CN00796419

Beloved Valley

THE

LIFE OF SAINT TEILO

SAINT TEILO

BELOVED VALLEY

THE LIFE OF SAINT TEILO

by

ANNE LEWIS

an imaginative biography

First Published by
LLANERCH PUBLISHERS

ISBN 1 897853 93 9

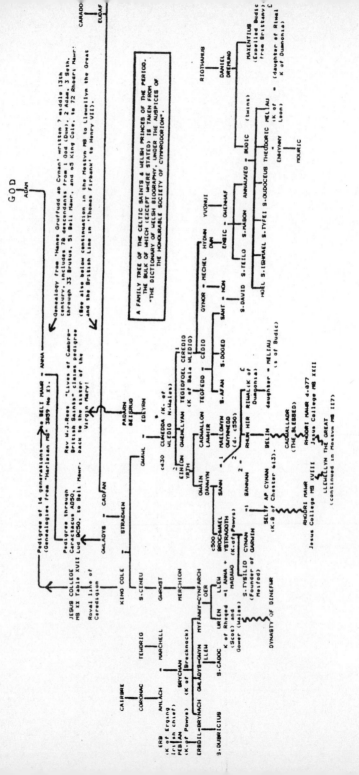

GOD
ADAM

A FAMILY TREE OF THE CELTIC SAINTS & WELSH PRINCES OF THE PERIOD.
THE BULK OF WHICH (EXCEPT WHERE STATED) IS TAKEN FROM
"THE DICTIONARY OF WELSH BIOGRAPHY" UNDER THE AUSPICES OF
THE HONOURABLE SOCIETY OF CYMMRODORION".

Genealogy from 'Hanes Gruffudd ap Cynan' written ? middle 13th
century, includes 78 descendants from 1 God (Duw), 2 Adam, 3 Seth,
through J33 Brutus, 51 Beli Mawr, and o3 King Cole, to 72 Rhodri Mawr.

(See also below continuation in the Mostvn MS to Llewelyn the Great
and the British line in 'Thomas Firbank' to Henry VII).

Pedigree of 14 generations. BELI MAWR = ANNA
(Genealogies from "Harleian MS" 3859 No X).

Rev W.J.Rees "Lives of Cambro-
British Saints" claims pedigree
back to the sister of the
Virgin Mary!

Pedigree through
Caractacus AD50,
to Beli Mawr.

JESUS COLLEGE
MS XX Table XVII Lud BC50,
Raval line of
Caredigion

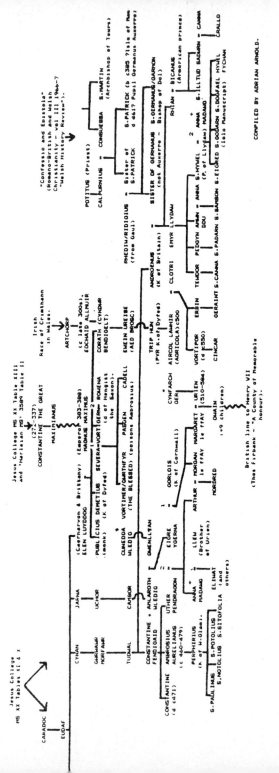

COMPILED BY ADRIAN ARNOLD.

THE BELOVED VALLEY

THE LEGENDS SURROUNDING THE LIFE OF SAINT TEILO

The Man. The Book. The Church.

OUTLINE.

CHAPTERS 1 - 12
Novel: ST TEILO - the man.

- CHAPTER ONE: 'The wedding'. Teilo - parents - early life - relationship to the royal family. Teilo's sister Annauved marries the exiled King Budic of Brittany. First mention of Ygrain meeting at the wedding after many years. Teilo is poleaxed. Why shouldn't he marry Ygrain? Question begins to dominate him. (Ygrain is the sole fictitious character).

- CHAPTER TWO: 'The Task'. Saint Dubricius on Caldey Island gives Teilo the task of helping to establish the Celtic Church in Wales, as exemplified by Teilo's work in Prince Vortipor's camp. Teilo is drawn to the religious life by the example of Dubricius and his inspiration. Task of the church and its ministry in Wales.

- CHAPTER THREE: 'Argol'. Teilo aims to set out for 'Argol' the stronghold of King Aircol Lawhir (Agricola), when news of the death of Aircol's father the old King Pyr, is brought to him by Ygrain. Overview of the political and cultural situation. Departure of the Romans - near chaos - Arthur as Dux Bellorum and supreme King and his relationship to Aircol. The battle for Wales in both its political and religious aspects. Cadfan from Brittany organises the building of church settlements (llanau) in Ceredigion. Teilo dedicates the hill as his main monastic centre with appropriate celebration and is called upon to build Llandeilo Fawr, but decides to go on pilgrimage to Jerusalem first

- CHAPTER FOUR: 'Soul friends'. Teilo, David (Dewi), Paul and Samson - friendship and growth together - Old Paulinus at Caio representing early Christianity already well-established in Britain.

- Teilo's Welsh friends move to Brittany via Cornwall and Devon. Teilo and Dewi remain to work together in Wales. King Mark father of Tristan.

- CHAPTER FIVE: c518. 'Journey to Jerusalem'. Teilo, Dewi and Padarn set out for Jerusalem . Conversations with Dewi and Padarn about marriage and women. How single-minded does God want us to be? The voyage as background. Why was Teilo loving and why was Dewi austere? Two role models compared - Dewi's position is safe, Teilo's is dangerous. Does God want Teilo and Ygrain to be unhappy?

- CHAPTER SIX: 'The visit' to Jerusalem - consecrated Bishops by the Patriarch of Jerusalem. The saints there are impressed by Dewi's austerity, by Teilo's love and by Padarn's theological brilliance. Overview of the church organisation in Jerusalem at the time. Return journey via Alexandria and Hippo. Introduction to the great debate between Saint Augustine and Pelagius. Teilo's unease - becomes convinced that he must forever reject Ygrain and fight for the Gospel; increasing dangers of Pelagianism and the threat from the Saxons. Return journey past Marseilles and Glastonbury.

- CHAPTER SEVEN: 'The building of Llandeilo Fawr'. Teilo sets about the building of his monastery - Travelling through his mountain settlements to his parents in Penally. He meets Ygrain again and tells her of his decision - she is very unhappy. THE DEDICATION - Teilo's greatest day and his worst. Ygrain refuses communion from him - Teilo preaches against Pelagianism and meets Ygrain who accuses him of the very same heresy and hypocrisy. Teilo is shaken to the core. DEPARTURE OF KING BUDIC to Brittany with Teilo's sister Annauved, Ygrain and the family, escorted by Agricola's Demetian fleet.

- CHAPTER EIGHT: 'The Synod of Llandewi Brevi'. Dubricius invites Teilo, who refuses to go - feels he cannot take part; Dewi goes instead - Dewi's speech. His popular acclaim. Teilo becomes Dubricius's constant companion until Dubricius retires and dies on Bardsey Island.

- (Optional chapter) CHAPTER NINE: 'Civil War'. 520s, 530s and early 540s, the vision dims. Death of Arthur. Death of King Aircol and his dream of Argol. Vortipor takes control in Demetia. Teilo and Llandeilo Talybont (Llandeilo Fach). Gildas writes castigating the five bad kings in south west Britain. Dewi, Cadoc, Gildas and others concentrate on training the Irish monks.

- CHAPTER TEN: late 540s. 'The Yellow Pestilence' follows the bubonic plague in Wales. Teilo is nominated to lead the refugees - can't bear to see Ygrain again. Dewi shows him that he is a true pastor, called by God to walk the dangerous path of love - only he who loves can be hurt. Dewi remains - tells Teilo to be the shepherd to his flock. Story of the storm and journey, during which he thanks God for his preservation for something special - but what - Ygrain? Teilo's work and experience in Brittany with his old friend Samson.

- CHAPTER ELEVEN: 'Brittany' (Armorica) c 547. Teilo visits his old friends now established in Brittany and travels to the south where his sister Annauved and King Budic rule. He meets Ygrain again in fear and trembling - but she has changed - she has suffered too but thereby has found God - she realises that Teilo is not a Pelagian but is motivated by love for God - she realises how 'loveable' God is and that it is possible to follow Teilo's path with good motives. Teilo's ambivalence, but he is a full-time man and unhappy 'tied down'.

- CHAPTER ELEVEN B: 'The founding of Landeleau' in Brittany. (little Britain) Teilo decides to build a centre for his followers in the middle of the country on the river Aulne. Many Breton legends remain of Teilo, including records of his many foundations there.

- CHAPTER TWELVE: c 555-580. 'Teilo's return to Britain' with his countrymen. Teilo retakes control of his own and Dubricius' work area. Development of language and poetry. Urien Rheged and Teilo fighting back the Saxons. Teilo's death at Llandeilo Fawr around 580.

Appendix (i)

THE BOOK. A detective story - a conversational piece.

Subsequent history of Llandeilo Fawr and the Gospel Book (written 720). How it came to be in Lichfield Cathedral and to be known as the 'Lichfield Gospels' or the 'Book of Saint Chad'. This is told in the form of a conversation between two men (an old man and a younger) the conversation taking place in the library tower at Lichfield Cathedral.

Appendix (ii)

THE CHURCH: Llandaff. How Llandeilo was disbanded, the Normans claiming Llandaff to be the centre of Teilo's work, a story fabricated in this Book of Llandaff.

Dramatis personae.

Author's notes. Appendices.

Bibliography.

Mirror image maps of south Wales, Cornwall and Brittany. Small family trees and relationship to Arthur inserted in appropriate chapters. Large composite family tree 'Arthur and the saints'.

ACKNOWLEDGEMENTS

I WOULD LIKE TO RECORD HERE
MY GRATITUDE
TO MY HUSBAND ADRIAN ARNOLD

FOR ACCOMPANYING ME ON ALL THESE JOURNEYS BOTH MENTAL AND PHYSICAL, ACTING AS THE DEVIL'S ADVOCATE IN SOME OF THE DIFFICULT ARGUMENTS, SUCH AS PELAGIANISM, AND HELPING IN MANY PRACTICAL WAYS, NOT LEAST IN COMPILING THE 'FAMILY TREE'!

In his words:

"The family tree of the Saints and Princes is a composite document. Anything before the year 400AD, i.e. above the generation from Cairbre on the left to St Martin (Archbishop of Tours) on the right is worthless as an historical document. Even the generations from 400AD down are a compilation of multiple 'Lives of the Saints' and other genealogies of princes, which were themselves built up with much patience and some imagination by countless monks and scribes in the middle ages.

"There is no doubt however that such 'genealogies' were a powerful influence in the middle ages, while that most glorious (and most readable) summary of the background ("The British Cymry or Britons of Cambria, outlines of the History and Institutions from the earliest to the present times" (1857) i.e. the beginnings of the British Empire) 'proves' in the finest detail the background of the Anglo-Saxon through the Druids and the best of the Celts, back to Japhet the son of Noah, Adam and Eve and even to the Almighty Himself! I have included these genealogies to show how serious but mistaken can be the aims of 'historians' with a 'cause celebre'.

"We have however in the bulk of the family tree been able to link by marriages St Patrick with Cunedda Wledig, Brychan and even St Teilo himself. The immediate ancestry of St Teilo comes from A.W.Wade Evans' "Vitae Sanctorum Britanniae et Genealogiae" p.320, to Padarn 'Beisrud' (i.e. of the red robe or appropriate pectoral of an Imperial title at the end of Roman rule). Even the writer of the 'Life of St Cadoc' however, as Dr Ralegh Radford has suggested, may be implying 'I don't believe a word of it' with his 'whom the experts say was the sister of the Virgin Mary'! Likewise the 'Vita Sancti Cadoci' gives the genealogy of Cunedda.

"Otherwise the genealogies come from manifold sources, collated in the following: 1) "An examination of the early Welsh Pedigrees" Geo. Owen Harry from 'An essay on the Welsh Saints' by Rev. Pryce Rees (1836) 2) "Lives of British Saints" Baring, Gould and Fisher especially (vol. IV" St Teilo"). 3)"Achau y Saint" as translated in the "Horae Britannicae"(vol II) 4) Dom Maurice's "Histoire Ecclesiastique et Civile de Bretagne" (Guincamp B.Jullivet 1835) 5) "La vie de Sainte Magloire" in "Medieval Studies" Part I(1957) and Part II (1959) 6) Jesus College MS XX and Harley 3859 as fund in the editions of Y Cymmrodor VIII and IX. 7) "The Dictionary of Welsh Biography under the auspices of the Honourable Society of Cymmrodorion 1959!.""

ADRIAN ARNOLD.

My special thanks go also to:

Dr Donald Moore.,

Prof. E.G.Bowen M.A., D.Litt, LlD, F.S.A, and to Dr.Ralegh Radford, and also to Dr E.D Jones, and many others, particularly to Andrew Solomon,Greg and John Solomon, without whom this book would not have been printed.

THE LIFE OF SAINT TEILO:

AN IMAGINATIVE BIOGRAPHY

Very little has come down to us in history about Saint Teilo except what was written about him by a Norman monk at Llandaff in the 12th century.

Canon Doble has written very fully on the sources still available for the study of the life of Saint Teilo; they are:

a) The marginal references to the cult of Teilo in the 'Lichfield Gospels' which we now recognise as the Gospel Book of Saint Teilo, written at Llandeilo Fawr near Carmarthen, south Wales, by a monk in the monastery there about the year 720 AD.

b) The 'Liber Landavensis' or the 'Book of Llandav' (Llandaff), written 300 years later by a Norman monk at Llandaff who copied from the identical but shorter Vespasian MS A xiv. (The additional material in the Book of Llandaff is listed by Mr Gwenogvryn Evans on pp.360-362 of the Book of LLandaff). Vespasian A xiv itself was written by Geoffrey, brother of Bishop Urban of Llandaff (d.1133).

However in the Llandaff edition the name Stephen is written over the name Geoffrey, so that it has been assumed that Stephen was another Norman clerk at Llandaff who added more material to Geoffrey's original work on Teilo. It is believed by scholars that Vespasian Axiv was written first at Brecon, which was in the diocese of St Davids at the time, the scribe here having access to other earlier material and certainly to the monk Rhigyfarch's version of the 'Life of Saint David' written at St David's in 1095. But Geoffrey apparently did not copy from Rhigyfarch's work and Stephen's extra material may have come from a Llandeilo Fawr version of the 'Life of Saint Teilo'. The whole question of sources is very long and complicated. Canon Doble worked on many of the lives of the saints and I have used his work extensively in my research for this book.

c) The third body of evidence for Saint Teilo is the witness of his very many foundations covering the area from Pembrokeshire in the south-west of Wales to Hereford on the eastern border. This of course is not evidence that Teilo was personally involved in all these places (although he may have been), for his followers may have founded them in his name. It does however show the picture of his activity in the whole area and also in Brittany. So much evidence has been destroyed in 1500 years that it is surprising to find his cult still so much alive. The time taken to sift through the available evidence has taken at least six years, with the aid of Professor E.G.Bowen M.A. D.Litt., Ll.D., University of Aberystwyth, F.S.A. who gave me all my original references and who was most generous with his time until his death. Thereafter Dr Ralegh Radford and many others helped me with my questions.

We know that Teilo was a cousin of St David and worked closely with him until the Yellow Pestilence; that his parents were Ensic and Gwenhaf and his brother was Mabon; their sister Annauved married the exiled King Budic of Cornouaille in Brittany and returned there with the help of Theodoric, the naval captain of King Aircol of Demetia; thus Teilo and most of the population of Wales left Wales in 547 for seven years or more because of the Yellow pestilence. We do not know when St David died, but since Teilo had the task of reorganising the country on his return from Brittany, it seems clear that David was no longer there.

The character of Ygrain is wholly fictional.

I have written Appendix [1] in the form of a detective story simply because the provenance of the Gospel Book is not known, hence although Appendix (i) is written in positive terms, there is no proof or evidence to support the belief that the book originated in Llandeilo. It is widely believed that it is Welsh however,.and could well have been produced there in 720. We may have to accept that proof of its origin will never be found. What is not debatable is that it certainly lay on the altar of Llandeilo Fawr until the time of Bishop Nobis.late in the ninth century. The next entry is of Bishop Wynsi of Lichfield[974-992]. It may well have lain at Llandeilo from 720 until it went to Lichfield with a small gap when it was found in the possession of Gelhi.

I was brought up in Wales, a country of beauty, of gentle hills, of lovely valleys with the sunsets on an ever changing sea. To me an exile in a world full of people in exile, the country grows ever more beautiful. At the most western point of the continent of Europe, Britain was always giving exiles a home. This story of a saint of the sixth century gives a picture of Celtic Christianity when the saints were often periginate, or exiles in this fleeting world for the life they sought in the nearer presence of their Lord, they deliberately chose this lifestyle for the love and service of God. Of the many hundreds of saints in this period, S.Teilo must stand out as probably the most important in Wales, and a crucial figure. Though the Christian Church was founded 2000 years ago, too many think that everything in Britain started in 1066, half way through the Christian story. A few may recall that Augustine was sent by Pope Gregory to England, just before 600, but little more, so that about half the history of Christianity in these islands is almost obliterated this book seeks to bridge that gap in some small way.

Since writing *The Last Siege of Dryslwyn Castle* under the name of Anne Solomon, for its reprint and all my further writing on Wales I shall use my maiden name, Anne Lewis.

List of contents

ACKNOWLEDGEMENTS   ii

Background   viii

Preface   PRESENT DAY SCENE AT LICHFIELD
CATHEDRAL LIBRARY.   1

Chapter one   THE WEDDING   3

Chapter two.   THE TASK.   10

Chapter Three   ARGOL.   27

Chapter Four   Perspective. Soul-friends: Teilo's friends and
contemporaries.   46

Chapter Five   c 518.   JOURNEY TO JERUSALEM   67

Chapter Six   THE VISIT   76

Chapter Seven   THE BUILDING OF LLANDEILO
FAWR   92

Chapter Eight   THE SYNOD OF LLANDDEWI BREFI. 110

Chapter Nine   CIVIL WAR. c537   130

Chapter Ten   THE YELLOW PESTILENCE.   137

Chapter Eleven   THE FOUNDING OF LANDELEAU   150

Chapter Twelve.   TEILO'S RETURN TO BRITAIN.   165

Appendix (i) A Detective Story 'THE BOOK'   177

Appendix (ii)   THE CHURCH   202

DRAMATIS PERSONAE   212

BIBLIOGRAPHY   230

Background

This is a story about Wales. The building of a nation, its life for about two hundred years and, as I will attempt to show, its virtual disintegration around 650 CE(AD) though recent centuries have been a long history of attempts at reintegration. My standpoint is as always from the vale of Tywi in South West Wales and the castle of Dryslwyn, Castle Argol with Grongar hill at this time, named after the then King of Dyfed, King Aircol Lawhir.

This story poses some problems. Only the writings of the monk Gildas are contemporary and his writing was not a history; it was a 'tract for his own time', chiding the five rulers for their lax morality and government, with long quotations from the Bible of his day, which we discover to be second century Latin, although he is writing around 540 CE). Gildas does not mention his contemporary monks by name, in fact he concentrates on the wicked kings of the period; his only reference to a good king is that of Aircol Lawhir, who ruled Dyfed in the 500s CE. Surprisingly he makes no mention of Arthur. I have also used a mixture of later literary work and much extra historical and archaeological evidence now becoming available. We have too the work of the contemporary poet Taliesin, the bard of Urien Rheged who gives vivid poetic pictures of this time.

It should be said from the beginning that there is a problem about the correct dating of St Teilo and his contemporaries. It has been suggested by various authorities that St David, Dewi Sant the great patron saint of Wales, died at widely different dates; some say in 544, others in 601. Sir J.E.Lloyd in his 'History of Wales' gives the date at c588. In a 'Life of St Teilo', we find 'On his return from Brittany after a stay of seven years and seven months, he found St David dead and the see of Menevia vacant' (The Book of Llandaff). On p.158 of the book of Gildas we see Teilo consecrating Ishmael to the see of Menevia 'because Dewi had migrated to the Lord'. As the supposed date of Teilo's death is c580, perhaps it is safe to assume that Dewi died before 580, and that he was dead when Teilo returned from Brittany.

St Dubricius, Teilo's tutor, who was in overall charge, organising the whole Welsh Celtic movement, trained Teilo to be his successor and this is commemorated at Llandaff Cathedral, together with Teilo's nephew Oudoccus, who was trained in much the same way. It is therefore fitting that these last three, who each in turn masterminded the movement, should have been commemorated by the Normans at Llandaff.

It is therefore obvious that no full biography of Saint Teilo is possible, although enough facts are known to build up a picture of his life and work. The conditions in the world of his day show us the frame in which his life was set, and, if we look around at his legacy to us today, a picture of the man emerges. This is what I have attempted to do. The most convenient vehicle for such a work seemed to be an imaginative biography based on what we have gleaned.

TEILO:- a few basic facts, as a background summary.

- Born at Penally (his family land) near Tenby c 500 CE.
- Educated at the monastery on Caldey Island opposite Tenby - under St Dubricius to become his successor.
- Later at The White House (Ty Gwyn) near Whitland under Paulinus.
- Further training with cousin David near Caeo (Llandovery).
- Worked closely with David, founding many churches jointly.
- The British Celtic movement was supported by Brittany with close interchange between Wales and Brittany. Founding of St David's, Llandeilo Fawr and Llanbadarn Fawr.
- Teilo, David and Padarn (a Breton) visit Jerusalem.
- The Synod of Llandewi Brefi.
- 537, Civil War.
- 547, Yellow Pestilence, Teilo taking many Welsh to Brittany.
- The founding of Landeleau in Brittany.
- Teilo's return to Llandeilo Fawr.
- Worked with his sister's sons in the Welsh Celtic movement.
- Trained Oudoceus, as Dubricius trained him, to be his successor. c580 Teilo's death - at Llandeilo Fawr.

I hope that the spirit of his work and that of his fellow workers will emerge, but first perhaps we should attempt a brief historical perspective of religious growth in the world.

THE WORLD RELIGIOUS BACKGROUND TO THE ARRIVAL OF CHRISTIANITY. *"The monastic life had its roots in the Near-east and the Indian sub-continent. The oldest of the world religions, Hinduism, had been developing for at least three thousand years before Christ. During this period a variety of major civilisations had developed, creating tensions within their societies. This, coupled with a need for a spiritual outlet and a religion which transcended superstitious polytheism created several religious geniuses in different parts of the world. These were especially noteworthy about the sixth century BCE, being the period of Confucius and Lao-Tzu of China, and Zoroaster in Iran and Gautama the Buddha in India, and was at the same time the period of flowering of Pythagoras in Greece and the greatest of the Hebrew prophets, Isaiah. Many of these civilisations claimed to be universal, and so founded 'Universal' religions.*

In the basin of the Euphrates and the Tigris, another great Aryan tradition was born, to be used with dire consequence much later in India, namely the belief in the once-born and twice-born; thus the fair-skinned Aryan invaders could claim to the black-skinned indigenous people of India that they were twice-born, a claim which was to be the fore-runner of a massive caste system in that sub-continent - a very different consequence from the profound use of this fundamental concept of spiritual understanding by Jesus Christ.

In contrast- Buddhism was a messianic religion which was unusual in that it did not centre upon God; its message was one of deliverance from suffering through the annihilation of desire. In China and in Egypt, the ancient traditions were more concerned with ancestor-cult and the worship of spirits of nature; the Tao of Lao-tzu meant 'the way', the Way of the Universe, a call for man to be in harmony with the Tao through the practice of quietude. Meanwhile the Jews acknowledged their means of escape to the Divine, called Yahweh or Jehovah, the Lord, with whom they made a covenant stating that they would be His people and He would be their God; the covenant demanded simple but profound morality through the Ten Commandments which were the basis of the Torah or the Law. The Dispersion spread this faith over much of the Mediterranean world and indeed further east.

This religious development required a few thousand years of religious thought, ethical rules and means to attaining higher standards of realisation in this world and of life after death. Some claimed that a period in one's life was required for education, followed by a period bringing up a family, a third period for prayer and contemplation, with a final period of return to the world without physical trappings after the manner of the east, as a revered beggar. Thus an eremitical tradition had been well established in the world, although the time in one's life that it should happen varied considerably.

The Druidical faith also shared a common core with India, developing no doubt from the same Euphrates basin and including human sacrifice, polytheism and abstruse philosophy. The Egyptian civilisation again was similar in that it worshipped animal gods, along with a great knowledge of the stars and mathematics. The Druids clearly derived their dress from the east, especially those Egyptians who also wore gold torques and amulets and long flowing white robes, as do the Arabs today; life was governed in its minutiae, including matters of feeding, social intercourse, appearance and dress, while the Druids ,it seems, believed also in Yahweh and were looking for Jesus.

But it was Judaism that gave birth to Christianity. Jesus Christ proclaimed His message for mankind, namely, salvation for all people who accept His Grace. No longer did salvation depend upon carrying out the Torah, ritualistic functions, by effort or incantations, but by the exercise of faith and prayer and belief in His death and resurrection; that was the simple message - too difficult for many to accept. "   Adrian Arnold, Joint Secretary, South London Interfaith.

The Christian Church by the sixth century had established main centres at Jerusalem, Rome and, more recently, Constantinople, (where by the mid-sixth century, when the yellow pestilence had done its damage and passed westwards to Wales, Justinian built his

Monastery at Justinia Prima). Just as the yellow pestilence spread partly through the trade routes, so did the faiths and practices of the religions of the world. The eremitical tradition in Wales for instance had developed from the practices of the Desert Fathers in Egypt, even to the hour of prayer and forms of dress, while the Druidical tonsure was similar to that of the later Eastern Orthodox Church.

In Brittany (also a major part of our story) Saint Teilo is remembered at Pentecost, when at Landeleau meaning Lan Deleau, llan (parish) of St Teilo, (the equivalent of Llandeilo in Dyfed), the priest leads his people round the boundary of the parish that Teilo founded. Pentecost or Whitsunday commemorates the day recorded in the Bible,when Jesus met with His disciples in an upstairs room. He had entered, although all doors and windows had been barred and locked, for the disciples were afraid. After His death on the cross, some had betrayed Him or run away; all were shattered at the way things had turned out for their Messiah, when suddenly He appeared and showed them His wounded hands and feet; He even allowed them to touch His wounds. St John's Gospel tells us all about His resurrection appearances in chapters twenty and twenty-one.

From that moment on, the disciples were changed men, filled with a new spirit of joy and love and hope; a consuming passion took possession of them and set them on fire with His love, and they were never their own men again. Now they were able to share His life for ever; He gave them a new Spirit and like Him they were given power to raise the dead and forgive sins in Jesus's name, which inspired them to go to all the ends of the known world to tell people this news, setting the Spirit at work in the world; until then this would have been unthinkable to those old frightened disciples.

LOCAL RELIGIOUS BACKGROUND AND ORGANISATION.

THE CELTIC MONASTIC SYSTEM, SOLDIER/MONKS AND THE MAKING OF WALES. This monastic system in the tribal life of the day would have at its head an abbot, who could be a layman, priest or bishop, inheriting his position by right of birth or suitability from amongst the monks of the tribe. His authority belonged purely to the monastery and to the district where he lived. In spite of the large number of bishops in the Celtic Church, real power remained local with the abbot. The form of worship was not yet ordered, although we do have Celtic liturgies in Latin dating back to this period. For about two centuries the Celtic church was cut off from Rome, until St Augustine re-established contact at the beginning of the 7th century. During this period the Celtic church was in contact instead with Jerusalem and with the Eastern church via the seaways and the strongest influence on the monastic church was the Coptic church of North Africa. Monastic discipline had been laid down by men such as St Jerome, St Augustine of Hippo and others. It was the practice of Christians to take on the indigenous faith and to build in Christian precepts, thus adapting for Christ both the beliefs of the people and their old place of worship.

People were under stress in many ways, as they turned to the missionary monks, many of whom were Kings or nobles who had given away all material goods, including land and their right to a private or personal life, in order to lead their people to a different way of living. These were men who had had the advantages of education, good food and a pleasant life, (because they were in a position to afford it) and yet they had chosen to abandon everything for their beliefs, which facts must surely have been most startling to that assortment of folk who came to listen: many were living in poverty themselves, beset by wild animals, with privations of cold and hunger and from time to time undergoing threats from those pagan Irish, now settled amongst them, since King Aircol Lawhir had subdued them and finally come to reign in Demetia. The people realised that something very powerful was at work in the lives of these men who had come to talk to them; if only out of curiosity, they came at first to stare; to their astonishment very often, they were won over by the things that these men came to say.

The Celts had always been a tribal people so that, when the Romans left Britain c410, less than a century before Teilo and with the Saxon invaders advancing ever further west, some fled from the towns, re-occupying their hill forts under local kings; many others stayed in their homes alongside their invaders so that some pockets of Celts continued to exit side by side with the invaders, although in the west the people remained subject to their overall king or Pendragon. Previously under the Romans, the Christian religion had come to be organised on diocesan lines and town - based. The town or city was the parish, while groups of cities with their territories (which the government already called provinces) became ecclesiastical provinces or dioceses, placed under a bishop from the chief city; indeed secular and religious power were often intertwined, as for example in St Patrick's time; Patrick's father not only had civic duties in local government as decurio or town councillor, but he was also a landowner and an ordained deacon.

WALES LONG TERM POLITICAL AND SOCIAL BACKGROUND. Magnus Maximus - Roman Emperor CE 383-388, and Elen of Caernarfon.

There are two extant accounts of the same historical period of Magnus Maximus's five year reign. First, highly critical but also showing gentleness, comes from the pen of the monk Gildas, living in the following century, who paints also a delightful picture of our country of Britain. The second is from the eleven stories of the Mabinogion, where it is woven into a romance, written down in the fourteenth century from the 'Four Branches of the Mabinogion', themselves written down in the eleventh century. We will also refer later on to the poems of Taliesin in the sixth century - contemporary to this story.

An example first then from the monk GILDAS 'THE WISE', writing c540, of the beauty of the island of Britain:-

"situated in almost the furthest limit of the world...protected by the wide...circle of the sea...the estuaries of two noble rivers, the Thames and the Severn, arms as it were, along which foreign luxuries were of old wont to be carried by ships, and other smaller streams; it is beautified by 28 cities and some strongholds and by great works built in an unexceptionable manner, walls, serrated towers, gates, houses, the roofs of which, stretching aloft with threatening height, were firmly fixed in strong structure. It is adorned by widespread plains, hills in pleasant situations....flowers of divers colours...like a chosen bride adorned with various jewels. It is irrigated by many clear springs....rivers flowing with gentle murmur, extending to those who recline on their banks a pledge of sweet slumber..."

Gildas then claims that Magnus Maximus crossed into Gaul with three legions of soldiers and thereby led to the downfall of a great country, Britain. It was through him that Britain suffered all the evils which followed.

He blames Maximus for robbing Britain of all her armed soldiery, military supplies and vigorous youth and thus leaving the country defenceless; he is responsible for the in-roads made by the barbarians and the beginning of the 'Ruin of Britain'. He speaks of Magnus Maximus's cunning and artfulness in bribing the soldiers of his enemy and how the young emperor Gratian was murdered by Maximus. However Britain's old enemies the Picts and the Scots were a constant trial to her in the west, long before the Saxons began their invasions on the eastern coasts.

Dr Arnold Taylor's précis of the Mabinogion story however shows the real contrast of the later romantic approach:-

"In the late 300s, ELEN OF WALES lived in north Wales at Caernarfon:- for her marriage portion she was given three strongholds - Caernarfon, Carmarthen and Caerleon. In Welsh medieval literature, we read in the Mabinogion the story of Magnus Maximus, a Roman Emperor and Spaniard, of the 4th century, who had a dream in which he was led to Elen - 'He had to journey from Rome to a land of high mountains and, coming to a river flowing into the sea, he found an island facing the land; at the mouth of the river he saw a great fortified city and in it a fort, the fairest man ever saw, with great towers of many colours on the fort: and in its hall a chair of ivory and the image of two eagles in gold thereon'. When he awoke, Maxen Wledig (his Welsh title) sent messengers all over the continent to find the owner and they journeyed the world for the space of a year in vain. However the tale ends happily, for Elen at last was found in north Wales at her chief castle of Caernarfon. After their marriage she went to live with her husband on the continent, until his death in 388 AD. She then returned with her children to Wales and adopted the religious life. Elen's brother, however, did not return to Wales with her, settling in Brittany instead, while his great, great, great grandson, Emyr Llydaw, was now to become important in the story of the saints".

This is the background to the time of St Patrick of the island of Man (according to Dr Ralegh Radford) and also St Ninian who founded Whithorn around 400 AD, the earliest Celtic site - in South-west Scotland. Ninian trained under St Martin of Tours. St Patrick was born close to Whithorn on the island of Man c385 (at about the time Ninian founded Whithorn) he was captured by Irish pirates and kept in Ireland, but escaped to the continent where he was trained by St Germanus of Auxerre. In 425 and 440 Germanus visited Britain to put down the Pelagian heresy which also features in the lives of St Teilo and St David. Patrick's sister also was of key importance, since it appears she married Rhediw or Rigidius of the royal family of Gaul; if this is indeed true then she was Emyr Llydaw's grandmother and great great grandmother of St Padarn. This would of course mean that not only St Patrick, but also his sister, were of key importance to the whole Celtic Christian movement.

(See family tree compiled by my husband Adrian Arnold from Jesus College MSS and dictionaries of the Welsh saints)

BRITTANY OR LLYDAW

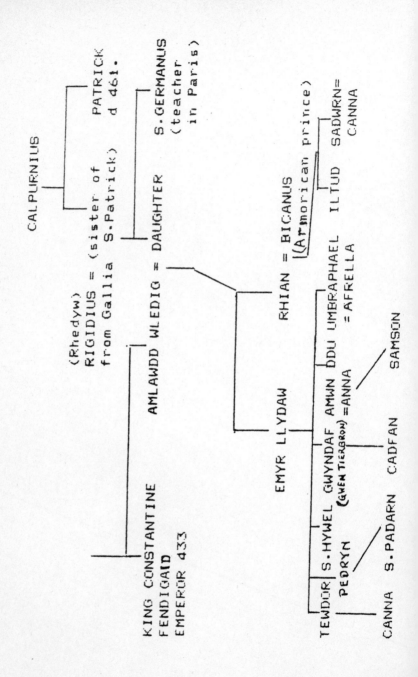

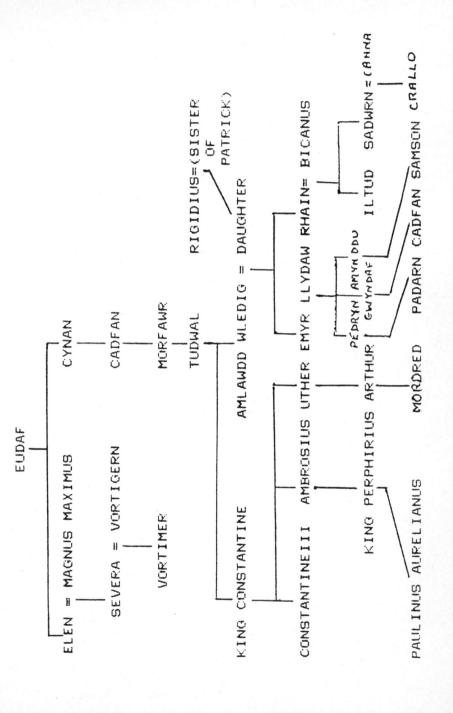

KINGS OF DEMETIA

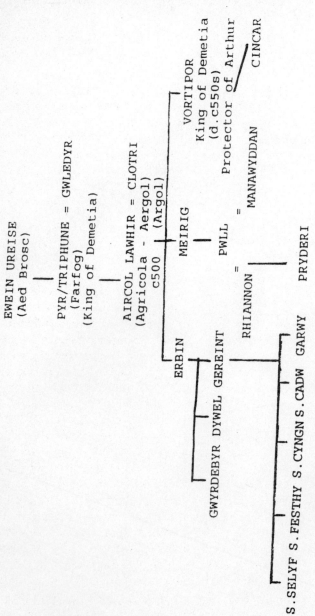

(All became members of the college of S.Germanus)

(King Pyr retired to his island off Tenby(Dinbych y Piscoed) to Ynis Pyr, Pyr's island (now Caldey) Manobier is also named after him.

The ruler of Demetia in Teilo's time was Aircol

SOCIAL AND POLITICAL BACKGROUND - A SHORT INSIGHT INTO THE MANY DYNASTIES.

During the THIRD CENTURY, an Irish tribe was expelled from Ireland. (This is developed in the 'Expulsion of the Deisi' by K.Meyer in Y Cymmrodor XIV 1900):-

THE IRISH DESCENT OF KING AIRCOL LAWHIR, KING OF DEMETIA. "Eochaid, son of Artchorp, went over the sea with his descendants into the territory of Demed (Dyfed or Demetia) and it is there that his sons and grandsons died. And from them is the race of the Crimthann over there, of which is Teudor son of Regin, son of AIRCOL, son of Triphun, son of Aed Brosc, son of Corath, son of Eochaid Allmuir, son of Artchorp". Aircol was King of Demetia in Teilo's time. (This tribe, along with most of Ireland, was converted by Saint Patrick).

BRITAIN IS WITHDRAWING INTO WALES.

By AROUND 500 CE, this AIRCOL LAWHIR (Longhand) WAS THE RULER OF DEMETIA (Pembrokeshire and west Carmarthenshire). He was therefore of the Irish tribe of the Deisi from Munster, a branch of the Ui Liathain, who had by now ruled in Demetia for several generations, had married into the ruling families of Britain and could claim descent from the Emperor Constantine and the British Royal line from Elen. His tribe lived peaceably alongside the local population, so that the language of Demetia was bi-lingual, British (Brythonic) and Irish (Goidelic) with Latin and Ogham as the written languages. King Aircol was an able administrator, who was even now welding the kingdom into a unity never before known. Still there were outlying bands of pagan warriors from Ireland who would make local raids - but these were chiefly on the coasts and especially those facing Ireland. Arthur, the overall ruler of the country, had given Aircol and later his son Vortipor the title of 'Protector' - of the Emperor Arthur - and, by taking the military name 'Agricola', Aircol was showing respect for the Roman style of rule in the country. In the same way his father, Pir y Dwyrain (meaning east, but now ruling in the centre of Demetia)with the title 'Tribune'. retired to his island Ynis Pir to enter the religious life. It was this island which later came to be called Caldey and where Teilo was trained.

ANOTHER PROMINENT IRISH DYNASTY DURING THE FIFTH CENTURY WAS HEADED BY ANLACH, who had marched through mid-Wales from the coastal area of Ceredigion and settled north of Demetia with his wife Marchell, who was daughter of King Tewdrig of Garthmadryn (now Brecknock); it was named later after their son BRYCHAN, who was born at   Goch, the stone fort of the red rock, just below Carreg Cennen (one of the largest British forts, possibly used as a slave camp to supply the gold mines at Dolaucothi). It is known that Spaniards were imported to work in the gold mines; certainly Brychan had a Spanish wife and probably raised his family just below Garn Goch in a Roman villa with hypocaust, still named Llys Brychan. His Spanish wife Proistri no doubt bore many of his twenty-three children, many of whom grew up to become saints.

THREE OF HIS GRANDSONS (DUBRICIUS, CADOC and URIEN) feature in this story. Brychan buried his father near Brecon, also named after him; he continued to thrust eastwards and married his son Brynach to Erbdyl, daughter of Pebiau, King of Archenfeld and Erging, the kingdom of the Golden valley and the Black mountains, between the rivers Wye and Usk; this area is now in Herefordshire, where there had been a Roman city at Ariconium and where their son DUBRICIUS was to make his ecclesiastical base at Henllan near Ross-on-Wye. One of Brychan's daughters, Gwladys, was carried off by force by King Gwynllew of east Glamorgan (Gwynllwg); the result of this union was CADOC, the saint who founded the great monastery of Llancarvan in Penychen on territory given him by a relative, Paul Penychen, not far from Gwynllwg or east Glamorgan. Another of Brychan's daughters, Myfanwy, married Cynfarch Oer and their son was URIEN RHEGED. Throughout, with so many characters in this story, it will help the reader to keep referring to the family tree of the saints in the index. There were of course no parish registers in these early days and there is no means of checking the validity of these family relationships.

ARTHUR AND URIEN Both Arthur and Urien are historical figures about whom legend and myth abound; stories continued to grow throughout the medieval period, so that it would appear at first wiser to omit them both, but the legend has been so powerful over the years that a mention of the 'myth' and its background is necessary. Certainly the Dynevor family, who were the ruling family in South-west Wales from this time onwards, trace their ancestry from

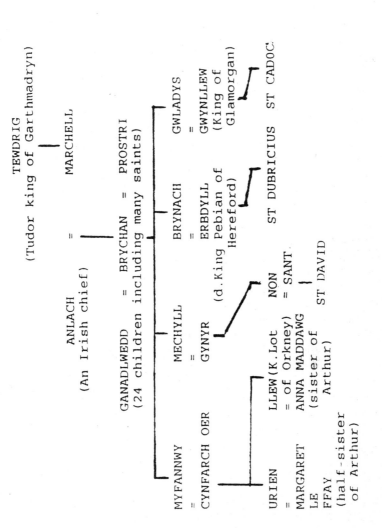

THE GRANDSONS OF BRYCHAN

TEWDRIG
(Tudor king of Garthmadryn)
|
MARCHELL
ANLACH =
(An Irish chief)

GANADLWEDD = BRYCHAN = PROSTRI
(24 children including many saints)

MYFANNWY   MECHYLL   BRYNACH   GWLADYS
=   =   =   =
CYNFARCH OER   GYNYR   ERBDYLL   GWYNLLEW
                            (d.King Pebian of   (King of
                             Hereford)   Glamorgan)

                            NON
                            = SANT
                            |
                            ST DAVID

ST DUBRICIUS   ST CADOC

URIEN
=
MARGARET
LE
FFAY
(half-sister
of Arthur)

LLEW(K.Lot
= of Orkney)
ANNA MADDAWG
(sister of
Arthur)

(simplified)

them both, so that an attempt must be made to piece together what we can. In the legends Urien had been sent down from further north, to the coastal area of Gower, and built his stronghold on the rock above the river Cennen, close to his grandfather's villa. From here he ruled the land between the Tawe and the Tywi which includes Gower (Gwyr with its old Roman fort at the mouth of the river Loughor and the river Lliw), Kidwelly, Carnwyllion (the Llanelly area), Cantref Bychan and Iscennen.

The poet Taliesin wrote in c 550 CE about Urien's exploits. Urien Rheged, believed to have been a man of the north, has yet left many apparent traces of his life in South Wales. We can immediately identify several. There is 'Gelli Wern Ganol'- a group of farms in the Felindre area of Pontardulais originally known as 'Gelli Urien', (Gelli Wyrain- Gelli Wren - Gelli Wern) called by the local inhabitants 'Gelli Wyren'. Similarly, at Tynbonau there was a famous spring with curative properties originally known as 'Ffynnon Yr Ien' or 'Ffynnon Rhean' originally 'Ffynnon Urien'. Again, further up the Loughor valley (in Welsh this is spelt 'Llwchwr'), 'Parcyrhun' originally 'Parc Urien' is another example, or so claims Denver Evans in his book on Pontardulais....'Tradition has it that Urien is buried in this area; he was the warrior who wore the raven insignia on his breastplate and the Loughor coat of arms features ravens, reputedly from well before the Norman era'.

Taliesin tells us that Urien was slain in battle at the mouth of the river Lliw but, while the river Lliw flows out to the sea at Loughor, traditionally it has always been understood that he died in the Strathclyde area of Scotland, and it must also be said that the balance of evidence puts Urien and Rheged quite securely in North-west England and south-west Scotland. However, as many place names are similar, if not the same, there is bound to be some confusion. There has been a 'Heol Rheged' on ordinance survey maps of the Llandeilo area until recently. It led from the church across the river and up the hill on the opposite side towards Carreg Cennen castle. Since Rheged has never actually been located, although it is believed to have been in the Strathclyde area, it remains an interesting place name. Dr Arbour Stephens produced a body of writing on Arthurian battlefields in the Gwendraeth valley, changing Nennius's place names to suit. In

Aircol's dream I have included some of these, but they probably remain dream material!

Urien, it is claimed, was married to Arthur's half-sister, Margaret le Fay.

HARLEIAN MSS 2300 (page 73)   These manuscripts in the British
HARLEIAN MSS 3859   Museum discuss Urien's family

One of Urien's titles was 'Leader of Christendom' (rwyf bedyd) in contrast to his enemies who were pagans. As Dux Bellorum, Arthur had Saxons in his army, fighting alongside the British, while Annales Cambriae tell us that Arthur fought for three days and nights at the battle of Badon, carrying the cross of the Lord Jesus Christ.

In his book, 'Arthur: Roman Britain's last champion', Beram Saklatvala also suggests what Arthur's court might have been like; I have used his account of the soldiers at this court. Several bases have been suggested for Arthur's strongholds and military camps including Chester, Caerleon-on-Usk and (across the Severn estuary in 'summer country', South Cadbury a hill fort covering eighteen acres-the legendary court of Camelot, near the marshes where 'the island of Glastonbury' lay; the word 'Ynis' or island was used in both its literal and metaphorical sense and could mean 'an island for Christ in a pagan world'. Nothing of substance has come down to us to support any one of the forts in connection with Arthur. Dr Leslie Alcock's principal evidence for South Cadbury was imported pottery (now suggested to be Roman) and a very dateable timber hall; of the entrances, only one is Arthurian. One of a dozen possibilities is Liddington, but Bath and its hillfort of Bathampton is the most favoured to date, which could also be the site of the Battle of Badon.

Whatever the date of the peace secured by Arthur, it is known that Hywel of Brittany, son of Emyr Llydaw came to his assistance with 15,000 men around 508. Hywel married Arthur's sister, Anna Madawg, connecting Arthur with the Breton dynasty. Years later Hywel founded a little church near St David's, a foundation known today known as Llanhowel. The manuscripts about Arthur's supposed relationships are however confusing. Morgan le ffay, Arthur's half sister, married the King of the Orkneys, Llew(Lot) the brother of Urien, whilst Morgan's son by Arthur, Mordred, also had a son, Gorfalk (See genealogical chart). The peace Arthur secured at the battle of Mount Badon (variously given as - 500 516 or 537!) lasted a generation. It was this generation of peace, which Gildas claimed to produce the five wicked kings, because they had never known the privations that war could bring and thus had become self-indulgent.

As to the character of Arthur, the 'Lives of the Saints' give a very different picture from the traditional; he does not appear as the hero we are accustomed to believe the very reverse in fact. This can be explained quite reasonably as suggesting that different people had different views of him, perhaps the Norman church had a desire to discredit or mock him, perhaps the uncharacteristic behaviour may have been occurred before he became a Christian. It is certain that he had enemies in his own ranks; his nephew or son Mordred perished with him in civil war at the end, so that people had their own reasons for jealousy and revenge.

Powerful men and princes figure in these tales, for the land belonged to them and, if the local king was converted to Christianity, all his tribe would turn from paganism with him. The king also gave the church permission to work in his kingdom along with gifts of land, while later recruits would come from the common people.

THE ORGANISATION OF THE CELTIC CHURCH AND SOME OF THE LEADERS.

Previously Arthur's uncle, Ambrosius Aurelianus, had made his military command centre, where he also built a monastery. Not far away DUBRICIUS organised and supervised from Henllan the plan for the great monastery from which the religious development of the British Christian movement emanated and to which famous school of over 2000 men came many future leaders for training. From here he was able to oversee the missionary movement in the south-west (Wales, Devon and Cornwall), where many including his illustrious forebears laid the foundations of the future church.

GERMANUS, ILTUD, BRIOC AND CADFAN. One of these leaders was ILTUD, who as a youth had been taught in Germanus's school in Paris. When the Goths overran the city, GERMANUS returned to his family in Brittany, closing his Paris school for ever; meanwhile Iltud went to fight as a warrior under Arthur, fighting as one of his fast-riding soldiers trained as cavalry elite, whose role was to push back the incoming Saxon hordes. Here he learned, along with the rest of Arthur's army, how to set up camp and many other skills, including knowledge of engineering and drainage, which were to be useful later in setting up monasteries and those small monastic settlements known as 'llannau'. As a young man of wealth and position, he enjoyed life both at court and as a warrior, until he was converted, it was rumoured, while out hunting in the forests of Glamorgan.

As a Breton, Iltud now joined his schoolfellow BRIOC in Brittany and was trained by Germanus for the work ahead. Their war then changed from the physical sphere to the spiritual, fighting for the minds and souls of the British. Local Breton tradition has it that Iltud and Brioc prayed for Wales here in Brittany at a place called Cadout. Germanus's mother was said to be the sister of St Patrick, while his own sister was the mother of Emyr Llydaw so that understandably his concern was to help the Breton family of Elen to return to Britain and to claim all Elen's old territory for Christ against this pagan inrush from the east.

Iltud returned from Germanus to Dubricius's monastery for further training and then on to Caldey island, where men flocked to him in such numbers that he returned to the mainland and founded his own monastery in Glamorgan - on family land at LlanIltud Fawr or Llantwit Major, as it is sometimes called (this was near to the site consecrated nearly five hundred years before). St Donat's church was said to have been that of King Caradoc (Caractacus) in the first century. St Donat's is in a cove under Atlantic college, on the south coast of Glamorgan. Llantwit Major is also said to be on the site of an ancient foundation where Caractacus's daughter Eurgain first founded a church.

To Iltud's school came many nobles and princes from all over Britain, sent as children, including prince Maelgwyn from north Wales, Gildas the wise, Taliesin (Urien's famous bard) Samson son of Amwn Ddu and Paul Aurelian.

Here they were taught every branch of philosophy, poetry, rhetoric, grammar and arithmetic, logic, Latin, Greek and astronomy, but above all knowledge of the Scriptures, both Old and New Testaments. Agriculture was most important in the founding of monastic settlements and Iltud devised an improved plough for greater efficiency and self-sufficiency. They were taught at first that the ideal unit was three hundred, to which other units of three hundred could be added as the work progressed. At Henllan, at Llantwit and also Cadoc's monastery at Llancarvan the number was over two thousand. Llantwit was well-sited being near the sea and was to become a useful sea-port, where travelling missionary monks could come to and from Brittany and across from Somerset, Cornwall and Devon, while the settled Romano-British stock around Caerleon made it a good rendezvous.

Germanus had arranged for Cadfan to organise the setting up of llannau in order to reinforce the border between Ceredigion and Demetia on the river Teifi; Cadfan was the present ruler of the house of Elen in Brittany and former warrior of great renown, later to be known as the patron saint of warriors. This defence of the border, keeping the marauding Irish out, was to be a joint venture between the British and Breton members of Elen's family and the grandsons of Cunedda.

Grongar hill is named after King Aircol Lawhir, could have been Cadfan's residence in Llangathen, at today's site called Llether Cadfan? (Cadfan's slope) perhaps a meeting place for those Bretons sent over by Germanus as missionaries? There is a chapel in Llangathen church today to Cadfan, but although there are several llannau credited to Cadfan in the Finistere area of Brittany, there is no other in this part of Wales. It is unlikely that this Cadfan founded a church in north Wales; a later man is commemorated on a stone found there. This monastic movement is however undeniable. Fourteen hundred years later, today, we still feel the mark made in Wales by these monks of the fifth and sixth centuries; some of these leading men, it will be noted, are descended in the Breton line from St Patrick's sister (see family tree).

To sum up then, as the Saxons pushed further west and the Irish invaded the coastal areas of Wales and Cornwall, the soldier monks put up a resistance which was both religious and physical. The result was the establishment of the Welsh nation which was to last about two hundred years, during which time a nation, a culture and a language were created.

CELTIC OVERVIEW

383-388.   Magnus Maximus, a Roman Emperor married Elen of Wales who lived in north Wales at Caernarfon, and took her to Rome.

385-461.   St Patrick of Man.

Whithorn

398   Founded by St Ninian. Candida Casa (The White House), - or 'the Shining place'(A.R.Paterson'Celtic Saga'). Ninian trained at Rome, later under Martin of Tours. Enormous extent of remains, the earliest date to 400 CE. Whithorn became a famous seat of learning. 5th & 6thC.Scholars throughout the Celtic world came to train here. Missionary monks went out to other parts of Scotland.

Ireland

5th century   Evangelised by St Patrick - Five main tribes. Patrick Romano-British, lived c 385-461 CE. Born Isle of Man (Dr Ralegh Radford) Trained under St Germanus of Auxerre, who twice came to put down Pelagianism in Britain.

6th & 7th   425-440. Since Ireland was never invaded by Rome, the Irish church continued to grow throughout 5th & 6th and 7th centuries. Patrick's influence on South Wales.

Wales

5th, 6th & 7th centuries.   A Christian province together with Devon, Cornwall and Brittany under the overall charge of Saint Dubricius.

Dubricius trained Teilo to be his successor.

Saint Teilo c 500-580 CE Llandeilo Fawr (great).

Saint David a contemporary, St David's - 'Menevia'.

Saint Padarn a contemporary, Llanbadarn Fawr (great).

Saint Germanus or 'Garmon' and Saint Deiniol, both in north Wales.

Saint Cadoc in the south, Llancarfan.

The above just a few - many thousands of others of course

Iona

Before the coming of Columba, Iona was a sacred island of the Druids (as was Anglesey).

563 In his 42nd year, Columba and 12 companions landed.

Trained in Ireland at Moville, then Leinster, completing his studies at Clonard.

Columba lived from 521-597, the next generation after Teilo.

The Northumbrian Church.

Lindisfarne

634 founded by Aidan from Iona.

THE NORTHUMBRIAN CHURCH

547 Ida, the English King of Northumbria founded the church (when Teilo was taking his people to Brittany to escape the Yellow pestilence!) = Urien the British king fought Ida. Urien shut up the English for 3 days and 3 nights at Lindisfarne.

625 King Edwin and Christian wife Ethelberg of Kent married.

633 Edwin defeated by pagans of Mercia allied to British of Gwynedd.

634 Oswald, Edwin's son, exilled to Iona.

634 Oswald returned, sent for Aidan to convert the Northumbrians. Aidan founded Lindisfarne close to Royal Palace at Yeavering.

637 Aidan was succeeded by Finian.

664 Cuthbert (635-687) succeeded for 12 years. Brothers Chad, Cedd, Cynebil and Caelin trained here.

698 Lindisfarne Gospels are begun.

698-721. Eadfrith produced these Gospels before becoming Bishop of Lindisfarne.

Jarrow Bede (673-735) started in Monkswearmouth as a small pupil he was then taken with his master to Jarrow to found a small church St Paul's where he stayed for the rest of his life. He wrote 'The Church History of the English people'. (There was 40 years between Aidan and Bede).

Whitby Saint Hilda was of the Royal House, born in exile 614 AD.

She was sent by St Cuthbert to be Abbess of Whitby.

664 The Synod of Whitby

680 - Hilda died.

Clearly these are some of the main Celtic centres, but one could expand the story greatly. Gospel Books continued to be written in the main monasteries throughout this period, many books coming from Ireland, while Wales had large monasteries devoted to scholarship of course. There are so many reasons for believing, for instance, that the Gospel Book of Teilo, which lay on the altar at Llandeilo Fawr, over 1200 years ago, was written in Wales, if not at Llandeilo, perhaps at Llanbadarn Fawr. It is earlier than the Book of Kells from Ireland being written c 720, and now called the 'Lichfield Gospels', or the 'Gospels of Chad'. The Book is housed in Lichfield cathedral where it has been since the 10th century, with a short break during the Civil War. I have chosen to make this a detective story trying to ascertain how it may have got to Lichfield. It is a tragic loss to Wales.

As for St Teilo, we have the Normans to thank for the fact that his cult is no longer at Llandeilo Fawr, but there is no doubt that they honoured his memory by taking the cult to Llandaff, their chief centre in Wales and an important area for Christianity for 2000 years. It is interesting that he is honoured with Dubricius, and his nephew Oudoceus at Llandaff. This would appear to give Teilo much more status than has formerly been assigned to him. It certainly looks as if the Norman church believed that he was indeed Dubricius's successor in pioneering the Welsh Celtic movement in his day. We have the Norman church to thank for writing this 'Life', and for perpetuating his memory at Llandaff.

Since there is so much valuable material that should be more generally known, and yet in the nature of things we have still more important gaps to be filled, it seemed good to me to take two imaginary men seated in the library at Lichfield cathedral and, through their eyes look first, into the time of St Teilo, which I have written as an imaginative biography, then at how the Gospel Book may have reached Lichfield, and finally how St Teilo's cult was brought to Llandaff by the Normans. Only one main character is wholly fictitious, that of the girl Ygrain.

At Teilo's death, three places claimed his body according to his 'Life'
- Llandeilo Fawr (his cult monastery), Penally (his family home),
Llandaff (the centre of his later cult).

Preface

PRESENT DAY SCENE AT LICHFIELD CATHEDRAL LIBRARY.

High in the library tower of Lichfield Cathedral an older man and a younger sat discussing the book which lay on the table before them. Its cover was made of hide, holding together a front and back of solid oak. The pages lay open at the last page of St Matthew's Gospel. In the margin the old man was tracing a Latin inscription, which translated says,

"Gehli, son of Arihtiud, bought this Gospel book from Cingal, and gave him for it a very fine horse and gave that Gospel Book for his soul to God and St. Teilo.

For some time they examined the text and decoration of the manuscript. It was written in Latin in a monk's hand, in steady flowing half-uncial (half-rounded) script. They turned the pages slowly wondering at the intricate design of the illuminated pages, decoration of animals and birds intertwined, and the stylised portraits of the Gospel writers, the whole coloured in fading soft blues and mauves, pale pinks and yellows. The fourth Gospel was missing. The Book held Matthew, Mark and part of Luke, but none of John; they wondered how the other pages had been lost.

The old man's finger touched the younger man as they traced the words, blood communicating through flesh in the present. But the finger on the page touched the steady writing on the vellum, communicating with the monk whose quill had formed the script , present with past. Above all, there was communication of the words of life and promise of life in the future; the meaning of the words, time and eternity.

"Are you able to translate the Latin on this page?" the younger man asked. The elder gave slowly its literal translation:

"Go to all foreign people, baptising them in the name of the Father and Son and Holy Spirit, teaching them to observe all things whatsoever I have commanded you, and behold I am with you all the days till the end of the age."

The two sat quietly for some time and then the old man broke the silence to comment on the words in the margins - these words were written in old Welsh, the oldest known written Welsh in existence.

"What you see here in Welsh under the first Latin sentence," he said, "is the record of a pact between Welsh families, who had long been in acrimonious dispute over a piece of land near Llandeilo Fawr". The last sentence of the Welsh states, "The good men said to each other, 'Let us make peace'; Elgu gave afterwards a horse, three cows and three newly-calved cows, only in order that there might not be hatred between them from the ruling afterwards till the Day of Judgement".

He slowly rose, folded the heavy book and carried it across the room, where there was an old casket specially prepared for it in the seventeenth century by the Duchess of Somerset, who used to call it 'the ark' and kept it in hiding during the Civil War. The old man looked at his watch; "Come," he said as he turned the key in the lock, "let us go and have lunch".

They climbed down the steps of the library tower and, passing the shrine behind the High Altar where the Celtic-trained St Chad was buried, they left the Cathedral and crossed the bridge over the pool and as they walked under the trees to the inn, they talked about the background to the book and about St Teilo in particular. As they talked a picture of him formed in their minds and it was as if they had been transported into the sixth century, when Teilo lived and worked.......

Chapter one

THE WEDDING

The soft sand trickled between his bare toes as he walked; then turning, he stopped to gaze at the misty island. This was the third day the treacherous sea wind had roughened up the waves. The sea still heaved a little as the chill spring breeze brushed white edges on the grey waves, but by noon with the changing tide it would settle and be calm.

"No time to lose now". He bent to check the boat on the beach, filled with supplies for the island monastery. "Soon we'll be off", Teilo smiled to himself, as he strode up the beach to take leave of the family and collect his younger brother Mabon.

His mother Gwenhaf looked up from her sewing as Teilo's quick stride brought him to the doorway of the long hall; he stood there strong and tall. His hair was shaved from ear to ear at the front, in the style of the Druidical tonsure, similar to the Eastern religious rite of fully fledged monks, and fell in thick brown curls on his shoulders at the back. Although of noble birth, he wore a thick rough tunic down to his calves, tied with a leather thong at the waist. The only concession to the cold was a thick woollen cloak, pinned with a metal brooch of Celtic design. His mother had given it to him when he left her as a child to live in the local monastery, to be educated by the great Papa Dubricius on Ynys Byr.

Gwenhaf's grey eyes sparkled with pride as her son stooped to kiss her - Eliud or "Sunshine" was his family name and it suited him with his brilliant mind and generous heart, but she was going to miss those merry brown eyes and the laughter he had brought to their home, especially since her only daughter Annauved was now married. Furthermore Teilo was taking Mabon with him to the monastery.

3

"I'll call Mabon; you will want to be off when the tide turns" said Gwenhaf as she bustled off to find her younger son.

She found him with her husband Ensic, who was struggling to fix a piece of wood which had slipped from the fence around the animal enclosure.

"The servants can do that, Ensic; Eliud has come to collect Mabon now, to cross to Ynis Pyr. Make haste Mabon; you don't want to miss the tide. You made enough fuss about following your brother, so don't hold him up now".

It had been a bit of a wrench to give in to Mabon's repeated demands a year ago, but eventually she and Ensic had agreed to let Mabon join the island monastery. This meant that there would be no one left to look after the family lands in Penally when she and Ensic were gone. Old Pyr had been very understanding as she explained to him that Mabon was not as robust as his brother Teilo; he promised to keep an eye on the lad, but it wasn't the other end of the world; he could even see his home at Penally from the island and now after a year Mabon's enthusiasm was stronger than ever. Gwenhaf couldn't help smiling to herself as he hastily left the fence to get his belongings together.

"There's no knowing how one's children will turn out" she said to Ensic. "Not only ours" replied Ensic, "there could not be more of a contrast between old King Pyr's grandsons either; that Prince Vortipor with his wild companions at Lydstep - he must be a constant worry to King Aircol; on the other hand, effete Erbin with his love of learning and his fishing fleet at Dinbych y Pyscod and his cell containing all those manuscripts, that's hardly the best successor to his kingdom either. Meirug on the other hand has his work cut out on the most dangerous west coast of Dyfed with constant attacks from the Irish pirates by sea and fighting continually to protect the monasteries and new foundations along the border between Ceredigion and Dyfed. Good King Aircol himself must worry about the future of his kingdom with such different sons to succeed him!"

To tell the truth, Mabon was a bit confused lately. He had been watching his brother for some weeks - glad to have him back from his travels. Teilo was a few years older and long ago had left both the school of Dubricius on Pyr's island and also the school of Paulinus on

4

PENALLY. Trefloyne
from a water-colour, c. 1810.

PENALLY. Old house

PENALLY
(THE PARISH CHURCH)

the mainland. Teilo was now a travelling missionary and Mabon saw him only on rare occasions such as this, the big family gathering for their sister's marriage to King Budic, an exile from southern Brittany.

"It was great to have the family all together" Mabon said as he took his leave of his parents.

Ensic took Gwenhaf's arm as they wandered down the beach to watch their sons push the boat off shore. Teilo stepped back to kiss his mother once more. "Take good care of Mabon" she whispered to him.

"Don't worry mother, he'll come to no harm" Teilo replied; then leaping into the boat the brothers were soon riding the bobbing waves to Ynys Byr.

"Oh well, that's that" said Ensic as the couple once more entered the empty hall. "You raise your children in a house full of noise and chaos and then all too soon they are gone and here you are again alone - what a strange thing life is!".

"At least Annauved is married" said Gwenhaf, "and we can look forward to a few grandchildren then ".

Ensic smiled at his wife "I suppose, old dear, its a bit of a disappointment to you, isn't it? Both our sons seem set on a life of renunciation of normal married life - whatever that might mean! Not that monks are forbidden married life; look at Gildas, Teilo's friend at LlanIltud Fawr; he has a couple of little ones already, but then he is not constantly travelling like Teilo. I think we should be glad that they haven't chosen to be warriors; they are at least concerned with a different quality of life - though I did see a change in Eluid at his sister's wedding - didn't you notice? Perhaps his choice is tinged with some regret after all".

His wife nodded "Who could fail to notice the change?- he was quieter and more thoughtful than I have ever seen him".

"I wonder what sparked that change off" Ensic murmured as he threw another log on the fire.

THE WEDDING

Mabon had been allowed to accompany his older brother to their sister's wedding. They had walked inland for a few miles, until the flat peninsula gradually gave way to rising ground.

"Come on little brother, you can't lag behind now, there are only a few miles left. Look! Do you see how the ground rises from here behind that old quarry? If you want a break, I'll race you to the top and you can rest there while I have a chat with the local priest. Ludchurch is an ancient settlement, but they didn't have a church here until recently and I expect there will be a few things to discuss".

As they climbed panting up the last and steepest bit of the quarry to the top, Mabon flung himself on the grass, exhausted. It was wetter than he expected and he jumped up again almost immediately, which made Teilo chuckle; he put his arm around Mabon's shoulders and guided him to a flat rock where they sat to regain their breath. The wild wind whistled round the hill, deliciously cooling their hot cheeks.

"Teilo, are you really going to wear that rough old garment at the wedding - or will you have special robes like the other guests"? Mabon turned his open face to his elder brother with a quizzical look. Teilo roughened his brother's short cropped head.

"Wait and see" he laughed; "I expect they will all want us to wear something to mark the grand occasion. Have you seen Annauved's wedding dress"?

"No of course not, the girls have made such a secret of it; I'm expecting something very fine. Aren't you? Annauved and Ygrain have been whispering together for months; there are to be lots of little flower girls - all the girls in the village are taking part. Why do girls like to keep all these silly secrets? I've felt quite left out just lately. I'm glad I shall be going back to the monastery with you this Lent; nothing will be the same again once Annauved has left home".

He gazed out across the flat plain down below them in the valley. He could see the sea from here in the distance where his home nestled in the hills which ran down to the beach. Mabon sneezed, he'd been here long enough; he wandered over to where Teilo was in discussion with the cluster of people on the settlement and soon they set off for King Aircol's main court at Narberth, where their sister was to celebrate her wedding.

Narberth was not many miles further inland and, as Teilo and Mabon arrived, the evening fires were burning and folk busying themselves cooking their supper in the doorway of their round wattle and mud shelters. Mabon was hungry by now and very much hoped that Teilo would find a place to stay as soon as possible, but Teilo took him up the steep sharp rise to the royal fort, where soldiers stood on guard at the entrance to the palisade. In the twilight Mabon could see many more soldiers wandering about inside. It was here, he realised, that they were to stay and soon they caught sight of their mother and father in a little family group, who excitedly greeted the brothers with much hugging and voluble chatter.

Teilo was to officiate at his sister's wedding to Prince Budic, Count of Cornouaille in Brittany. Budic had fled to Demetia when his brother Maxentius grasped his share of the kingdom on the death of their father Daniel, son of the great Riothamus. The marriage was a true love-affair; "So good", Teilo thought, "to see her happily settled and so much in love". He liked Budic, a strong, fine man, who would no doubt take Annauved back to Brittany as soon as things settled down over there.

This was to be their last evening together and, although they all intended to have an early night, Annauved and Teilo had not seen much of each other for some time and wanted to talk and make the most of it. Annauved, no less determined a character than Teilo, greeted him with a warm hug. They loved each other dearly and had been close companions all their lives. Annauved, though like Teilo in character, didn't resemble him in looks. He was tall and athletic; she was short, blond and dumpy with large blue eyes and a determined little chin. She would make every bit a queen on her marriage. Teilo didn't envy anyone who disagreed with Annauved; she always managed to have her own way in the end. Yet their love for each other was as firm as her little chin; anyone who disagreed with Teilo when they were children had his sister to reckon with - and so it would always be! They had so much to talk about; the evening passed

7

all too soon until eventually Gwenhaf bustled in to interrupt them and take Annauved to her room.

The wedding day started mistily but Gwenhaf and Ensic hoped that it would stay dry. Mercifully by mid-day the mist had cleared and it became fine and sunny, just as they had all hoped and prayed it would. King Aircol's court was a buzz of excitement with the kitchens at full stretch, exuding tempting smells. The wedding party being busy, Teilo escaped from them and went down into the church to make sure that all the arrangements would go smoothly and without a hitch. His mother had, for this special day, given him a long white robe, which not only dignified the occasion but made him, with his bronzed complexion, stand out in the crowd. The wedding party were to assemble beforehand in the King's great Hall and then make their way down to the royal church, a long low building of oak, lit for this occasion by many candles.

Annauved's close childhood friend, Ygrain, was her special attendant at the wedding. Ygrain was dressed in pale yellow, her dark hair and pale skin being thrown into lively contrast. As with the other girls, flowers were woven into her hair and a garland was hung around her neck.

It was some years since Teilo had seen her and he was taken aback by her loveliness. Her dark eyes met Teilo's as he entered the King of Demetia's great hall at Narberth, to lead the procession for Annauved's wedding. Teilo stopped for a moment, surprised at her beauty. He went over to greet her and in that quiet conversation it was for them both as if time stood still. The wedding preparations however continued, as Teilo turned with an effort to the task of organising the procession. Over the next few days he was to be kept busy, for the feasting followed the wedding ceremony and he was to be introduced to all the guests. In the centre of his being however a great stillness took over - something had happened in those moments with Ygrain, which could never be undone and with which on his father's land at Penally he needed later to come to terms. The unexpectedness of it and the bad timing meant that he could not allow himself to think, until some long time after, when all the excitement had died away and he could once more be alone with

8

himself; it was as if his whole integrity had been shaken to its roots and he was quite helpless to control his clouded thoughts.

Not only had his parents given him to the church, to spend his life for Christ, but always it had been his greatest happiness to do just this; he had gone along with it willingly - ardently even. But, faced with this crisis, he was obliged to think the situation through for the first time. Could he allow himself any personal life, when all his energies and powers were already given to God? Many monks and priests had renounced everything, he knew, but what had seemed to him an easy and joyful path before, now became a major test, one which was not to be resolved without a deep struggle. How could he explain to Ygrain the conflict passing through his mind? Perhaps he had made a big mistake by assuming that he was strong enough to live the life of a monk.

Ygrain on the other hand had also felt the power of that moment and it was less easy for her to understand. She was younger than Teilo and on the threshold of adult life. Yet what had happened to her just now was no passing fancy. It seemed to her a cruel twist of fate that such a deep pang should pass through her soul, which might never be resolved. Like Teilo she knew only too well that he was already wedded to the church. He had already given his life to the service of the kingdom of God.

Chapter two.

THE TASK.

The little boat carrying Teilo and Mabon pulled up on the the island's beach and, to their delight, his friend Samson was there to greet them. Tall and fair with piercing ice blue eyes and long lanky limbs.

"We've been waiting for you, Teilo. How did the wedding go?" began Samson, as he tethered the boat to a post held deep in the sand. He stood up to his full height and greeted Teilo with a broad smile. "How are my parents? Were they at the wedding"?

"So many questions" Teilo laughed. "Here's my young brother Mabon; he has been staying at Ynys Byr for a year already".

Mabon looked up, so overawed by Samson's severe and piercing eyes that he stepped back and nearly tripped over a rough stone.

They walked back together over the sand dunes, past the village, then on and up the steep path, where lay the fields. Many of his old friends were at work; they had come over to the island specially for Lent, making a welcome extra labour force, one or two recognising Teilo waving as he passed in the distance. Samson, glad of the chance to talk to Teilo alone, was rapidly explaining what was on his mind.

"'Papa' Dubricius used to bring me with him on his annual Lenten visit. I became very unpopular at LlanIltud Fawr when Iltud's nephews heard that the great master was going to put me in charge of the monastery after him. They even tried to poison me in their jealousy, so Dubricius decided to remove me and bring me here for a break - I think I must be a bit of an embarrassment all round, for jealousy forever seems to follow me". Samson looked down in dismay as he spoke.

"How's that, old friend"? asked Teilo looking anxiously at him. He knew how Samson's personal austerity always caused trouble. Samson had an unfortunate way of making the older monks' hackles rise

CALDY ISLAND

INSCRIBED STONE ON CALDY ISLAND

when they were faced with his almost fanatical masochism - a determination not to surrender to his personal needs. This self-discipline did not go down well with some of the older men, many of whom had been faithful courtiers to old King Pyr and had retired with him to the island; they were used to a more comfortable life than this ideal of Samson's.

He had been put to look after the jars of wine and honey in the cellar. "There was a near scandal the other day", Samson continued. "I went down to the cellar and many of the jars had been broken into and their contents stolen. Dubricius was sent for and in my panic I just fell on my knees and prayed. When Dubricius arrived the jars were full again - I was simply dumbfounded and with great tact the Master said nothing, but just smiled at me as he went back up the cellar steps again. I can tell you it did not make me any more popular with the older monks".

"You've got to expect that, Samson. Show some feeling for them too - some of the old ones have rheumatic joints and suffer in the cold more than they admit. What suits you does not necessarily help them to deal with an uncomfortable life in their old age".

Teilo had always admired Samson's earnestness; he was one of his closest friends, but his lack of tact was painful. Dubricius was not trying to cool his ardour for a life of discipline, but to develop some understanding in Samson for those not quite so committed as himself. Samson's parents were high officials in King Aircol's court, great landowners, and Samson had turned his back on all the prestige and wealth which could have been his; in the flush of youth this did not seem such a hard thing to give up. "Wait till he feels the trials of old age, though", the old monks murmured; "Let us see what his endurance is like then!"

By now they had reached the centre of the island. Although it was up on a rise, the encampment was sheltered and protected by a bank and fence which surrounded the main monastery. Here, in their clay and wattle cells like beehives, the monks would study the scriptures and join together to sing their praise to God. A good part of each day was taken up by hard manual labour in the fields.

11

As for Dubricius (Dyfrig) he was a native Celt. Although his main monastery was at Henllan near Ross-on-Wye, being in overall charge of the church in the South-West he travelled much of his time. There were relatives everywhere, for his grandfather, King Brychan, had had twenty or more children most of whom became saints and had founded churches in the west - some in Wales and others in Devon and Cornwall - so that like a successful businessman Dubricius travelled and taught all over the area. It was his example which Teilo had always found so attractive, together with his organising flair, his ability to get alongside men of very different temperament, not to mention his great skill as a teacher. "He could have made a comfortable and wealthy life for himself if he had only chosen to do so", thought Teilo. Dubricius had been Teilo's hero as a youth; he had looked up to him as a great man who tirelessly gave himself to the cause; he had that kind of dynamism that Teilo admired; he could ruthlessly drive himself for the cause which was always more important than any selfish need.

Teilo also admired Dubricius's farsightedness in realising that the battle against pagan Saxon infiltration of the country must be fought in the hearts and minds of his countrymen. He had planned the resistance with Ambrosius Aurelianus like a military campaign. With the aid of their countrymen over the Channel in Brittany, great leaders such as Illtud and Cadfan had fought alongside Ambrosius's family, Uther Pendragon and his son Arthur and others, turning their military skill towards the spiritual campaign with all the energy they could muster.

For his part, none knew better than Dubricius himself the many strains and privations his ardent monks endured in their calling; many a time they slept out under the stars as they travelled from place to place, carrying their Divine message. They wore only the simplest of garments, a rough woollen tunic or cloak, their feet bare but for sandals, carrying a Gospel Book and a bell to ring and attract the local population when they reached any small settlement. Once an adequate crowd had gathered, they would open the book to read and explain the passage to the crowd. If enough people showed interest, the evangelist would lay down the staff which supported him on his long journeys by foot and stay in the place for a while, baptising as many as professed to believe at a convenient stream. Water, the symbol of life, always flowed past the little wattle churches which the monks built for permanent worship and teaching with the help of the local people.

Dubricius had early marked Teilo as his successor and, when he had taught him all he knew, he sent Teilo to Paulinus the great teacher on the mainland for further instruction, which included Latin and Greek, logic, rhetoric, mathematics, philosophy, grammar, poetry and astronomy, but above all knowledge of the scriptures, all of which Teilo ably mastered with Dubricius as his inspiration.

"It's good to see you my son," he said as he scanned Teilo's face which looked unusually drawn: "I hope this Lenten time will prove refreshing to your mind and spirit. Mabon, how you have grown this last year; it must be all that rich creamy milk they give you here. Go off and explore the island until its time for vespers; you'll hear the bell when it's time to come in; I want to have a word with Teilo and catch up on the news."

Mabon wandered off to the other side of the island, which was scarcely a mile wide, where he could watch the fat seals basking on the rocks, sleek and lazy as the tide lapped gently round their huge hides. "One could spend hours here," he mused lazily as he rested his head on his chin; "There must be more varieties of seabirds here than almost anywhere along the coast". He rolled over on to his back and stared up at the sky, counting the birds as they wheeled past, an exercise calculated to send anyone to sleep, and very soon he was doing just that.

As Dubricius and Teilo went inside the monastery room, Samson slipped away to join the monks at work in the fields. His chat with Teilo had put his mind at ease. Of course he knew that he must appear so very intolerant to the old monks; he just had a different point of view that was all. He'd work it out somehow.

"I have something of importance to tell you, my son", began Dubricius looking grave as Teilo turned anxiously towards him.

"You don't have to give me an answer now; think about it first and then we'll have another chat before you go. Did King Aircol mention anything to you at Narberth?"

"No, I hardly caught a glimpse of him; we were taken up with the wedding celebrations and King Budic was royally entertained. As you know they are great friends; it wasn't a suitable time for serious talk" replied Teilo regretfully; he was in fact thinking again how it would have helped both of them had he managed a private word with Ygrain.

"Oh well then, I shall have to tell you myself. It's much too warm an afternoon to sit indoors. Let's go out into the courtyard; I can tell you there."

And there they sat in the monks' compound with the warm spring air blowing the grasses gently in the field beyond, as Dubricius looking very serious explained the problem.

"That young tearaway Vortipor has turned his father's property at Lydstep into a drinking den; the rumours of course are rife, as you must know with your home so close. It seems that during these drunken brawls a number of murders have taken place. King Aircol has despaired of his son and wants to put an end to these scandals. He has done all he can to stop this disgrace, but Vortipor is headstrong. Aircol does not deserve such a son; in great sorrow he has asked me to see if the church could bring any influence to bear; I have suggested sending you, since as a local man you know the situation and the people only too well"

Teilo sat with head bent, his eyes lowered. A powerful feeling of reluctance overcame him, nausea almost.

"Do you realise what an impossible task this is? Vortipor is arrogant and cruel and unlikely to take any notice - least of all of me! In fact he could as easily arrange to have me murdered for my impudence!"

"You seriously underrate yourself" laughed Dubricius; "You have been in much more difficult straits than this; Vortipor is just thoroughly spoilt, not wicked! See what you can do and I suggest you take young Mabon and an older man along with you. Lydstep is very close to this island and we can keep an eye on the situation if need be."

"Mabon", spluttered Teilo; "he's far too young!"

"I have had excellent reports of Mabon; I think he will surprise you;" Dubricius's kindly old eyes had read the expressions across Teilo's open face, as they passed from astonishment to dismay.

Dubricius was always full of surprises and, although Teilo knew his judgement was usually to be trusted, this really was too much. However he had been Teilo's inspiration in his callow youth; who was he to deny another youth now? This was just how the work expanded right across Wales and beyond, youth and enthusiasm harnessed under the leadership of this holy man and the magnetism of his personality. He always seemed to believe that the impossible was possible and had already stretched Teilo, as he trained him for future leadership. Now a second challenge was to come hard on the heels of Dubricius's first.

Teilo looked at the saint and braced himself, for it was clear that more was to come: "The king has noted with growing interest what you have done already in his kingdom and feels that now is the time to consolidate your work. He has given me a hill near castel Argol in the Tywi valley where he would like you to build a main center for your work. You will be entirely responsible for it and, when all is complete, King Aircol himself will come and worship there. What do you say Teilo? Do you feel ready for this step? I will back you all the way of course, but the inspiration will have to come from you."

They talked late into the afternoon, not noticing the time, until with a jolt they heard Samson's voice, leading the brothers in from the fields; the afternoon was mellow with their voices, as the tired monks rounded the bank into the encampment. Samson's tall strong frame cast a shadow over the two as they sat, for the afternoon sun lay low across the fields; raising his eyes, Teilo saw playful shadows on the grass setting each blade into relief and for a while Samson sat on the grass and joined their conversation, until it was time to wash and prepare for the evening meal and prayers.

15

"How lovely, how pleasant the Lord is," said Dubricius, as he led their meditations, "let us adore the Lord, the maker of all things."

From dawn till dusk the monks gathered together at intervals in their little church to praise God. The rhythm of monastery life soon cast its spell on Teilo, as from the little church the monks followed the day through with singing and praise and prayer. There was no set form of prayer; Germanus in his missionary efforts in Wales had influenced the church with his Gallic form of worship from northern Brittany, but the church rubric was simple, unfixed and unsophisticated, now that the Roman influence had been so long gone from the country. A few of the churches still clung to the old Roman ways, but now that they had been cut off from the mainland of Europe by the Saxon invasions, the only contacts left to them with the wider church were the seaways.

The old Phoenician sea routes back to the Mediterranean touched Brittany, Spain and the north African coastal areas. Jerusalem rather than Rome was now the inspiration for the Celtic church, while the pagan occupation of eastern Britain endured.

The days passed quickly and soon Teilo's retreat was at an end. As the monks gathered that last evening, the final communion was particularly sweet; Christ's presence seemed so close, the heavenly longing so poignant, that he would have dragged it on for ever. As the brothers broke bread together, the sacredness of Christ's body broken for sinners bore down upon Teilo; he felt himself so inadequate to perform the will of the Lord, but when the cup came, Christ's blood shed for all sinners, which included himself, those in Vortipor's camp and all those others he would have to minister to in this coming year, caused the strength of the Lord to flow through him.

The monastery boat left early the following morning to catch the tide; it was cold and grey but the water was still, as Teilo said farewell to his master Dubricius and friends.

"When you judge it right to leave the camp", said Dubricius, "leave two men there; we will keep an eye on things from here; you will then be free to join King Aircol as soon as maybe at Castell Argol, for

I know he is anxious to get on with his new plans and there will be much to discuss."

As the boat cast off from the causeway, Teilo sat looking at the row of friends waving him off from the shore; he continued to stare as the little boat moved further away, until his friends were but little black dots in the distance. He had not been his usual cheerful self, most times good company and bubbling over with life, for he knew that that day he must face Vortipor.

The boat struck the sandy beach below Vortipor's camp, a small cove, but deep enough for boats from the continent to anchor in the bay. Dark swarthy men unloaded a variety of cargo as Teilo jumped ashore. There was an exotic smell of spices mixed with the guttural oaths of the crew shouting in a foreign tongue, the hubbub breaking the peace of the little cove. A burly sailor was struck by a piece of falling cargo; he lurched to the ground holding his bleeding head. Other sailors gathered round him as the blame was laid and a brawl began; it all created a rough awakening for Teilo as he faced the unwelcome task ahead.

VORTIPOR'S CAMP.

Teilo and Vortipor, both of Royal descent, were brought up in the same district in south-western Wales. They had had many a tiff in the past, not that they had met very often, for Teilo's destiny as a monk, like Vortipor's as a future king in Demetia, were set in early childhood. But Vortipor's education had also been in the hands of monks; he knew the standards expected of him as the son of a Christian King, but he had been a rebel from the start.

Whenever a royal occasion demanded his presence as a nobleman's son as was Teilo also, Vortipor had taken the opportunity to goad Teilo, jealous of his popularity. Seeing his restless spirit and energy, Arthur had made him (like his father before him) his personal 'Protector' a title which meant that Vortipor was in Arthur's body-guard; this was a great honour, of which he was justly proud, but in times of peace such as those now being enjoyed, following

Arthur's conquest of the Saxons, Vortipor's duties were minimal and at such times he could become frustrated and bored.

Teilo took two companions with him to Lydstep, Mabon his brother and an older man Iouill. As they climbed the cliff path from the beach, the little boat which had brought them from the island was pulling away. A wind was getting up, but fortunately the distance back to the island was not more than half a mile. Teilo was conscious that this grey afternoon reflected his own mood, as he and the brothers reached the white well at the top of the cliffs and sat down to regain their breath.

They were unable to see the cove from here, but more brawny sailors were dragging up the cargo with a good deal of shouting as the men from Vortipor's camp haggled for their foreign goods. The three monks went to the camp and, turning a bend in the path, were aware of the voices becoming suddenly louder, as they were also blown by the wind. A bonfire in the centre of the clearing was burning high - almost too high because of the rising wind; a couple of youths stood poking it with sticks; they had obviously been set to look after it and had misgivings about piling it too high.

At the entrance to the camp two ill-kempt armed men grasped their weapons when they saw Teilo and his companions approach. The taller of the two challenged them to come no nearer. "Stay right there," he growled and with black tangled hair hanging from his shoulders, disheveled and ill at ease, he looked toward the other guard, hardly more than a boy, with a vivid scar across his cheek, standing legs akimbo. His spear threatened the monks, as he questioned them about their business.

"What do you want then?" he snapped.

"I bring a message from the King for your chief Vortipor", Teilo calmly explained.

The guard frowned. "From 'oo ?" he retorted briskly, making his swarthy face even more sullen. However he let the monks through and, as they entered the camp by a gap in the banked defences, groups of young men looked up as they passed.

"King's men, huh," some jeered.

18

But more took little notice, continuing with their dice-throwing and raucous chatter. Teilo guessed that the larger hut in the middle was the best to make for.

"That must be the one," he murmured to the others, "Lets hope Vortipor's there."

Seeing two guards at the entrance, they made their way towards it, followed by a group of chattering young boys. The normal life of the camp was undisturbed; a few women - again most roughly dressed and disheveled - stared at the monks from the entrance of various huts or looked up from their cooking pots with brazen expression. It seemed generally a disorganised place, with a strong feeling of hostility and repressed violence just below the surface; Teilo felt it would break out at any moment, should he make a false move. He looked at his brother Mabon - he had gone as pale as a sheet. Iouill put his hand on Mabon's shoulder.

The three monks were challenged again at the entrance to the largest hut.

"Who are you then? It's no time for seeing anyone, this."

A piece of cowhide hung about the doorway for protection from the wind, icy by now. A loud voice from inside shouted obscenities and abuse at the guard, who went in with Teilo's message.

"My holier-than-thou father wants to interfere again with pious snooping spies , does he?" the loud voice sneered.

But the three men were taken into the hut without ceremony.

It was dark inside. A fire in the centre gave welcome warmth and, as they grew accustomed to the light, the three men were appalled at the scene which met their eyes. Vortipor lay stretched out on a couch of goat skins. His long tousled black hair framed a strong and ruddy-looking face. The sandals on his bare feet and the thick red mantle were those of a King's son and his frame was that of a tough well-built warrior, but his expression was menacing, unfriendly, hard and not calculated to encourage Teilo to explain the purpose of his visit. His voice was gutteral and cruel.

"An odd bunch here, all right." he murmured as he looked at them slyly without bothering to turn his head.

Teilo observed that his speech was a little slurred already, although it was not far into the afternoon. Vortipor did not ask Teilo and his companions to sit down, although there were rushes on the floor and a few benches on which they could have sat; instead he filled his goblet with more red wine from the pitcher on the table in front of him and said to Teilo:

"Get on with it then; what does the old bore want now? State your business and get on your way."

The three monks stood their ground, surrounded as they were by armed youths and girls; two girls were attending to Vortipor's slightest needs, one sitting with him on the couch and the other standing behind with her arm about his shoulder. Teilo could only repeat the very words used by the King.

"Let me know how you are received; stay a while and report back to me what is happening there," had been the KIng's commands.

The prince snorted, but before he could interrupt, Teilo hurried on.

"These rumours of murders taking place nightly have reached King Aircol in his stronghold and he is displeased. Disorder in his son's house reflects on him."

Even as he spoke, Teilo could see more pitchers of wine being brought in to supply Vortipor's table, merchandise which had arrived that day by sea and was being unloaded earlier, even as Teilo and his companions had landed on the shore; these pitchers of strong red wine had come from the warmer lands of the Mediterranean. Teilo saw his chance and, pointing his finger dramatically at the pitchers, he pressed on, whilst Vortipor seemed temporarily and unusually at a loss for words.

"Prince Vortipor, it is this very wine which inflames your camp each night; the more the red wine flows the more the blood is heated; with but the slightest argument you know that red blood will flow from any man attacked. You know also that a single command could stop all this violence; you are bringing the good name of your father into disrepute."

Teilo knew by now that he had said enough. Vortipor already inflamed by wine, threw his goblet with an oath across the floor at Teilo and his men; his sullen face grew livid with hate and violence, but a touch of anxiety and even respect was creeping through.

"You have come from the King; otherwise I would have had you all thrown out," he said; "I will give you safe conduct in this camp, for if anything happens to you, I know I'll be answerable to my father; do what you can to stop the killings - I give you a free hand with that - only leave me out of your pious reckonings."

Whereupon Vortipor left the hut in a fury, pushing those in his way as he went. No one dared follow him in such a mood. Teilo, Mabon and Iouill were left standing in the middle of the room and a youth who had been slouching nearby, but who knew Teilo's family well , came forward and set a very different mood. "Please, wont you sit down," he said.

Teilo was after all a local man himself; his family were local landowners of noble stock, so that of course a few of the young men knew the family well. They all fell into heated debate, until Teilo was called to elaborate on what the King really thought.

By now the hut was so full of young warriors that it was necessary to move outside and let Teilo have a bench to stand on, to talk to such a large group. He stood against the hut and reasoned;

"Many of you are known to me and I know your parents well, so I talk to you as friends; you know my message already, for the King has made his feelings about this camp quite clear. Your parents are worried too and they need you badly at home. Surely you have now had your fling and some of you can see the end results; it is just not worth the candle."

Some of the youths were of good family but others rough and uncouth; Teilo's message to them was therefore received with mixed feeling - some agreeing that the drinking was now out of hand; they murmured amongst themselves - "It's not like it used to be any more."

Others resenting the interference shouted, "Who the hell does he think he is? Tell him to clear off and leave us alone."

Teilo could hear a muttered oath, "He sounds just like my father" and Mabon, catching the boy's eye, suppressed a smile of agreement.

But the mood was testy and the general feeling was one of contempt for the monks; "We'll continue just as we please," was the gist of some of the comments.

At last the three monks were offered space in a small hut to rest and spend the night. After a light meal they retired early, not really able to relax, but feeling that all that could be said had been repeated that day; they could do no more for the present. Teilo sat up on his bed of rushes listening to the noises of the night in the camp around him, for the yelp of the wild boar would respond to the howl of the wolf and the dogs in the camp would bark back their hollow challenge; all this as well as the bellowing of the camp drunkards. Vortipor was feasting in his usual style; singing and dancing could also be heard, while the smell of roasting meat pervaded the camp. The fresh provisions of oil and wine from the continent added to the feast and everyone was merry. The three monks quietly prayed in their small hut, asking God to show them how they could do His will here. It was very late now, a man was sick against their hut, the stench was vile; music and dancing reached fever pitch, when suddenly across the night air came a piercing scream, a blood-curdling male voice strangled with pain and terror.

The three brothers had not slept and in a few minutes they reached the hut whence the hubbub had come. They stood and took in the scene. Girls in various stages of undress sat or lay around the room, most however clasping clothes to themselves, rather drawing away in horror at the sight of two mangled and bloody bodies in the centre of the rush floor. A frightened youth nearby whispered to Teilo what had happened;

"The big fellow, Tudwal, on the ground over there said something, I think to Gwrwst's girl; Gwrwst didn't like it and said so, giving Tudwal a real good clout; Tudwal did his usual and really laid into Gwrwst; he's the dark one flat out over there; all the others then jumped up and laid into Tudwal who groaned as he fell hitting his head on the edge of the table. Neither of them has moved since". The boy shuddered as his voice trailed off into silence.

22

As usual the cause had been boredom; the youths had just been sitting around with nothing much to do, drinking more than was good for them to fill in the time. The girls created their bit of diversion too, until one warrior went too far with another's girl friend and a fight started - not an unusual cause of trouble. However, on this occasion, it was a bit more complicated; the same fellow also had a reputation for bullying; he'd done some nasty things to people to extort money - and, because he was being attacked for molesting another's girl friend, those he had previously been bullying also joined in the fight. It became violent and ended by both the original warriors, as it turned out, being killed. Gore sullied the rushes; the molested girl friend had been caught up in the fight and she lay sobbing at Teilo's feet, blood pouring down her neck where the knife had just missed killing her.

Stooping down, Teilo called for a basin of water and a cloth. A slovenly older woman hurriedly brought them in. The bodies of the warriors were lifted and prepared for burial, as the cold light of dawn spread across the camp. The normal custom here was to get rid of the evidence of the past night's debauchery as fast as possible the next day and with little ceremony. With the monks in their midst however, they were obliged to observe a bit more common decency on this occasions, as a splattering of rain fell on the shivering crowd who had scrambled down the cliff to the burial ground.

Teilo, Iouill and Mabon, pale and drawn from their sleepless night, stood waiting for the burial party to assemble. They quietly sang a psalm as more warriors and girls joined them. In sharp contrast to the mood only shortly before, everyone stood silent as they looked down at the graveside.

"Holy God," said Teilo as the service began, "look down on us from your Heavenly throne in pity for our helplessness and forgive."

The bedraggled little party stood shivering, the rain falling now relentlessly; when the short service was over, they trailed up again to the stronghold on the cliff.

Vortipor had not been there among his men. He remained in his camp in that same sullen mood as when the brothers had arrived. He called them to his presence, but this time he was prepared to listen to what they had to say. Nothing could be said to exonerate the situation

- he knew his standing amongst his warriors would soon deteriorate, if he was unable or unwilling to restore some order and decency in his stronghold; even more disastrous, his father would take him to task and this could lead to all sorts of unpleasantness. He was therefore determined to let Teilo have his way and take control of the situation. Teilo spoke quietly to Vortipor.

"I will leave Mabon and Iouill at the camp and this drunkenness must cease. Then and only then will good sense replace this wild behaviour. You must take charge once again. I will return when I have done my business with your father and taken his orders. Mabon will soon have to return to Ynys Byr to continue his studies, but no doubt Dubricius will send some one in his place."

Teilo knew that he was taking a grave risk leaving young Mabon at all, but Mabon had proved himself well able to relate to the boys of his own age; he was in fact a positive asset. Teilo went hot all over at the thought of the risk he was taking and of the promise he had made to Ensic to look after Mabon, but the boy wanted to stay a few more days; he felt the risk was justified and that Vortipor was on the whole to be trusted to keep his word and protect the monks, for King Aircol's sake, not to mention his position of honour under the Emperor Arthur's authority.

Indeed when Arthur was in his prime the king had won his kingdom with many such men, warriors who were willing to risk all, to drive the invading Irish out of their coasts. With just such renegades was Urien Rheged still holding back incursions in the Gower peninsula and had not Dewi so defended himself when he was set upon by the Irish chief Boia, at that time when Teilo was helping him to build his monastery in the valley Rosina, the marshland by the ports of the west. But of course Vortipor was of the generation who were too young to have fought a proper war and all his contemporaries too soft and spoilt as compared with their fathers.

"He is subdued, but not for long," Teilo thought; "His nature is full of turbulence; it will as likely break out again in some other way; one must be thankful he has at least agreed - and take it from there. As for the youths they had too much spirit and required a challenge; but many were fairly inarticulate and needed guidance, whilst the girls

24

would come to see themselves as people who mattered and, as they gained in self-respect, could also gain in beauty and in poise. But it would not all happen at once, it would take time."

Teilo stayed a week or so with his fellow monks; there was a good deal of talking to be done with both the warriors and the girls at the stronghold and this opportunity had come unexpectedly as the result of extreme distress. As Teilo took his leave of his brothers he turned to Mabon.

"You will have a replacement coming over from the island monastery soon, Mabon, and then you will have to return to your training, but at least this has given you a glimpse of the task that lies ahead for the rest of your life, should you decide to become a fully-fledged monk. I'm sure you've found it an extraordinary experience, haven't you?"

Mabon was sitting by the same white well where they had first begun the enterprise; it seemed to him much longer ago than it actually was, since they had last been there; now they were sending Teilo off to his next commitment and he had to admit to a slight sinking feeling in the pit of his stomach at the thought. Not to be given in to though! Mabon looked up at his strong brother and with a grin wished him 'God-speed', lowering his eyes quickly as they moistened. Teilo pretended not to notice but gave him a warm hugs, As he said goodbye also to Iouill and walked away from the camp down the rough cliff path.

He reflected on the magnitude of his 'Task', which demanded all his resources and much more besides. To get alongside one person in love and understanding was demanding, but his mission was first to those many monks in his charge and then to the multitude of those in need, of little purpose and less faith around him. It was of course beyond his own strength alone; this was his mission but he needed all the support he could muster. He could only do it by total dependence on his Lord Jesus and by maintaining constant prayer to Him as he went about his business.

Teilo also knew his monks were not fearful of Vortipor, neither were they afraid to face the reality of their own inner-being - Vortipor's men faced this with wine, but the monks had learnt to face it head-on; they could now teach by example. They were practical men

25

and knew for themselves human feelings of joy, remorse, of love and fear and all else that was common to man. But what they had learnt was to bring all that they were and all that they wanted in the future to the feet of their Lord, confessing their failure to live up to His standards, yet willing daily to submit themselves to His will for their lives and, as He daily reformed their attitudes and filled their lives with peace and joy, they slowly gained in insight and understanding; they could show how to cultivate the soil with a tranquil spirit, gained through openness to God, by living that simple life, where luxuries were despised.

Teilo knew only too well however the pangs and heartaches, which had not left him untouched. Was he also on a treadmill? What was God's will for him concerning Ygrain? Should they give each other up? No sacrifice would make any sense if God did not exist. Had he got any right to run his own life? His parents, Dubricius, and his own will had all led his life in its present direction, but it now appeared to be taking on its own momentum. Bemused, Teilo looked once more at the misty island, as he turned inland on his journey to the valley of the Tywi, to King Aircol's court at Castell Argol.

Chapter Three

ARGOL.

Stumbling down the cliffs, he jumped on to the soft sand and stopped to take his breath. Looking up he was surprised to see a figure in the distance hurrying towards him across the beach. As it approached he came slowly to realise who it was - Ygrain - of all people! His feet were rooted to the ground.

"What on earth was she doing here?"- a sensation of lightness and joy filled his whole being - already warm from his climb down the steep cliff, now tears of amazement stung his eyes. Unable to think he started to move towards her and as he did so she began to run also, until they met in warm embrace - he seemed just to enfold her in his strong arms - and so they stayed for a while, unable to think or move. At last she looked up into his face and smiled - and his automatic response was to return the smile. As the breeze blew her dark hair across her face, his hand smoothed it back - and he kissed her very tenderly.

"What are you doing here?" he asked.

She found it difficult to reply; at first it was in a faltering voice that she tried to explain, but gradually it became more controlled. "I have been staying with your parents; they invited me when Annauved married but I decided this was the time, and so I come now, when I thought they would be missing her. But why am I here in your arms now? - that is really your question!

moved away slightly as Teilo searched her face trying to understand.

"Well", she murmured, "the news of the sudden death of old King Pyr has reached the mainland and seeing you coming down from Vortipor's camp, your parents sent me to let you know - I suppose they are still watching us now", she murmured, as their embrace ended and they stood just looking at each other. eyes filled with tears. as he took her hand and led her across the beach toward his parents' home.

Indeed Gwenhaf had been watching and was now looking at Teilo in stunned amazement.

"Don't say a thing", Ensic warned, "there's no reason why they shouldn't be fond of each other; they've always known each other. Let the youngsters work it out for themselves."

But when Gwenhaf discovered that Teilo had left his brother Mabon in Vortipor's camp, she could contain herself no longer. "Do you mean to tell me that he's there with but one other monk!" she spluttered. "What has come over you Teilo? Have you completely lost your senses?" she scolded.

He tried vainly to explain that he had Vortipor's word for it that the monks would not be harmed in any way.

"But do you really believe that a single word of his can be trusted?", exclaimed the distraught mother, stumping off to recover herself. This was not the behaviour she expected of Teilo; he had never behaved in this way before, neither had Ygrain; where would it all end? His future was so promising and he had been so happy in 'the life'; he couldn't change course now, just when bigger and better opportunities were being presented to him. She was so proud of her elder son; Ensic was certainly wrong; she had a duty to make him pull himself together."

For once in his life, however, Teilo was able to take his time. If Pyr was dead, there was no point in going back to Argol immediately, for the King and court would have to return to Narberth for his funeral - it was probably up to him to make the preparations anyhow - unless Dubricius was still on the island. With these changed plans he would be able to stay on at his parents' home for two or three days at least and he and Ygrain would have a chance to talk. It was just the opportunity he had hoped for.

Having discovered that Dubricius was still on the island and that he would not be needed to make the funeral plans, Teilo found himself free. The more they talked the more he realised that she was just the girl for him. It was a happy time, just chatting and getting to know each other, with Gwenhaf and Ensic trying to be discreet, but privately able to judge the situation much more clearly than the young couple. The house was alive again with warmth and laughter for a short while, until Teilo had to leave - never had he felt less like going than he did then.

"I can't return after the funeral I am afraid - I shall have to make my way up to Castell Argol; the king has something to show me there", he said with sudden misgivings, so he turned to Ygrain and told her what he knew of the King's future plans for him. Both knew it was going to be a major task and as Ygrain listened she paled; she felt herself go cold and it was in subdued mood that she had to say goodbye, wondering when she would meet him again.

He set out on foot with his staff in hand and strapped on his back the gospel book. He knew the countryside well as he struck inland past Ludchurch, where the preaching cross that he had planted some years ago now stood solid, as if addressing the landscape; people loved to hear Teilo preach in this place, where the wind always seems to blow. Teilo himself felt a great sense of elation there, but he passed on to Narberth once more to the King's main fort, where King Aircol could be seen quite regularly, holding court for the tribes of the countryside around. Men would come to him to settle their disputes and his judgement would usually be considered fair and wise.

At Narberth the gossip was rife; it seemed that Pyr had had an accident and word had gone about that he was drunk. "What did really happen?" Teilo asked of Dubricius, when he met up with him in the town. "Poor old Pyr", replied Dubricius, "you remember how old and frail he had become; he drank rather too heavily on that last night, as much as anything to warm his poor old bones, so that wandering in the courtyard of the monastery on his way to his cell, he tripped over the stone which surrounds the mouth of the well, fell in headfirst and drowned. It really was a very sad death for the noble old fellow and a great tragedy that he could not die with dignity in his bed; we are all grieving about it".

Dubricius was busy with the funeral arrangements, seeing to it that everyone who had to attend the old King's funeral was notified and would be there on time. He had told the immediate family. King Aircol had ridden down from Argol with soldiers and officials; the town was milling with people arriving by the hour from all directions. The grandsons who were to stand behind Aircol in the procession were also there by now, including Vortipor, looking resplendent in his military uniform - and his guards, all properly turned out for once. "What a difference!" Teilo thought to himself, as he caught sight of Vortipor's brothers; Erbin the eldest was pleasant enough, but fairly ineffective, really better suited to life as a scholar, with his many manuscripts in the safety of his fort near Tenby. The middle son Meirig, with his young lad Pwll; the child stood solemnly behind his father now. Meirig spent much of his time near the west coast beyond the Prescelly mountains in the ancient fort of Nevern, near Dewi's monastery at Menevia. He was glamorous and as fair as Vortipor was dark. His handsome charm made him look every inch a prince with his gentle manners. Aircol's daughters stood around him also, the two favourite staying by his side throughout the ceremony.

Dubricius and his monks led the procession, chanting in unison as they went down the steep path leading through the settlements from the royal fortress high on the overhanging rock above; King Aircol and the royal mourners followed, honouring the old king. Wearing their finest garments they slowly proceeded past the main buildings of wood or wattle and clay, until they reached the large church of sawn oak, built long and low within the encampment.

That evening there was a banquet also in honour of the king. Many nobles spoke of his achievements - in laying the foundations for a peaceful Demetia and fighting alongside the mighty King Brychan to clear the Irish out of the coastlands- and how with Uther Pendragon, father of the great Arthur, he had helped in the fighting around the goldmines near the Roman fort at Llanio, now the home of five saints - how he had left King Aircol a great legacy of peaceful co-existence with those Irish who had remained - and how he had then retired like a good Christian to that more peaceful profession of Abbot, donating his own island to the church. King Aircol proudly listened to the many tributes to his father, remembering how as a young man he had taken over when his father, friend and colleague of the Emperor

Arthur, had retired. It was Arthur also who had welcomed him to his bodyguard along with all those other lesser kings and princes.

Teilo sat silent at the dinner table; he had a lot on his mind, personal thoughts and emotions which he could not easily cast aside. His silence was misunderstood for mourning. He found himself sitting with some important court officials, Anna and Amwn Ddu (Samson's parents),and his uncle Umbraphael who had come over from Brittany. Amwn Ddu and Umbraphael were both brothers who had married two sisters of the royal family of Gwent; they were senior officials at King Aircol's court and had been on Pyr's island for Lent.

Umbraphael turned to Teilo, "Have you heard about Samson?" he asked. Teilo looked up to see the amused expression on Umbraphael's face; "Dubricius has appointed Samson in Pyr's place as Abbot!" ; he turned to see Teilo's reaction.

Shaken from his reverie, Teilo could not help a slow grin again steal over his face at the thought of the ardent young Samson in charge at Ynys Byr. "The monks will have a hard time of it meeting his stringent rules - they entirely need someone to rule them, but in moderation."

"It will only be an interim appointment", smiled Umbraphael. "No doubt you know that Samson hopes to leave for Ireland soon. I daresay Dubricius thought it would teach Samson a short lesson in gentleness, but he has persuaded me to go over to Ireland and take charge of a monastery there also."

"Well," Teilo replied "Samson has certainly turned his own family upside down lately! Didn't he convert them all? - all, that is, except one of his sisters, I think!"

Samson's parents sat quietly listening and his mother Anna's cheeks glowed with happiness hearing about his work amongst the family. Her husband and his brother were part of a large contingent of Bretons, descendants of the royal line of Elen of Wales and the Roman Emperor Magnus Maximus, who had settled over a century ago in Llydaw or Brittany. Now they were coming back to Wales to help convert the nation to Christ; it was an adventurous campaign fought for the soul of Wales by men who had been great warriors in Arthur's war with the pagan Saxons; indeed they had held them at bay. Now they were anxious to fight just as virile a campaign, but this time for the souls of men.

Anna had waited many years for Samson to be born; when she became pregnant, she was so overjoyed, that she and her husband had offered him even before his birth to God for His service. Samson was then sent at the age of five to Iltud's school on the coast of Glamorgan where Anna became proud of his brilliant progress. When her husband saw his ability however, he seemed to forget the vow and wanted Samson to assume control, take over the family land and to serve in the court of King Aircol like Amwn Ddu himself. Anna became most distraught reminding him of his sacred vow, until in the end he reluctantly gave way and agreed to honour it. Now he was also to watch Samson with pride.

The King sent word to Teilo that he would still meet him at Argol as arranged, as soon as he could get away, so Teilo slipped away after the meal and set out on foot again to the river Tywi. On his way he had fortunately to pass his monastery at Llanddowror, where he stayed the night. Rising early the following morning he stood by the stream and could hear the strangest of noises.

"What on earth is all that crying" he thought, "not one baby surely but a whole nursery by the sound of it". Peering through the rushes by the stream, sure enough he could make out seven tiny babies lying in the wet grass. A man stood there who, after busily stripping off his clothes and furtively looking round, grabbed the nearest, and shoving its face below the surface and held the wriggling baby hard down in the water. Teilo burst out of the rushes and hit him hard on the chin, sending him flying. In so doing he released the baby, by this time nearly dead, and grasping the limp little form, held it upside down by its feet and gently massaged it, until it took a convulsive breath and was violently sick. Thankful that it was still alive Teilo pushed it inside his cloak, massaging it gently until instead of that bundle of blue skin he could gradually feel wriggling limbs, pink and warm once more.

The man huddled there dripping wet and cringing with fear. Recognising Teilo he was on the point of taking to his heels, when Teilo seized him, remembering him as the poor father of a local

32

family whom he had met some years before; even at that time he had had a family too large to feed and had come to Teilo for help; Teilo had counselled him and his wife even then to abstain from intercourse and to concentrate on rearing the family they had already, but could hardly manage.

Teilo's hackles rose. So angry was he that he could have hit the man again and again; but instead, controlling his voice he knew not how, he told the man to help him carry the children into the monastery where they would be fed and housed. "You are unfit ever again to care for children", Teilo burst out when the seven boys were safely fed and cared for by the monks. "Go away and don't let me ever catch sight of you again."

The boys grew up to bless Teilo and eventually Dubricius was to give them a monastery near Dewi's at Mathrey.

Teilo however was in no mood to stop now, for by the King's command he had to join him and the court at Argol as soon as was practicable. Hurrying to regain lost time, he broke his usual habit of walking on foot and took a mountain pony from his monastery at Llanddowror. Riding as far as the seaport of Moridinum, he took the first boat he saw going in the right direction. which turned out to be a flat- bottomed one carrying supplies to the King up at Castell Argol.

The river valley was very wide down here by the sea, as the boatman pulled at his oars, singing softly as they travelled up river. The meadows were full of the marsh flowers and birds of early summer, while the hills beyond were held in blue mist as they plied slowly along with the incoming tide. Teilo now had plenty of time to rest. He dozed a little in the afternoon sun, lulled by the oarsman's steady rhythm and the gently rocking boat. He was still nodding away as the boat passed the lush green meadows where cattle grazed and on the river bank, camouflaged by bullrushes, he missed the perennial sight of a heron resting on one leg after a satisfying meal. Each day a siege of herons flew out from their heronry below Grongar and set out in line, dropping off in turn as they came to their own section of the river bank. Over the boat two black birds also crossed the valley together on their peaceful expedition. Spring was showing her colours everywhere.

But Teilo awoke with a jolt when the oarsman called out to a fisherman on the bank. As he looked up he saw Argol in full view, set right in the middle of the valley, almost surrounded by its lake of tidal water. The sun was shining through full clusters of cloud; and high above, where the buildings of the stronghold could be distinguished, the hill appeared as yellow and green, shading to darker greens and blues below the skyline. Clouds moved across the hill and over the water, creating reflections of clarity and colour which took Teilo's breath away. It was the look-out on Grongar who first saw Teilo approach. His journey from Narberth had taken nearly three days.

King Aircol had various strongholds throughout his kingdom of Demetia, but his favourite was the stronghold of Argol with its steep sides descending to a ford on the Tywi river, which wrapped itself around the foot of the hill. In winter, when the waters spread across the valley, flooding the fertile fields, the stronghold was almost cut off from the land, except to the north-east where a spine of high ground stood out, almost connecting it to Grongar hill, 'the round fort' where Aircol's fighting men were encamped and being trained to keep a vigilant eye up and down the wide valley. It was along this spine, one finds in the 'Laws of Wales', that the ancient white cattle with long horns and pink ears would stretch in a line, head to tail, with a bull every ninth as ransom for the King. From the top of Grongar could be seen Urien's stronghold, like an eagle's nest perched on a rock, three sides plunging down to deep chasms where the river Cennen flows. Aircol's men would signal to Urien in his fortress at Castell Cennen over that range of hills, at the first hint of danger in the valley.

With a bump the boat arrived at the base of the hill and Teilo stepped out to begin his climb to the top of Argol. It was very steep but he strode strongly upwards; he took the opportunity half-way up however to pause, turning to look back down the valley. The country was generally well-wooded, but this hill was covered only with thorn bushes. Here and there the grazing sheep had left skeins of wool, stuck fast but blowing in the wind. Going on again he found the entrance bank well fortified and guarded by soldiers of Aircol's army, dressed in leather and sandals, with protective breast plates also of

DRYSLWYN CASTLE.

Soft ground etching by John George Wood, 1812

National Museum of Wales

leather; about their shoulders hung thick woollen cloaks; they now stood at the imposing entrance gate smartly attired, welcoming Teilo. He passed through the entrance yard, up and through the inner defences where the court officials had their dwellings and further into a private courtyard, where the King's living quarters were to be found.

The court official greeted Teilo warmly. "It's good to see you again; how many dusty miles have you travelled, I wonder, since you were last at Argol? I have set aside a wattle shelter for you to refresh yourself and rest, with food after your journey. You have now time to yourself until dinner, when the king will see you in the large banqueting hall - but after dinner he has told me to say that he wishes to speak with you in private."

It was a welcome pause for Teilo; he settled down on a stool at the entrance to his hut and opened his Bible; he needed to pray about the discussions ahead and to prepare his mind. He could hear the gentle murmur of sheep and cattle far below, while the occasional skylark sounded so clear high above. A butterfly settled on the nettles near his feet, its painted wings fluttering, well spread to enjoy the full warmth of the sun.

The call to dinner came as the sounds from the river below faded with the early evening light. Teilo made his way up to the top of the hill, where a long imposing wooden hall stood; it was here that the evening banquet had been prepared. As he entered and was shown to a table, the court officials were already seated; he looked around; there were many familiar faces - it was not for nothing that Teilo had been named 'Sunshine' (Eliud) by his family - people warmed to him as he exchanged greetings with them as old friends and they laughed and chatted.

As the King entered, everyone rose to their feet. King Aircol was now approaching sixty, taller then average and of powerful build. His face was long and tough but, when he laughed as he frequently did, the hard lines of the famous soldier softened to give the impression of a man of great goodness. He was of course still in court-mourning for his dearly loved father and looked grave and pale. When the King was seated, the rest of the court made themselves comfortable on benches set around the tables. Close to him was the official cup-bearer and on the other side his master of horse alongside the King's falconer, all in their appointed place.

Aircol had ambitious plans for south Wales; he planned to turn the whole country to Christianity with the help of the Breton missionaries, the leader of whom was Cadfan, sitting on Teilo's right; he leaned across to attract Teilo's attention.

"Tomorrow will be a momentous day for us all", he said, " We have had much discussion about it. I expect you will have an audience with the King tonight after the meal."

"I've had orders to attend," Teilo said thoughtfully, "I know roughly what he has in mind, but so far there have only been hints from Dubricius and of course I need to know the order of events for the dedication. The implications of such a centre are multiple so that much careful planning is required."

"Teilo, it's been a long time since you were up this way; where have you been hiding out recently?", a local official interrupted.

He was Aircol's chief huntsman, a man with a keen eye and open ruddy countenance, who knew the woods around like the back of his hand. He had a way of taming his precious hunting hawks; they might fly so high that they became mere specks in the sky above the hunting party - yet when the huntsman gave his soft call they would drop like a stone, landing gently on his padded arm.

"Teilo's been at Vortipor's camp", came a quick reply from across the table.

Teilo looked up at Cadfan keenly; they had had many discussions at Cadfan's house just to the north, on the slope of the hill facing Argol. He was a renowned warrior who had left Brittany in order to help co-ordinate the work of his fellow countrymen in the area. As the powerful ruler of Elen's family from over the sea, he was leading the Christian mission to Wales from the Breton point of view. His jet black hair was greying now at the temples; he spoke quickly with a slight accent, but their language was so very similar that they could understand each other well. Cadfan's brother Sadwrn also lived with his wife a few miles away in the hills near Caio, where they had founded a church up in the hill region nearby.

The brothers had planned with Teilo strong Church settlements in undefended territory along the borders of Ceredigion and Demetia, a Christian enterprise in most vulnerable territory. There was nothing new in this; Dewi and Teilo's forebears had been sent from northern Britain a few generations before to deal with the wild Irish who were constantly invading the coasts of Wales. They had all read what the great Patrick had said about the raiding party which captured him only a decade or so before. Patrick had told how he was living with his family (perhaps on the Isle of Man) in comfortable circumstances of minor nobility with Potitus, his grandfather, an ordained Christian priest in the village, and his father, a decurion or local official of the national government as well as being a Deacon of the Christian Church. Their circumstances were well-to-do, with servants in the house and Patrick at the age of about sixteen when Irish pirates had descended on his parents' villa and forcibly taken him away as a slave to Ireland.

Urien Rheged it was (the most distinguished of the thirteen kings of the north and whose mother Myfanwy, was a daughter of King Brychan in Wales) who now defended this area between the Tawe and the Tywi rivers and, in addition to being King of Strathclyde, was also known as Lord of Iscennen and King of Gower, Carnwyllion and Kidwelly; he was thus King Aircol's immediate neighbour and friend. From Carreg Cennen to the mouth of the river Llew, near the Roman fort of Leucarum, he maintained a strong presence, for all around the Welsh coasts the people still had to be vigilant. Thus it was Urien's men who were patrolling Gower and around Kidwelly to the east and south of Argol, while to the west the raids still continued.

"Recently", Cadfan told Teilo, "a priest-in-charge of one of our new churches on those weaker border defences to the west has been murdered at the altar - in the manner of a Druidical sacrifice."

Teilo was working to convert those clans who remained primitive and pagan in Wales and who still practised human sacrifice. Some believed in the transmigration of souls, while folk-lore often referred

37

to men assuming the shape of animals and women being created out of flowers; visits were still made to the underworld, while magic still held sway in a cannibalistic world, where the special prize of war was the head of an enemy, as was the case of course throughout much of the world and the Roman Empire in particular. The mission being continually planned at Argol was directed at this local situation.

The meal continued with quiet conversation; tomorrow would be a great feast day to celebrate the consecration of the hill, but today remained a normal evening gathering. The fire in the hall was kept burning, while on the floor, spread with rushes, two of the King's favourite dogs were asleep after their hard day's hunting in the forest.

Apart from the warriors' camp above, the stronghold was filled with hungry young men who could each consume great quantities of food. Fortunately the land was very fertile in this wide valley of Ystrad Tywi, grazing was good and milk and butter rich and plentiful when properly husbanded.

A bard strummed quietly by the open hearth and the flickering flames threw the king's great shadow on the walls, mingling with the lesser shadows from rush tapers.

At last Aircol stood up and withdrew to an ante-room beside the great hall - it was here that Teilo had been summoned to attend later. He went in quietly, his brown hair smoothed down and for once, as he stood there straight and tall, his merry brown eyes held a solemn expression. Aircol took in Teilo's demeanour with some satisfaction; he was well pleased with the tough work that Teilo had already accomplished and felt that this was a man of outstanding physical and moral courage. He motioned to Teilo to sit down.

"I believe that Dubricius has already given a hint of my plans for you? The hill further up the valley is now given to the church, for the building of a great centre to consolidate the work in the area. Is it your wish that you take on this great task?"

Teilo nodded as he looked at the King, who continued:

"I know that you and Dewi already have a large church organisation at Llanarthney, close to Argol, but this new centre is now required to train those many young men coming forward to work for the church, due in large part to the work you and Dewi have already accomplished in the area".

Aircol had worked all his life for a more settled country and valued the men of his race who had supported him in his endeavour.

"I remember the work you did to help Dewi build his monastery to the extreme west of my country, in the marshy ground of the Valley of Roses on the coast. Dewi's monastery serves busy seaways from Devon, Cornwall and the continent and is the point of embarkation to Ireland, not to mention shipping from lands further east in the Mediterranean. But Teilo, your future centre is at a point where several land routes converge, those from Urien's territory and the south-east, as well as those west through Ceredigion and north to Brycheiniog and on through the centre of Wales to Dubricius's area in Henllan."

Teilo realised that Aircol was sending him to a very strategic place; his mind went back to the time when he assisted his cousin Dewi to build his monastery at the most westerly point of their land facing Ireland. The Irish pirates would land in the bays and set up camp on the cliffs above. Teilo vividly recalled the pagan camp of Boia nearby and how he had become curious to see what Dewi was up to. Boia's wife had made violent objections to Dewi's work and sent her maidens to the lake close by, to bathe naked in order to tantalise Dewi's monks. They had been shocked by this suggestive behaviour and begged Dewi to leave the place. He however refused and stood his ground.

Boia's wife had then sat down and, taking her step-daughter, laid the girl's head on her lap, pretending to show her affection by combing her hair, but then in pagan Druidical fashion had taken out a knife and slit the girl's throat, cutting off her head. Some demon then appeared to seize her and she had fled, her step-daughter having been duly sacrificed to her pagan gods. Boia, himself a Druid as well as chieftain, decided in his anger and distress to attack Dewi's camp. By a strange coincidence however that very night, another Irish raider named Liscki invaded Boia's camp, cut off his head and burnt the camp to the ground. Fortunately Liscki then left Dewi in peace to get on with his work, which had grown and thrived in spite of this macabre incident.

But Teilo was woken from his daydream as Aircol continued:

My son Erbin shall be at your disposal, together with the men in the camp adjacent to your hill, so that you will not want for builders, but the plan must be yours and you will be in charge from the start. Tomorrow the court will adjourn to this hill and you will consecrate it to the Lord Jesus Christ and dedicate it to His work for ever."

This moment was perhaps the most memorable of Teilo's whole life. He realised that he would now be able to consolidate the work of many years throughout this valley, but Aircol, seeing Teilo deep in thought, decided that this was not the time to talk of practical detail - such could wait until Teilo had understood the wider significance of the project; he allowed Teilo to withdraw.

Teilo walked back to his little wattle shelter and as he was dropping off to sleep he had a dream. The dream was of the Holy City, the new Jerusalem, sent down to earth from Heaven by God. Unable to sleep, many other thoughts came tumbling through his mind; his cousin Dewi's monastery had been set in a valley after the Welsh fashion, but now in contrast he was being offered a hill after the Irish pattern of monastery building. In such hill forts tribes normally lived together in enclosures for protection; they built earthworks all around, leaving a gap in the embankment for traffic in and out; outside this outerbank there would be fields for cultivation.

But monasteries required two embankments providing three zones of increasing sanctity: the outermost was for the dwelling houses of the townsfolk and a market cross. Next would come the street-trading area between two walls for protection and in the centre a third area, the monastic enclosure, usually circular or oval in shape. The ideal city should possess four gates, with a stream of water flowing through the centre for cleansing and baptism.

With his mind racing so fast, it was little wonder that Teilo slept little that night. He rose early for prayer, preferring to go out upon the hillside, to commune with his God. As dawn rose across the valley, the tips of sunlight again lit the camp on Grongar hill high above, while over the whole mountain range Urien's camp, perched high on the stronghold of rock above the Cennen river, could just be seen.

Teilo looked east from Argol in the direction of his future monastery - a hill soon to be called Llandeilo after him. The birds were fluttering and flying in the spring sunshine and he could hear the sounds of the camp, as breakfast was prepared. "It's time to return," he thought; this is going to be one of the most exciting and important days of my life". He breakfasted along with other members of the court; the King was absent but Teilo was told that he would appear later that morning with the Royal procession.

Tremendous excitement ensued and, when all was finally prepared, the procession set out up the valley with the King and bodyguard on horseback, Teilo leading the procession on foot. They reached the hill around noon. The early promise of the day was gloriously fulfilled. Below wound the beloved river, the wide valley curving at this point towards the foot of the Black mountains and the higher Brecon Beacons. They came to the edge of the hill, down the side of which a stream was flowing to the river below. The King dismounted from his horse and, with the Gospel Book strapped as usual to his shoulders and staff in hand, he began to walk, thereby setting the boundary for the new monastic centre. He was followed by and a vast procession of followers, chanting as they went.

As soon as the ceremony was over, Teilo surveyed the scene - a large expanse of land dedicated to God - with of course the stream flowing through for baptism and cleansing. It was here beside the stream that he would build his church; he had had considerable practice in choosing a site. His eye was unerring; he would always choose a most prominent spot, laying the firmest foundations, as though to last for ever. This his most important church was to be no exception. He was now able to speak to the people about the Eternal City.

"Dear friends," he said echoing the thoughts of Augustine of Hippo, "the only basis and bond of a true city is righteousness raised to a higher plane, a system of right relationships between men, but it must begin with a right relationship with one's God. The city of God belongs to the great society of the universe, where first there is faith in His will and in His system of loving relationships; through His grace man is then able to set his other relationships aright; 'Order in me my love for my fellow men' should be our prayer, for while we are only temporary residents here on earth, we must each try to learn to be permanent residents of that Heavenly Kingdom. These words by the great Augustine of Hippo are most apt to our thoughts today. We are taught in Holy Scripture that we must not rest in our work until the kingdoms of this world are become the Kingdom of our Lord God and of His Christ. It may not happen in our lifetime, for the rule of the one God amongst all nations throughout the world will take much more understanding and tolerance than we have yet attained, nor for many centuries to come, but here on this spot we pledge to live and fight for that world kingdom of the future, to play our little part to bring it to pass."

So did Teilo preach the word of God and all the people prayed; they sang their psalms of praise and finally Teilo dedicated the land to God's use forever. Then it was time for the whole procession to return in good order to Aircol's stronghold, to feast and celebrate.

Conversation that night at the feast was animated. Samson's father, Amwn Ddu, seated near Teilo began to talk of his birthplace in Brittany (Armorica as it is sometimes called), while Cadfan, the present head of Elen's family in Brittany, joined in the reminiscences. They were going over the old familiar story of the plan for Wales - for it was again in the forefront of their minds, now that Aircol had given this special piece of ground for the building of Teilo's monastery.

"When I was a youth in Brittany", Cadfan recalled, "all my family were watching with great consternation, as the Saxons surged westwards across Britain; we decided to formulate a plan to save Wales. I remember my father telling me how the British Emperor Constantine Fendigaid and his wife had been killed by the savage invaders; many of the leading families had died with them, and so from the court at Brittany they sent back Ambrosius Aurelianus, the son of the dead Emperor who had been brought up in Brittany for safety. He returned to lead the British resistance, partly because he had an hereditary claim, but also because he was an able general, a quiet and modest man loved and revered by all. He landed in Britain with ten thousand of our Breton soldiers to carry out the counter attack and he ably defended the west for at least two decades. Then suddenly and inexplicably Ambrosius, who had done so much for your country, was poisoned."

Teilo knew the old story quite well, but it was particularly fitting that it should be remembered at this time. Cadfan continued - "On his death his brother Uther took his place."

Teilo knew that after the fighting, one of Ambrosius's brothers, Uther Pendragon, with Uther's son Arthur and his foster-brother Cai, had given the lands to the north of Demetia (in the region of the gold mines near Dolaucothi) to the Princes of Powys; these Princes were Brochmail 'Ysgythrog'(meaning with teeth like tusks) and his sons, one of whom was a friend of Teilo, named Tysilio, who had become a disciple of Dubricius. He was very different from the other son Cynan, who was both warlike and acquisitive and whom Teilo had long thought might become a future trouble-maker in the area.

"Still", thought Teilo, "Ambrosius's son King Perphirius and his family live close to the area."

Teilo was friendly with Perphirius's son, Paul Aurelian, who was a few years older than himself. Paul had refused his inheritance, or to rule the large estate in East-Glamorgan close to Iltud's monastery; instead he had built for himself an isolated monastery on the range of hills opposite his home in Llandeusant.

"We are not fighting just for our country", Cadfan burst out, "we are fighting for an ideal- an idea concerned not just with things temporary, but with eternal truths!"

He continued - "The Christian faith in these islands must be preserved. We have been guardians of this faith from the beginning; we defend the vision and imagination of our great forbear, Elen, who on returning to Wales after the death of her husband Magnus Maximus established our dynasty here."

Cadfan turned to Teilo and spoke in a quieter voice.

"Teilo, there is an enormous task to be done from your new base; you've got to be outward-looking: with Dewi you have established many 'llannau' in Demetia and I'm trying to consolidate your work in the Ceredigion area; in fact my nephew Padarn has brought many men from Brittany with him to help, while Dewi's thriving centre in western Demetia on the communication routes couldn't be better placed - everyone must pass his monastery there whether they are entering or leaving the country; we'll be relying on you to face east against those incoming Saxons and to support Dubricius in his stand at Henllan. We are forging here in south-west Wales a wedge of resistance which I hope will become so strong that no-one can ever break it, chiefly by winning the hearts and minds of the people for Christ; then will this nation have passed down an unbreakable spirit in perpetuity."

The fire burnt low and, tired after the meal and animated conversation, the guests began to realise just how late it had become and appeared anxious to depart. Before dismissing them however, Aircol turned to Teilo:

"This is your day; today we have given you land on which to build your monastery to the glory of God. What do you say? Have you made your decision? Will you conclude the festivities for us at least with a few words?"

Teilo stood up and, as the guests hushed to listen his face became grave, his voice earnest:

"King Aircol, today we have so much to be thankful for and, as we celebrate the consecration of this hill, we are reminded that our Lord Jesus Himself came to this earth. I have a deep yearning to go to the land of our Saviour's birth, to re-dedicate myself before starting on such a new venture. I wonder too whether you would give me your permission to take one or two companions with me on such a pilgrimage?"

The company were silent, but at length the King replied:

"I think your request is more than justified and at this point in your life, Teilo, you would be likely to gain much from that experience. Have you anyone in mind to accompany you?"

Dewi, his friend and soul-mate, the cousin who had laboured with him so hard in Christ's cause, came immediately to Teilo's mind, but he said nothing; it would be God's will and not his own, which must prompt Dewi. At length Aircol understood his hesitation and, as Teilo had hoped, asked the company to pray for God's blessing on the journey.

So Teilo at last found himself alone and wended his way slowly down the path to his shelter for the night. The thoughts that occupied his mind were many and muddled. He must come to terms with himself, his mission and Ygrain and it seemed to him that the journey to Jerusalem could be a wonderful chance to do just that. He slept in fits and starts that night. The next morning awakening early before the rest of the camp, he slipped quietly down to the waiting boat at the foot of the hill; as the boatman pulled away from the shore, the lapping of the oars was all that could be heard as the boat glided unobtrusively downstream.

Chapter Four

Perspective. Soul-friends:
Teilo's friends and contemporaries.

Teilo sat in the boat, drifting slowly downstream from Argol, with skeins of tangled thoughts twisting in his mind. He needed to get away at this juncture to think things through. The trip to Jerusalem would serve such a purpose and a lot more besides. He must say goodbye to Ygrain, but first he would have to find Dewi and see what his thoughts were about joining him on the journey to Jerusalem.

Dewi and Teilo had been friends since their school days. They first met at old Paulinus's school near Narberth. He remembered that winter still, cold with every twig pointing bare across the winter sky, a puffed out bird or two standing silent under the bushes, to shelter from the snow as it began to fall - breaking from white clouds above, to float upon the earth. At a time when all who could stayed sheltering by the hearth, the silence was broken by the whistle of a youth as he ran across the path calling his dog to follow him. Teilo was tall and strong, of noble bearing with merry brown eyes, a gangling youth, with short brown hair. He and his cousin had been sent to gather firewood, by the monks at the monastery of St Paulinus where both boys had been sent to be trained when very young, and both being very bright where they had taken to the life of study with ease. Teilo with his eagerness and enjoyment of life was a good friend for the more serious Dewi and would often laugh him out of his more sombre moods. Dewi's black hair and eyes sparkled as they raced across the scrubland and, though smaller and lighter than Teilo, he was tough too, with that wiry strength which often has deep reserves of energy. A wolfhound had bounded past them as they struggled with their load of brushwood back to the monastery, to leave the cold air silent again - closed up tight and quiet, after the warmth and brightness of the boys had cut through the winter world with their moment of joy and laughter - one of those days lodged forever in Teilo's memory.

After Teilo had completed his early schooling with the great teacher Dubricius on Ynys Byr, Dubricius had decided that, since he had taught the boy all that he could, he should be sent to the mainland for further training with old Paulinus. Dewi's early schooling on the other hand had been at the old monastery of Hen Fynyw, near the west coast of Ceredigion, under the care of his uncle, the learned Bishop Gustilianus, his mother Non's brother; from the start therefore the boys had a different approach, although they were both second cousins-once-removed to Arthur.

Dewi was son of Sant, King of Ceredigion; his mother was Non; but he himself did not want the life of a king, instead disciplining himself so severely that he would often only drink water and eat bread; he later came to be called 'Aquaticus' because of this strict regime. Dewi represented the western culture, being exclusively Welsh, whilst his cousin Teilo was greatly influenced by the culture brought by the Romans to the eastern part of the country through Dubricius, who represented both cultures. Dubricius had been brought up in the centre of Britain, on the Roman highway close to the ancient lead mines on his father's land near Ross-on-Wye. He had both Welsh and Irish forebears through his grandfather King Brychan, while the Welsh name of Dyfrig (Waterbearer) was symbolic of Dubricius as leader. Wells and water playing a great part in the Celtic church, Dubricius was the bearer of special cleansing and spiritual qualities attributed to water.

Old Paulinus had been a disciple of Germanus; he played a most important part in the monastic movement in Wales. He was known as Paul Hen, or old Paulinus of the north, his sons Peulan, Guidivel and Gwynfench also founding churches. At his famous college near Hen Dy Gwyn, Whitland, as master of schools there, he had placed under himself as superintendents, Flewin and Gredivel, two sons of Ithel Hael an Armorican prince who had joined Cadfan's immigration. However, old Paulinus had another monastery up in the hill country near Caio, at a place known as Crug-y-bar, where his brother Urthwal presided and nearby a Roman station, now abandoned but called

Louentium, had been established earlier to supervise the gold mines there.

It was to old Paulinus's second monastery near Caio that it had been decided to send Teilo for retreat before beginning his ministry, after he had completed his training near Narberth at Hen Dy Gwyn. But first he was sent to visit another Paul, the young Paul Aurelian, who was a little older than Teilo.

Paul Aurelian was tall with mouse-coloured hair and grey-blue eyes, his bearing that of a nobleman, but his expression more that of an ascetic, slightly withdrawn and yet of compelling power. He was not strictly handsome, with typical strong features of Roman nose and long face, but he was clearly a man who would make his mark whatever his chosen profession.

Paul's home was close to Llandovery. As Cadfan had recalled earlier, Paul's father, King Perphirius of Bovium in mid Glamorgan, was the son of Ambrosius Aurelianus, his great grandfather therefore being Constantine Fendigaid, so called 'King of Britain', a Roman Emperor. Paul's father was thus a brother of Uther Pendragon, and Paul himself first cousin to the great Arthur.

King Perphirius had left Bovium to settle in this region near the gold mines at the time that the Princes of Powys were given the land round about by his brother Uther. He settled in the 'Grove of the Crows'(Llwyn y brain), near Caer Bannauc, where he raised a family of nine sons and three daughters - the third son being young Paul. His land around Bovium included the land on which Iltud's monastery was built and which King Perphirius had donated to the church.

There was thus a deliberate strategy. Paul's grandfather Ambrosius Aurelianus had worked for many years from his main base in the centre of Britain alongside Dubricius, throwing back the Saxon advance. This great base near Cinderford, six miles from where Dubricius was born (Weston -under-Penyard) had been used by Caractacus to repel the first Roman invaders, it looked down the winding Severn river right up through the centre of the country beyond. Here he built a monastery and, with the reserves of coal for warmth and protection in a long winter of hiding in the dark forest in which they could withdraw, making a natural fortress against enemy

48

attack. With Dubricius, Brychan's grandson, at Henllan, they prepared a strategy which was both religious and military during the last quarter of the fifth century. Thus the families of Constantine Fendigaid and Brychan had been closely involved in religious and political affairs for several generations.

Another contemporary of Teilo was the great Cadoc, both a rich prince and a saint, who like Paul belonged to both Glamorgan and the area close to Llandovery, for his mother was another of Brychan's daughters (Gwladys, who had been carried off by King Gwynllwyw, his father, the King of east Glamorgan). Cadoc was yet another king's son of this generation determined to throw off worldly power and to become a servant of Christ. Cadoc founded a church at Llangadoc close to Paul's in Llandovery, but his important monastery was Llancarvan in Glamorgan close to Llantwit Major.

Since young Paul's home was very close to Caio, it was convenient for Teilo to visit him before he made his way to old Paulinus's monastery there. It was a great time for them both; young Teilo with his open smiling face had found a friend in Paul who could match his brilliant mind; they were soon getting along famously, as though they had been friends for years; there was so much that they could learn from each other.

As a child Paul had begged to be sent to Iltud's school near the coast, in the vale of Glamorgan. Probably he had heard about the land his father had given to the church there. Iltud's pupils exceeded two thousand, all housed in four hundred houses and seven halls. Many nobles and princes from all over Britain passed through Iltud's school, Prince Maelgwyn of north Wales, the writer and historian Gildas, and the poet Taliesin, later to become Urien's famous bard, to name but a few. Here they were taught every branch of philosophy, poetry, rhetoric, grammar and arithmetic, astronomy and so on but, above all, knowledge of the Scriptures, both the Old and New testaments. Agriculture was included, as most important in the founding of monastic settlements, Iltud even devising an improved plough for greater self-sufficiency.

The monastery grew so fast that soon Iltud needed to reclaim further land from the sea. He was also hard put to it to feed all the visitors to the monastery , so that pupils were even set to keep birds off ripening crops. When Paul's turn came for this, he failed miserably, the birds swallowing all the grain. Next day however his friends came to the rescue and together they drove all the seagulls into a big barn saving the remainder of the crop, whereupon he was forgiven by St Iltud!

Like Samson, Paul Aurelian first went to Iltud's school at the age of five and by the time he was a teenager he knew that his vocation was to follow the example of St Anthony and the Desert Fathers, to the great distress again of his father who wanted him to rule his large estates; was to leave Llantwit monastery for the hills across the valley from his home in Llandovery, to build a monastery of his own, calling it Llandeusant after his two brothers.

When Teilo visited young Paul, they followed the path of the Tywi river up to its source at the end of the valley (Ystrad Ffin), where water gushes out into an ice cold pool. Here they built their little retreat, a mountain shelter, with its spring of fresh water close by, and found that their joint insight into the Scriptures was able to reveal things which had puzzled each before; it was a highpoint in Teilo's life - here he learnt deep spiritual truths, which were to serve his ministry well in the future. Now was his resolve strengthened, not, that is, to succumb to temptation. Paul, like both Samson and Dewi, fasted a great deal - as much as two or three days at a time; normally he ate very little, perhaps bread with salt weighed and measured, dipped in water from his cup. He never touched meat, only occasionally fish and water, never wine, except at Holy Communion. All this he did to avoid satisfying his human desires, drinking in short only to slake his thirst.

This beautiful retreat, set deep in the Welsh hills, gave Paul and Teilo the opportunity both needed to contemplate God. It was formative for both, as they faced their call to take the Grace of God's presence into the dark evil of the world. Familiar as they were with the writings of Augustine of Hippo only a century before, they were conscious that though he had contemplated how the ideal city should be, when they studied their scriptures together the ideal was always far from reality. The Book of Lamentations, written by Jeremiah the prophet six hundred years before Christ was born, was a lament for the city.

Christ himself wept over Jerusalem. But Teilo and Paul were aware that they could only bring about a change of heart in the people by facing the challenge and being true to their own very different callings - Paul as an ascetic, Teilo in the midst of people.

Their training needed to be tough, but they were resilient; nevertheless their retreat ended all too soon, since Teilo was due back at Old Paulinus's monastery near Caio. The boys set off through the mountains, parting when they reached the old road, Sarn Elen; Paul went to his father's house, while Teilo crossed the ridge along Sarn Elen to Porthrydd, high above Paul's home, following that same route to the gold mines past King Mark's villa Banhedos. King Mark, father of Tristan, had watched young Paul grow to manhood, noticing his gifts as a brilliant scholar and monk and forever pressing Paul's father to let him come to his court at Lantyan on the Fowey estuary in Cornwall. Now at last Paul had received the summons from King Mark to instruct his people in Cornwall and to be their leader in the 'heavenly warfare' but, since the people of Cornwall felt their King had been Divinely directed, Paul was not only invited to go but told further that if he did not obey 'Extreme force would be used'.

King Mark, known as 'Great Dog' of Dumnonia, was later to be known as the king who ruled four nations, each with a different tongue, his brother, King Constantine of Dumnonia used to stay at this villa Banhedos.

Llandovery was a lively place in Roman times, with a Roman fort at Llanfair near the river Tywi and a civilian settlement of twenty or thirty dwellings, where tanners and workers in precious metals lived in the hubbub of their small settlement. Gold torques and other ornaments have been found near these gold mines, including a model snake, a small golden statue of Diana and a chain of very similar pattern to those found in the ruins of Pompeii. With his villa on the route between the forts of Louentium near the gold mines and Alabum(Llandovery), King Mark as military commander was well able to supervise operations under Paul Aurelian's father King Perphirius. Although the gold mines had only been used for about a hundred years by the Romans, there was still precious metal left.

Teilo travelled along with a light heart after parting with Paul Aurelian. As he climbed the ridge, he was surrounded by panoramic views. Passing over the top, he dropped once again down the valley to Old Paulinus's monastery (which was close to the gold mines) at Crug-y-bar. Paul took with him twelve monks and, leaving Llandeusant monastery in the capable hands of his two brothers Potolius and Notolius, departed from that loving home, his many good friends and the comfort of a wealthy ruling family.

With their 'mountain top' experience now over, the two young men set out on their life's work separately, but with fresh dedication.

The movement of Teilo's friends into Brittany via Cornwall and Devon.

As Paul said farewell to his parents, they stood in the doorway of his home in the Welsh hills under that great crag of rock where he was born and looked across the valley to the ridge of hills beyond the river, faintly blue in the morning haze - hills on which Paul's monastery was built. King Perphirius gave his son his blessing. The tall king stood at the doorway a long while as Paul set out across the valley to his monastery carrying with him a letter to Arthur, his father's first cousin, to be delivered on his way to the court of King Mark at Lantyan, near Fowey in Cornwall.

Secure in the knowledge now that his work would progress under his brothers Potolius and Notolius, he took leave of his friends and set out with a stout heart from Llanddeusant monastery high on that ridge opposite his father's home. Of his initial twelve companions, Tigernomalus (Dyrfal), Hercanus, Lowenamus and Bretowennus (Brydwen) came with him initially, but later many more friends and relatives were to join him before he took ship for Brittany.

The little party were leaving the thriving monastery for ever. They might have followed the old route which Paul had taken so many times to his school at LlanIlltud Fawr, following the Roman road leading to a ford over the river Loughor where there was an important base in the old Roman fort of Leucarum; from here they could well have picked up the coastal route through his father's territory at Bovium, to the monastery of his master Illtud at Llantwit Major (LlanIlltud Fawr). However hoping to see Arthur at his court of Caerleon first, they followed the Roman road east, which drops down the hillside at Trecastle near Brecon and follows the river Usk into the Gwent and down through the valley bowl of Glamorgan.

This was the country of the Silures, the warrior race ruled by King Gwynllyw, Cadoc's father and where Cadoc himself was educated by the Irish monk Tathan at Caerwent. The Romans had ruled these strong people by forcing them to come down from their hill forts to live in the town, where they could keep an eye on them. Now that the Romans had left, the people reverted to their hill forts again, leaving Caerwent in the middle of the valley with its Roman shops, baths and basilica, a very pleasant market town for the Silures and a staging post before crossing the river mouth of the Severn.

Paul avoided Caerwent however, going straight to Caerleon in the hope of seeing Arthur there The Romans had called it Isca after the river Usk which flows alongside, but it was also known as Caerleon - the city of the legions laid out in AD75 as the headquarters of the Roman second legion of Augusta (that same legion which had the custody of the Apostle Paul in Rome, many of whom St Paul converted to Christianity).

The enormous barracks were now deserted, but the magnificent city still had Roman baths, an amphitheatre for sport and entertainment and many centrally heated houses with gilded roofs, enclosed in mighty walls and surrounded by hills and meadows. Up this river ships sailed to the legendary site supposed by some to have been one of Arthur's courts, from many foreign countries; here the missionaries Fagan and Dyfan were sent by Pope Eleutherius in AD156, so that the legend says that by AD 185 it is claimed that it was important enough to be made an archiepiscopal see, one of the three in Britain, the others being London and York; here too Julius and Aaron were martyred for their faith in AD303. For Arthur may have been an important city, while Cadoc had a church there to carry on the work of the early founders, although Dubricius of course would officiate on important state occasions.

Discovering that Arthur was not here, but gone to the summer country, Paul went on south-west across the fertile plain of Glamorgan, where Cadoc now lived like a prince in his enormous monastery of Llancarvan. Cadoc had been forced by his father to maintain some secular rule over a small portion of his inheritance, although his chief desire was to serve God as a monk and he was also known as a great traveller.

Though their lifestyle was so different, Paul and Cadoc had much in common. Both fathers were great Kings in Glamorgan; both had wished to give up all, to live their lives for Christ. The old ruffian King Gwynllyw was as sad as Paul's father that their boys had taken such a step; it seemed to both that they were making a big mistake. Cadoc's monastery Llancarvan was therefore in the centre of events; where he showed hospitality on a lavish scale to the poor and the widows, by feeding them from the monastery kitchens and teaching his monks to work for the common good. Like Paul he had connections with Llandeusant, for his other church at Llangadoc was nearby, though later connected with Dewi.

After a short stop Paul travelled on to say farewell to his master Illtud at Llantwit. The old man was in the best of spirits, amused to hear that Paul was to go to King Mark's court at the latter's request.

"I wish you well," laughed Illtud, "but I can't imagine how you will fare; it will be interesting to see how it all turns out!"

Illtud knew Paul better than Paul did himself and realised that he was called to be one of the 'peregrinati' whose destiny and mission was to leave all and go out into the unknown . Illtud told Paul that he had been talking one day with his monks about a vision that he had of his death, how an angel with golden wings had come to carry his soul away; close by another monk was also thinking about death, but Illtud had just laughed and told him that the poor angel would in his case have leaden wings, for, although the monk lived a very holy life, his love his possessions and the things of this world, which would weigh his angel down!

"That wont be the case with you Paul", he smiled," your soul will have no weight to drag it down!"

It was time for Paul to leave Llantwit and Bovium and so he led his people out of his inheritance, his father's capital city. With his little party of followers he came down the sea-path to a sheltered cove where near the beach there was a little church called Llanwerydd (St Donats). And so Paul waved Illtud his master goodbye and set sail across the Severn channel - for the coast of north Devon. There was a good following wind and a shoal of porpoises played and swam, racing the boat across the channel.

When they landed, the party travelled south-east to Glastonbury, a place of power and of great holiness from ancient Druidical times, where many Celtic monks chose to be buried. The monks at Glastonbury welcomed Paul with words of encouragement and showed the party the old mud and wattle church, traditionally dedicated to the Virgin Mary and believed by some to have been founded in Apostolic times. Here Paul left his friends and went to visit Arthur at his stronghold close-by.

He climbed up the steep entrance and entered the fort through a massive gateway. Arthur had closely identified the British with the Christian cause. It was known that at the great battle which gave Britain this period of peace he had carried the cross of Christ three days and nights in the midst of the fighting. Now that the fighting was over he retained at his court many of his military commanders and their ladies. He greeted Paul warmly for, although their methods of Christian warfare were different, their cause was the same. Hardly could two men of the same family have differed more. Paul was young, lean and earnest; Arthur in full manhood was commanding and tough; he looked on Paul kindly and bade him sit down and give him all the news of King Perphirius and the district round about. They talked quietly for a while.

"My father Uther Pendragon gave the land around Caio to the Princes of Powys, so that Brochmail and his sons could have territory stretching across mid-Wales to Shrewsbury." Arthur continued - "Strange that he should have had two such different sons, Tysilio building churches on the Ceredigion border, whilst Cynan remains a real warmonger if ever there was one, with one overwhelming passion, the conquest of more lands and possessions."

Paul agreed and smiled to himself as he remembered the story of the family - the founder of the dynasty was Cadell Ddyrnllwg, the swineherd of the tyrant king Benlli, who churlishly shut the doors of his stronghold against St Germanus of Auxerre and his companions when they needed shelter. Cadell and his nine sons sheltered the men of God in their poor cottage and killed and dressed the calf of their only cow to feed them, whilst fire from heaven consumed Benlli's stronghold. Even so did Cadell, the blackfisted, become the new ruler of Powys.

"My foster-brother Cai", Arthur continued, "was brought up with me in Caer Gai in Merioneth. When my father subdued the unrest in the area round Caio, Cai helped him to bring order to the area. Then your father King Perphirius agreed to leave his home near the coast at Bovium in order to settle nearby - between the old Roman base at Caio and the Roman fort at Llandovery. We call it the 'Grove of the Princes'," Arthur laughed, " or the grove of the crows! After the call we all used to contact each other in those mountains in periods of danger!"

"It was thus that you came to be born at that junction of the two roads from the forts at Louentinum and Alabam. Had you chosen to take another path in life, you and I would be talking now as military leaders - but you chose otherwise."

They talked on quietly for some while; then Arthur stood up and they both went out into the compound.

"Whilst you are here", he said, "I would like you to see how my peace-time court is run, for still we have to be vigilant; trouble may break out again at any time. Although I am overall commander, I depend on the local kings to rule their own territories. You will know Urien, the grandson of Brychan; he and King Aircol both subdued their territory locally and now run it with a free hand, but it is vitally important for us all that they remain subject to me overall. Urien was not truly a man of the south, being born in the north, but since his mother was a daughter of Brychan and married to Cynfarch Oer, who with Cunedda's men had expelled the Irish from the Gower coasts many years ago, I sent him down to his grandfather Brychan, to defend the coastal land between the Tywi and the Tawe. See what a man he has become! From his stronghold at Carreg Cennen and the old Roman sea fort of Loughor at Aber Lleu, he is now able to control the coastal area and also signal down the valley to King Aircol's men at the stronghold Argol if and when the Irish invaders become troublesome again on the coasts of the Gower peninsular."

Paul felt that he had already taken up too much of his uncle's time and prepared to withdraw. Arthur smiled and said:

"Look around my court whilst you are here. Just as all my bases are tough and military, so is this one, although disguised to some degree by the presence of my Queen Guenever and her ladies. Although our marriage was originally a political alliance, she has brought beauty and joy into our mundane military lives."

"Sir, I thank you for welcoming me so kindly", Paul replied, "I shall be interested to meet the people at your court; but can you tell me what to expect when I travel on to the court of king Mark at Lantyan; will it to be anything like this? Or will it come as a rude awakening after the military order found here?"

Arthur told him of King Mark to the south. "You will have a full schedule if you wish to change anything there", said Arthur, "Mark is headstrong and has a violent temper. Still he has demanded your help, so that will obviously facilitate your mission; I wouldn't have your job for all the mead in Britain! You will already be aware of his unhappy marriage to Yseult?"

Paul nodded, for news like this travels fast. Having been persuaded by his council to marry, somewhat against his will, King Mark had sent his son Tristan to Ireland to bring back the daughter of the king of Ireland as his bride. The council felt that a political alliance with Ireland was urgently needed. On the return journey however whilst escorting 'Iseult the fair' back to her future husband, Tristan had fallen hopelessly in love with her himself. They tried to keep their love secret, but they were discovered and fled to the woods, living there for some considerable time, causing great unhappiness and chaos at the court of King Mark and division and desolation amongst the countryfolk, who took sides in the affair. The country was in a sad state when Iseult returned to her husband and Tristan crossed the sea to Brittany to start his life afresh with another 'Iseult of the fair hands.' Paul Aurelian had been sent for to help heal the situation in the country.

Paul did not stay in Arthur's stronghold many days, but he was well received throughout the camp and came across several familiar faces, including some of those he had known from his days at St Illtud's school. Queen Guenever, daughter of the Saxon King Leodegrance of Cameliard, was not much older than Paul, with long fair hair and clear blue eyes. She and the other ladies of her court made a colourful sight, softening a tough military base into something more like a peacetime court with their laughter and conversation.

It was, however, only one of Arthur's strongholds, although perhaps the most attractive. Arthur himself as 'Dux Bellorum' had a mobile field force. Launcelot the Saxon, 'the proud one', whose homeland was in the Loire valley near Beaune was a heathen by birth, but had been baptised when he entered Arthur's service, as commander of the escort of a hundred knights accompanying Guenever to the court of Arthur.

In the early days of Arthur's rule, his foster and half-brother Cai, at whose home Arthur had been raised as a son, tried to seize power himself. However Arthur succeeded in establishing his position and later even appointed Cai to be 'Senechal of England' and his deputy. Cai, Kay, Gaius or 'Chei' was a leader in war and terrible in battle. There were garrison commanders of the Roman type and in his government Arthur planned for nine commanders of the Saxon Shore and nine garrison commanders including the fourteen needed to man Hadrian's wall, nominal and unmanned though it had been for many years.

There were also provincial governors and petty kings under the 'Dux Bellorum'. Arthur had his mobile field force of men such as King Mark and other local kings. These cavalry commanders ranged freely across Britain keeping peace and order, Arthur's nephew Gawain or Walwyn being one of the two more important commanders or consuls in control of consular provinces.

There were twenty-eight knights and in the second generation of these came Galahad, whose mother Elaine was the daughter of King Pellas. Galahad occupied the Siege Perilous; he was Governor of one province, with the same Gawain (Arthur's nephew and son of his half-sister Margaret and King Urien) Governor of another. Gildas, the son of Caw who was in school with Paul, was one of the scholars of the court; he was later to write down his thoughts for posterity. These men - thirty one in all - who sat on the council with Arthur were working soldiers " commanding their garrisons, completing the paper work of their offices, victualling and arming their troops and fighting their campaigns with vigour and efficiency. "The last of the Roman style troops in Europe.

But Paul's brief stay at this stronghold was over. The bustle of court life, the coming and going of military men were very different to his equally busy but quieter schedule. It was a Celtic court and Arthur and his men had Celtic names, but many took Roman names and tried to revive the Roman style of ruling which they so much admired.

For all his Roman blood, Arthur felt himself a Celt; he was a son of Eigr, who was herself daughter of Anlawdd, son of Gwen, the daughter of Cunedda Wledig, which of course meant that he was not only a cousin of Paul Aurelian but also of David and of Teilo. They were all fighting for the survival of their country in their own different ways.

Arthur's way was not Paul's way. It was time for Paul to take his leave; he had found Arthur to be not only a great leader in battle but also a great Christian. Whether he sat in his great audience chamber, council or the chapel, the court was conscious that Arthur was ruling under the authority of Christ; whether he was making decisions about his campaigns or presiding over disputes in law or taking the oath of allegiance from his enemies, the Christian faith was seen to be the great secret of his power. Paul stood a while on the banks around the stronghold, looking down on the summer country:

"Why is it so impossible to live up to a dream?" he thought; "All in this idealised court should be well and yet there is a twist in human nature which works to destroy."

The busy court hummed around him as he stood and looked out across the country. He could hear the clang of a breastplate on an anvil as one of the knights' armour was being repaired; below the horses grazed in the warm sunshine in the meadows; Gwalchmai, the master of the Household, put his hand on Paul's shoulder.

"Will you be staying with us tonight again Paul?", he murmured - and it broke Paul's reverie.

"No" he said" it is time I set out for the court of King Mark, although I have enjoyed my few brief days here, Gwalchmai. I have already taken my leave of the King; it simply is quite an effort to tear myself away!" Gwalchmai smiled kindly at young Paul, bade him farewell and wished him good luck in his mission. Paul took the steep path down again, the same way he had taken up to the stronghold and off across the country to collect his monks from Glastonbury.

The movement of Teilo's Welsh friends into Brittany was now to begin with Paul Aurelian's call from King Mark. But Paul could not help chuckling as he recalled his conversation with Arthur about King Mark, 'Great Dog' as he had called him, 'Conomorus' as he was more usually known. King Mark was a powerful ruler, who later was to rule four nations and 'Great Dog' summed up his snarling defiant brutal attitude to life, as Paul was soon to discover. The court at Lantyan was close to the sea and could have been an idyllic place; instead it was a troubled world of uneasy inhabitants. Mark had been thwarted by Tristan, in gaining not only Iseult's love but also the sympathy of many of the inhabitants of Cornwall (little Wales as it was still called).

Paul and his twelve friends did not have an easy time of it at the court. Mark was impossible to deal with, subject to fits of rage and keeping his young wife Iseult more or less captive at the court. The officials did everything they could to help Paul and his companions based at court, as they travelled around amongst King Mark's subjects teaching the Gospel and endeavouring to soften some of that bad feeling local people had towards their king. They stayed many months and little by little gained the esteem and love not only of the people, but also of the King who wanted them to stay. All the people clamoured for Paul to be made their bishop, but this was the last thing that Paul wanted for himself.

While Paul wondered what he should do, he had a vision in which he saw an angel telling him that he must cross the seas, for this was where his life's work was intended. When he told the King, Mark refused to let him go, praising Paul for the work he and his followers had done in the country and saying that they could not manage without them. He wished to give him a present to show how much Paul meant to him; Paul replied that he would love to have the bell, one of the seven rung to call the court in for meals. The request was refused and Paul took his leave.

Whilst arranging for a ship to take him and his companions to Brittany, Paul went to visit his sister Sitofollia who had set up a little nunnery at Mounts Bay; she was quite overjoyed to see her beloved brother Paul. She told him all her news and then with tears in her eyes made said:

"Paul, dearest brother, beloved of God, if you have to leave your native country and all your loved ones, your brothers and sisters and neighbours and friends, at least leave some permanent memorial of your goodness and virtue, by which you may be remembered in time to come."

Paul then asked her what she meant and she explained that her religious house was much blessed by God and a most suitable place for the religious life, but she was much troubled on the one hand by jealous relatives, who lived on adjacent properties, and by the encroaching sea on the other, so that there was never enough land for the sisters to cultivate for the needs of the nunnery.

She asked Paul if he would cause the sea to retire and leave them more room. Paul said that he would pray about it and asked her to kneel down with him and commit the matter to God. Then at low tide they went down to the shore, for it used to retreat a mile or so and he told her to place stones at the low tide mark. As they crossed the sands with their hands full of pebbles, it was in fact very low tide; they all knelt down to pray and Paul commanded the sea in future not to pass the limit marked out by those stones. Whether or not the stones were reinforced by the local people into a dyke, the sea has never since encroached on the land here again ..so they say.

Sitofollia's many efforts to delay Paul's departure were at last abandoned and he set out for Brittany in the newly-fitted ships, taking with him many companions, nephews and relatives. 'Being on fire with love of the heavenly kingdom' Paul first reached an island called Ossa, about sixteen miles off the Breton coast, to land at the 'Port of the Oxen', where he found a little fountain with the ground around it fresh and green. Here he built a small shelter for prayer but after a time he and his companions decided to move on and eventually landed on the mainland at Ploudalmezeau, where they found a deserted farm with a clear sweet bright spring. The place was known as the Villa Petri and here he built a little church.

The countryside was deserted except for a few wild animals. The members of the party all settled themselves in the country round about and one of them, Justinius, found a particularly lovely spot near a spring in a thick wood with the whitest of sand around. Every day a wild ox would come to drink at the spring and each day he trampled and tore down the little hut and the fence around it, so Justinius asked Paul what to do. They agreed to exchange shelters and Paul, enchanted by the beauty of the place, tamed the wild ox and built a little monastery there.

Tired after one long journey, he saw a deserted villa - the Villa Wormawi - deserted since the Romans had departed, although not yet entirely reverted to nature . He decided then to find out how the country was governed. He came upon a swineherd who told him he was one of the swineherds of a Count named Withurs, a Christian man who ruled the country according to the Christian religion under the Emperor Childebert. He offered to take Paul to him, so he followed the swineherd as the sun was setting and came upon a deserted city, which they had to enter by the western gate, for it was surrounded by a high earthen bank. As they explored further, they came to a deserted castle, in which a wild sow was suckling her piglets and even better, to their delight, above them in a huge tree was a swarm of wild bees and the tree full of honey. The legend continues that the party settled down for the night, but were disturbed by a fierce bear which had ravaged the countryside, causing havoc amongst the country folk; the bear fled when it saw them and fell into a pit. Paul was also to banish a wild ox from the place. Later a party of them went round the deserted city and blessed it; this city, deserted

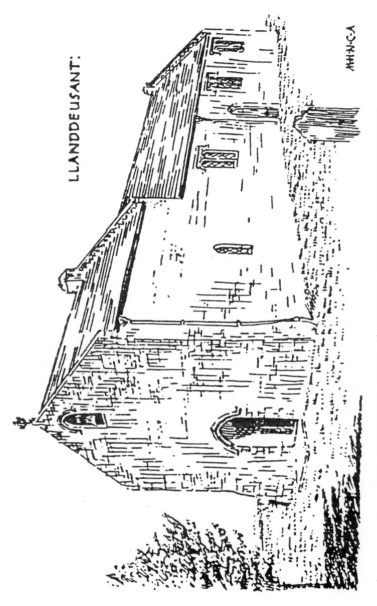

LLANDDEUSANT:

MHNCA

LLANDDEUSANT CHURCH, CARMARTHENSHIRE.
The site of Paulinus's first monastery (from a drawing by the
late Mr. M. H. N. C. Atchley).

when the Roman occupying army withdrew as the pagans overcame Rome, is now Pol-de-Leon.

The swineherd eventually led the party to the island of Batz, where Paul met Count Withurs and, discovering him to be a relative of his, found they had much in common. Count Withurs had retired to the island in order to withdraw from society. Here they found him transcribing the last words of the Gospel Book. Paul told him how he had also travelled to Brittany to seek solitude and how he came to be in Withurs' land; he had just spoken of how he came to part from King Mark and how he had asked him for one of his bells and been refused, when a servant brought in a gigantic salmon in one hand and in the other a bell, the handle of which had been gnawed through by marine leeches. It proved to be the very bell for which Paul had asked from King Mark. It performed many miracles later in Brittany, healed the sick and in a certain place its touch was to raise a dead man to life. It came to be known among all the Bretons by the name of 'Longifulva'. Paul was credited with many miracles including the removing of a serpent/dragon.

Withurs, foreseeing many difficulties for Paul, sent him with sealed letters to King Philibert (Childebert) in Paris. Paul took twelve presbyters with him and everywhere they stayed they built a little church. The sealed letter asked the King to make Paul a bishop, 'even against his will', which the King duly did and also gave Paul gifts of money and land for the church. Paul returned and remained at Leon, until he was old and ready to retire to the island of Batz, which Count Withurs had given him in perpetuity.

Thus Paul spent many years in this area, after the grant of the land for his monastery. He never returned to his native land. It was a strange fact that the Breton saints travelled to Britain to evangelise, whilst so many of the Welsh saints left Britain for the coasts of Brittany. Both Paul and Samson became famous for their work in Brittany. Both originally travelled there in order to seek solitude and to live lives of prayer, far from the worldliness of the life they saw around them.

Samson also travelled to Brittany about the same time as Paul, perhaps a few years before him. They both followed much the same route from Wales. As he left the monastery in Ireland, the monks had given him a present - a chariot in which to carry his books and to travel around the countryside. Soon after in Wales he decided to make his retreat in the upper Severn valley at a place called Cressage (Christ's oak) and here in the middle of a deep wood he built a little church almost on the edge of Saxon territory.

After some years he was made abbot of a monastery, possibly Llantwit, for Iltud had returned to Brittany at this time. Much pressure was put on Samson to become a Bishop and finally Dubricius ordained him along with two others, three being the usual number of ordinations at that time. It was soon after this, whilst praying all night, that he was told in a vision that his life's work was to be in Brittany. He visited his mother and his aunt on the way down the Severn. They had founded convents in Glamorgan, for after he had converted his family, his father and his uncle Umbraphael and all his brothers and sisters (except one) took up the religious life, all their money being given to their religious houses.

Samson had by now become a traveller or peregrinatus for Christ's sake. He travelled with two horses harnessed to that chariot which the Irish had given him and there are many stories about his time with this chariot in Cornwall too. Landing on the north Cornwall coast at St Docco (now St Kew) where he passed a group of people worshipping a symbolic figure (phanum)"after the manner of the Bacchantes". Samson climbed down from his chariot and stood watching the worshippers. Then he took two of his companions with him and climbed the hill to talk to them about the magical rites which they were practising. At first he had a mixed reception, when suddenly a boy who was horse-racing was thrown to the ground, twisting his neck and dying immediately. Everyone was very distraught, but Samson said:

"See if your image can do anything for the boy now."

He promised them that if they turned from their devil-worship he would, by the power of God, raise the boy to life. He prayed over the corpse for two hours and then presented him to the people alive. When they saw this they fell at his feet, destroyed the idol and were all baptised. Samson now carved a cross on the large menhir which was being worshipped when he first arrived. He was also to found a church near the court of King Mark in Lantyan, although he did not stay at the court there.

Again whilst travelling from Padstow in the north to Fowey on the south coast, passing through the area of Tricuria, he met people worshipping another idol. A wise man of the country named Juniavus stopped him and asked him why he was travelling through the country. Samson told him the purpose of his journey to Brittany and the old man gave the gentle reply:

"O most loving Father, the journey thou hast undertaken is a thing to be desired by a servant of God, for God in His gospel praises him who becomes a pilgrim for His sake."

The old man went on to tell him that things were not as they should be in the area and that the people had fallen away from their former good way of living. Samson took this as a sign from God that He had work for him there. It was this that had persuaded Samson to take his books and sacred vessels off the ship and to cross Cornwall by land instead of rounding the coast by boat. He was accompanied by a large band of brothers, all riding in his little chariot with him. .

The journey from Padstow to Fowey is not a long one and yet there are churches commemorating St Samson throughout the area, from high in the wild moorlands to the sea estuaries. He was there a year or two and on a second visit to that foundation of Docco at St Kew, he found that the monastery had fallen away from its former strictness also and one can well imagine the monks' horror when they heard that Samson and his large band of reforming monks were about to descend on them. The Celtic monks remained true on the whole to their original ideal, but others were known to have fallen into slacker ways as time went by. Golant, Padstow and Southill all commemorate Samson's visit to the area. Southill seems to be the site of Samson's monastery in the area; the parish was very large including the town of Callington.

Both in Wales and in Cornwall therefore Samson encountered strange heathen practices, belief in witches and idol worship. He encountered a wild woman who had eight sisters (there are nine for a coven) and who lived in the woods, her clothes all in tatters. Samson however finally left Cornwall and stayed for a while in the Isles of Scilly on his way to Brittany where one island is named after him; he also spent some considerable time at Guernsey on his way to Dol, which was to become his headquarters for the rest of his life.

When Samson at last reached Dol with all his travelling companions, 'Very many monks', he found a host of his countrymen already there, people who had fled from the Saxons, mainly from the regions of south western England and eastern Wales. He was to become known as Bishop of Dol and Pental on the lower Seine. Paul and Samson are but two of Teilo's many close friends, who gave their lives to work for God in Brittany.

Saint Samson's window (XIIIth century)
His arrival in Dol.

THE ROMANO-BRITISH IMPERIAL LINE.

CARADOC AND CONSTANTINE THE GREAT.

(four generations)

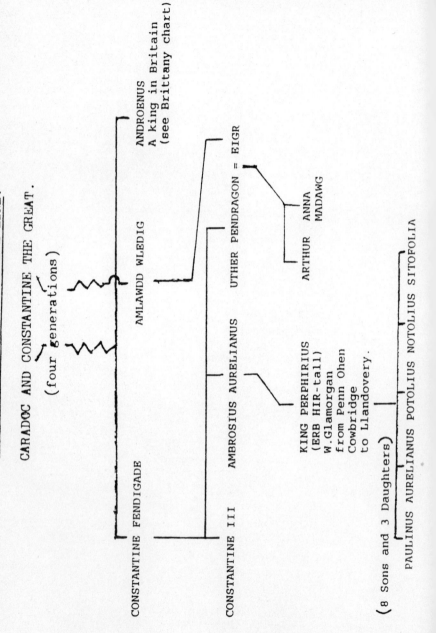

CONSTANTINE FENDIGADE

AMLAWDD WLEDIG

ANDROENUS
A king in Britain
(see Brittany chart)

CONSTANTINE III

AMBROSIUS AURELIANUS

UTHER PENDRAGON = EIGR

KING PERPHIRIUS
(ERB HIR-tall)
W.Glamorgan
from Penn Ohen
Cowbridge
to Llandovery.

ARTHUR
ANNA
MADAWG

(8 Sons and 3 Daughters)

PAULINUS AURELIANUS POTOLIUS NOTOLIUS SITOFOLIA

A LINK BETWEEN S.TEILO & KING ARTHUR ?

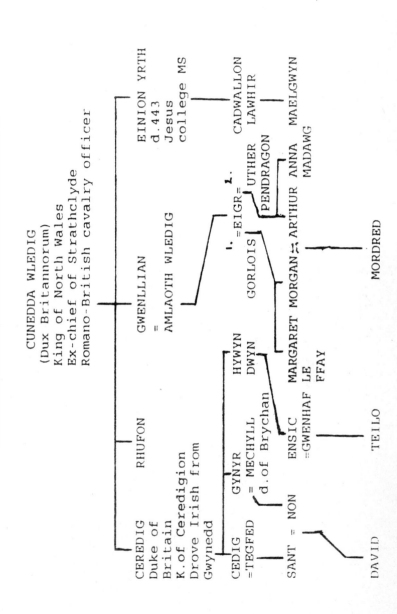

CUNEDDA WLEDIG
(Dux Britannorum)
King of North Wales
Ex-chief of Strathclyde
Romano-British cavalry officer

CEREDIG
Duke of
Britain
K.of Ceredigion
Drove Irish from
Gwynedd

RHUFON

GYNYR
= MECHYLL
d.of Brychan

CEDIG
=TEGFED

SANT = NON

DAVID

GWENLLIAN
=
AMLAOTH WLEDIG

HYWYN
DWYN

ENSIC
=GWENHAF LE
FFAY

TEILO

EINION YRTH
d.443
Jesus
college MS

1. =EIGR= 2.
GORLOIS   UTHER
           PENDRAGON

CADWALLON
LAWHIR

MARGARET MORGAN ≈ ARTHUR ANNA MAELGWYN
LE FFAY   MADAWG

MORDRED

Chapter Five

c 518. JOURNEY TO JERUSALEM

After leaving Argol, Teilo soon quit the boat to go to Llanarthney close by. Hearing that his cousin was in the district dealing with church administration there, Dewi went to join him some days later.

Dewi jumped eagerly from the boat as it pulled up in the gulley at the base of the church mound; some yards away in one of the huts by the edge of the settlement he could see Teilo with his back to him, talking to a group who were helping to tie down some fodder which had slipped from its storage in one of the huts by the edge of the settlement. Hearing that Dewi had come, Teilo swiftly turned to greet his cousin.

Dewi's face was flushed. "I've exciting news, Teilo. Where can we go for a bit of privacy? I need to talk to you urgently."

"Follow me" said Teilo hoping against hope that it was the news he wanted. They disappeared through the doorway of the wooden church and pulled it to after them.

Very soon they were in deep conversation.

"I have a strong impression that the Lord wants me to go to the Holy Land, Teilo. What shall I do? What about the work? Do you think it can keep going under its own momentum while I am away? My mind is racing with all the possibilities ahead. What can it mean?"

"Hold on a minute", laughed Teilo "Just stop and listen! The same thing has happened to me! I feel very strongly that I must get away and assess my future too. King Aircol has just released me from the work for the very same journey. He wanted me to find one or two companions to go with me. But I was waiting to see how God guided before asking. This is my much needed confirmation! We must go back to Argol and tell the King."

67

"Wait Teilo. That's not the end of it! In the same dream I was told that Padarn was to accompany us on the pilgrimage. I suppose we ought to find out if he also feels prompted first? Do you know him? I confess that although he brought over that large contingent of missionaries from Brittany and at first we were so delighted to see him and liked him well, I haven't had much to do with him recently. Is he still working in Ceredigion?"

"Come, let's go and find out", was Teilo's quick reply and they hustled the boatmen who were already deep in discussion with the locals to take them back up river straight away. Grabbing his meagre belongings, Teilo threw them ahead into the boat and they were very quickly again at the foot of Argol and soon standing once more in the presence of the King.

It was not many hours before they had Aircol's permission to proceed on their journey accompanied by Padarn, with Cadfan's blessing; Padarn being ranked fourth leader of the Breton mission, Cadfan's agreement was required also. But Teilo was now secretly working out how he could manage to see Ygrain before leaving for Jerusalem.

Padarn had come from Brittany with real zeal for the work in Wales, many monks following him to a place near Aberystwyth; and so it was decided that he be consulted without delay as to how he felt. Dewi and Teilo set out for Ceredigion, where Padarn's work was now centred. They found him as they expected, up to his eyes in work, surrounded by a group of young lads and teaching them to sing - they could hear him long before they saw him and, as they rounded the last bend before sighting the sea, they were greeted by the combined sound of the breakers on the shore and the clear voices in unison, borne towards them on the wind.

With his usual enthusiasm, Padarn was determined to get the best from his choir, calling on them all once again to repeat from the beginning, when he looked up and saw Dewi peering down at him; as for Teilo, he was laughing out aloud unable to conceal his amusement.

Padarn quickly abandoned his task, dismissed his young choir and, delighted to see his friends, held wide his arms in greeting, inviting them to his shelter for refreshment. There was much to discuss. The next day Padarn gathered his people and told them that together with Teilo and Dewi he was convinced that the time was ripe for their pilgrimage Jerusalem. Since Padarn was a little older than the others, well recognised as a brilliant theologian and therefore a valuable companion for them, they all felt as they discussed details that the journey was going to be a momentous one.

All three found their work well blessed, but Padarn realised now that the time had come for the building of a larger monastery - a more permanent place for the training of these young lads in his area; he had great plans, but felt deeply the need to re-dedicate himself for this major task of the future; the timing was just right. But first they must consult with papa Dubricius and seek his permission for the voyage. Between them they represented Dubricius's three chief areas of south Wales.

The matter decided, they agreed to meet at Dewi's centre on the coast and take ship from there.

"First I must say farewell to my family," said Teilo, for he was again thinking of Ygrain, hoping to find her still at his parents' home. He hurried there to take his leave.

He met her in the hall as he entered his home. Her dark eyes glowed as he approached and they held each other in silence for a while. At last she spoke.

"We had no idea you were coming, Eliud." She used his family name as she had always done as a child.

"Ygrain, I have come to say goodbye." Teilo's voice was low, speaking quietly to her as he held her. He felt her tremble as he spoke and, looking up, her eyes were filled with tears, her expression uncomprehending as she looked into his face, trying to make out what he could possibly mean.

"Here, sit down and let me tell you what has happened," he said.

As he spoke, her open face hid nothing at all. He watched her with increasing dismay, as she listened to the end she then burst out with all that had been held back for so long.

"Oh Eliud! Whatever can I say! I know its been difficult for you, torn as you are between what your family expect, your own wishes and God's will for you - the future is unknown to us. Certainly I cannot tell you what to do or say; all I can do is to ask you, beg you, to remember that we have our one life and that your decision concerns not you alone, but me also. I have always known the importance of your work, but why can't we do it together? There are plenty of married priests; you don't have to live the life of a celibate. I might even be a help to you, even giving you a better balanced view of life. I know it is not easy to change course when you have set out on such a definite road, but please consider what God's will really is - did He really mean us to meet and to be together? At least consider this on the long journey you are going to undertake. I shall be thinking of you and praying that you will resolve the matter rightly before you return, for I know it will take you many months travelling. Goodness only knows when you will come back again". She started to cry, something almost unbearable for Teilo. He sat there with his hands helplessly at his sides, longing to take her in his arms again, desperate to know what to say to comfort her. Agonising enough about his own feelings, he could only watch her distress.

It was his parents who relieved them of their embarrassment, coming in just then to find Ygrain in floods of tears and Teilo utterly dejected sitting opposite.

"What is all this?" gasped his mother, moving quickly to her son and putting her arms around him, as her husband stood quietly by. Quickly however he had assessed the situation and soon with something for them to drink and a warm fire brought things back to normality and they began to discuss the journey and the likely course it would take.

There were innumerable things to be done the next day as Teilo went up to see how things were in Vortipor's camp. He was relieved to find that Mabon's place had been taken by an older man and that all was progressing well. It was best to leave home as soon as possible, now that Ygrain was putting a brave face on things and that his parents would keep an eye on her. It was really just as much a shock for them and they were determined not to make it public until Teilo had had a chance to sort himself out.

So the three men set out from Dewi's centre at Menevia; they set sail with King Aircol's blessing, taking with them no staff, nor bag, nor bread nor money, as the Lord had commanded - but they preached the Gospel and helped, healed and prayed throughout the many trials during that early part of the voyage down the west coast of Europe.

The boat was a large merchant trader from the eastern Mediterranean, the sails filling with a gentle breeze as they crossed the wide channel keeping well clear of Finisterre or the Lands End of Armorica, Padarn's native land. His strong face was bronzed with the summer wind as he wistfully scanned the rocky cliffs of the coastline, but there was no chance or need to step ashore until they were much further south, off the Spanish coast in fact. The oarsmen in the galleys knew the ports well, for there was constant movement of Spanish people in the Celtic world - indeed King Brychan had taken a Spanish wife, Prostri, while the Romans had long brought Spaniards from the Spanish gold mines at Rio Tinto to help at the gold mines near Caio.

There was no need because the boat had been well laden for its return journey; chickens clucked from their baskets tied to the deck, while round the sides of the boat fresh green cabbages and root crops hung, all securely tied, to feed them during their journey. An odd assortment of travellers were sailing south with them; men, women, and some very noisy children it seemed, taking the air on deck. Standing there beside Padarn, Teilo was pale and deeply thoughtful; "Does it ever cross your mind how much you have given up for the Gospel?" he asked.

Padarn turned slowly towards him, "I was thinking just the same!" he replied.

Neither of them spoke for some time; with the monotonous waves lapping gently on the sides of the boat, the steady, regular movement from the galleys and the oars swishing in unison drowned their thoughts which were much too deep and difficult to articulate anyway.

"Some things are better left unsaid," thought Teilo, but the thoughts which so pressed upon him would not go away. Both Ygrain and he were living breathing people; they both had a life to lead somehow.

She may have had something in what she said. What could God mean by suddenly upsetting their lives in such a way? Yet, without the Lord and all that He meant to them, nothing made sense. If there were no God, they could do just what they pleased; they could marry and live out their lives privately and no doubt exceedingly happily. But if there were no God, there was no Gospel either, his own work would be meaningless and the hope for the British nation non-existent. They might just as well have given in to the Saxon threat and their paganism without so much as a whimper.

"What do you think about women?" Teilo said at length. Not at all what Padarn expected to hear, he was so taken aback that he simply burst out laughing.

But Teilo was not laughing, not even smiling and Padarn quickly realised that this was a deadly serious question, to be treated seriously. He turned hopefully to Dewi who had joined them by now and was looking in some consternation at Teilo. But Dewi was no help at all; he was waiting to hear what Padarn said.

"In general", Padarn looked straight at Teilo "I think they are charming, warm hearted and intelligent creatures. In particular" he continued, "I think they are to be feared, for their power over us men is such that we can lose both faith and reason if we allow ourselves to get too involved. I'm a man's man, much happier dealing with a good challenge and a tough programme; a woman has no place in my life, when I try to think what work God has in mind for me. The theological problems we are faced with and the hours that I need to spend in prayer and communion with the Lord, all preclude a normal personal life for me. With a woman in my life I would have to think continually of her needs, when all my time at present is free to think the next challenge and what God expects of me. It would be hopeless for anyone to try and share my kind of life, hopeless for me and my work, hopeless for her and her happiness - and if I became a father it would be much, much worse. At present I can help dozens of men and boys of all ages; just think of the pressures on me if I were trying to divide myself between a private and public life. It simply couldn't be done!"

Quiet till now, Dewi had been watching Teilo - just as Teilo had been watching Padarn; he was seeing as if for the first time the vulnerability of his friend, whose wide open face revealed all. He felt frightened for him, not knowing the cause, but guessing and not being far off the mark; he had never seen Teilo so pensive and withdrawn. Dewi was worried that he might be losing his old friend, for he had the greatest respect for his steadfastness; he was truly upset that anything could come between Teilo and all that he stood for; he was jealous for his dear friend's ideals, his good name and future plans for his work for God.

Dewi was the only son of his parents, who themselves had abandoned everything for the cause, knowing little of family life and living in many ways a rarefied existence, just as was now expected of him. No such traumas had ever passed through his mind as were now faced by Teilo. Warm and human himself, Teilo had had the warmth of a family, of a brother and a sister and their friends as constant companions; he had joined in the rough and tumble of normal family life. His calling was just as genuine as Dewi's, but his humanity was such that he understood human frailty and compassion from early experience. His master Dubricius also came from a large family, which had helped him in his work and understanding of those committed to his care. How could he now explain to Dewi how he felt? This was the first time they had ever had a real misunderstanding, the first time that he had ever found Dewi wanting. Dewi's ideal of the Desert Fathers, John the Baptist and other great saints was excellent, but they were of little avail to him now. For the first time Teilo was unable to talk to Dewi, his cousin and soul-friend from childhood.

At last Dewi burst out "The thoughts and passions of our life must be ruled by austerity and discipline, if we are to conform to the will of God; our bodies must be our servants not our masters. Like the Desert Fathers we must train them to endure cold and hardship, heavy manual labour and little sleep, but we have to work at it. Sometimes as I stand waist deep in a mountain stream, I feel tremendous exhilaration: exhilaration which I express in singing God's praise from the psalms, as you well know Teilo. It is just when things are at their worst and the situation quite unbearable that His greatest blessings seem to flow. Don't you remember Peter in prison and many others too, how they just praised God with psalms and hymns and how the angel came right into their cell and led them out to freedom? Then there's Paul too; many of the soldiers guarding him in prison were converted by his behaviour. Spiritual truths have a curious way of being quite the opposite to our human understanding sometimes. We just don't know where God is leading us; we have given up control of our own personal destiny."

These words of his dear friend David were to echo in Teilo's thoughts until his dying day ....'we have given up control of our own personal destiny....we just don't know where God is leading us.....'

Just for now however Teilo was not convinced. He certainly did not feel like making a clean breast of it and telling his friends of his pain, yet he was not convinced that God could show him such momentous happiness and then expect him to renounce it just like that. Did God really want two of his special creatures to be unhappy? If so why? What was it really all about? Just how single minded did He expect him to be? These things were just tearing him apart. Why shouldn't he marry Ygrain? The others obviously hadn't even wanted to get married, so they hadn't really grasped that there was even a problem. It was in this dangerous mood that young Teilo stood daily looking rebelliously at the grey waves and the heavy Atlantic breakers as they crashed against the boat. For a moment the best that he could do was to agree to differ; he glared silently back at the ocean.

As they sailed now between the north coast of Africa and the southern tip of Spain, the weather changed and the gusty breakers of the Atlantic ocean gave way to much calmer waters. What struck them most forcibly about the Mediterranean sea was the blueness of the water shining and glittering around the boat. They had excellent weather for the last part of the voyage and by dint of good exercise on deck were both sunburnt and fit when they reached the Holy land, disembarking there to the sorrow of the whole ship.

It was impossible for Teilo to be morose for too long. His natural exuberance was quickly evident when the prospect of being in Jerusalem so soon approached. Some of the passengers came with them some of the way, passing through many a dusty little village, the three friends being commended, even eulogised in front of villagers by some passengers. It all became rather irksome after a while however, for the three were young and fit and soon outstrode their followers. By the end of the second day, they found themselves on the road alone; they were free to laugh more easily, chat more fully and sing their praises to the Lord as and when they wanted.

Deciding that they would avoid some of the villages and sleep under the stars one night, they made themselves comfortable not far from the roadside. The night was clear and the moon bright. Tired after walking all day, they soon fell into a deep sleep; but Teilo awoke to hear a curious muffled sound and, conscious of someone fumbling amongst his scant belongings, he sat up with a start and was just quick enough to avoid a hefty blow from what appeared in the moonlight to be a gleaming knife.

He leapt to his feet and gave the alarm; "Got you!" he hissed between his teeth.

His companions scuffled to avoid similar attacks, but managed to grab the filthy beggar firmly; they forced him to sit down and confront them. Two others had run away by this time but on seeing their fellow kindly treated, curiosity overcame them and they crept back - a poor bedraggled group, flea ridden and skinny.

"Come on, lads" murmured Teilo "we must find some food to give them. They look starving and even their teeth are chattering."

Flinging his cloak round one of the group he rummaged around in his pockets to see if by some lucky chance there was a crust of something. Padarn, with his usual foresight had kept a bit back from the evening snack and soon the beggars were snatching it eagerly.

Dawn by now and still quite chilly, it seemed pointless to sit around any longer and they could already see Jerusalem on the hill ahead of them, so they set off.

Chapter Six

THE VISIT

The thieves, still wrapped in the young men's cloaks, refused to leave them, so that they were obliged to enter the city accompanied by the three beggars, who started shouting and making a highly embarrassing commotion which soon attracted a crowd of curious spectators. Spotting a young man beckoning to them, Teilo pushed his way through the crowd and was just able to hear him say in a hurried whisper:

"Come, I'll show you a way out of this."

The young man slipped deftly through the crowd, so that Teilo, Dewi and Padarn could only follow with some difficulty and found themselves in a quiet backstreet alone with the stranger.

"My name is Mark; I belong to the Christian community here. We were told of your arrival a few days ago;" he said, extending a hand in greeting.

He was dark and colourfully dressed with a twisted turban made of rich silk, evidently an educated man by his cultured approach. He led them swiftly on down the streets until they came to a doorway where he knocked twice. Thereupon a girl called from within and, evidently satisfied with his reply, opened the door; they stepped in to find themselves in a courtyard, cool and shaded with flowers rambling up the wall and a pool of water in the centre. They were led across the courtyard and through a dark doorway, into the house of a sympathetic family, who gave them a peaceful moment to wash and refresh themselves with food, before having to go back into the throng once again.

Their fame had gone ahead and before long two or three Christians arrived to greet them and to see if there was anything they needed.

It had been a dusty journey from the coast to Jerusalem. The three friends were unaccustomed to the heat and Dewi, with his insistence on drinking only water, had suffered from an upset stomach and learnt that first lesson, to drink only fresh well water which was in constant use. All three had had to rest on the way a little so that they could become acclimatised. The food, the flies and the heat of the sun were not the only things which were trying; everywhere they went they found the people so different, the noise of the bazaars, the colourful dress and long flowing robes together with the mixture of race and language were all more than a little confusing. At each town they entered, crowds of small children would greet them, pressing them for gifts of money or food. They had hoped for a quiet day or two to recover before entering the city, but unfortunately the robbers had prevented that.

Although the Christian fellowship in Jerusalem were expecting Celtic monks, they were taken aback to find them heralded by three beggars. As they strode down the streets of Jerusalem, their hair cut in that characteristic Druidical tonsure, they soon recognised them however from their bearing and their manner as dear brothers in Christ.

After enjoying Mark's initial hospitality, Teilo and his friends' first thought was to make for the church of the Holy Sepulchre. Here they spent three days in prayer prostrate on the pavement of the temple, outstretched in the position of Christ on the Cross, as was normal practice for Celtic Christians in prayer. In the city where Christ was crucified, three days seemed to them hardly long enough to pour out their hearts to Him in praise and adoration. Teilo felt humbled to his very heart, as he lay there in prayer with his companions.

After those three days the Christian community welcomed them into their homes. There was so much that the three wanted to know from them; of course there was the language problem, but Teilo, Dewi and Padarn were all well versed in Greek and Latin, so that communication was not difficult. They wanted to be shown all those places associated with Christ in the Gospels and one or two men were chosen to take them round.

At last, rested and refreshed after their long journey, they were called by the Elders to the meeting place of their church of Jerusalem to preach; here they handed over letters of introduction from Dubricius to the Patriarch in Jerusalem.

Three chairs were indicated; Teilo chose the wooden one, leaving those ornately worked in metal for the other two - Teilo felt that the wooden chair was closer to the wooden Cross, upon which Christ was crucified; to those present his choice was taken as a sign of his humility. When invited to speak, like the first apostles, he found that all the audience understood what he was saying. Although he was speaking in Latin, everyone heard him in their own language.

From now on Teilo's ministry was to be conducted at a deeper level and this gift of the Holy Spirit was never to leave him his long life through; it was an added blessing in a totally dedicated life. Dewi and Padarn were also invited to speak, after which the Archbishop of Jerusalem, assisted by other bishops, laid hands upon the heads of all three, thereby ordaining each to be bishop in their own Celtic church. Each had distinguished himself, Dewi by performing the service, Padarn by his singing and Teilo by preaching. The saints there, impressed by Teilo's love, took him to their hearts. Dewi was recognised by them as one of themselves, for from John the Baptist onwards there had always been holy men who chose to live the ascetic life; they recognised the authentic nature of his calling. As for Padarn with his theological brilliance, they just clamoured for more, glad to welcome someone who explained simply so many complex things.

The city of Jerusalem was crowded and bustling, full of monks and nuns as well as lay people. Teilo particularly wanted to see the church now built over the room where Jesus and His disciples had celebrated their last supper; here Jesus had appeared to them after his resurrection and here was the place where He had breathed on them and given them the Holy Spirit.

There were many places to explore and others which could be reached by short excursions from Jerusalem, but after five hundred years and foreign occupation some of the locations were scarcely remembered; as interest grew, so the crowds gathered to see the places mentioned in the Bible; they could have spent many months and years just tracing these, the Mount of God where Moses received the tablets of stone, that other mount 'Horeb' where Elijah had fled from the presence of King Ahab and hidden in a cave, or the lake of Galilee where Jesus spent so much of His ministry teaching the people.

Teilo, Dewi and Padarn knew the historical background of Christianity, which had developed in the eastern half of the Roman Empire in an ancient culture that was predominately Greek, well before it became the official religion of the Roman Empire in the fourth century. The Empress Helena had married the Roman General Constantius Chlorus before he became Emperor, although he later divorced her, to marry the step-daughter of the Emperor.

His son, to become Constantine the Great, remained loyal to his mother and put great sums of money at her disposal, with which she built churches from Germany to Palestine. In her old age she travelled to Jerusalem to see the Holy places, many even then lost beneath new Roman buildings built by the Emperor Hadrian on the ruins of old Jerusalem. There she discovered the Holy Sepulchre and the Cross of Christ , her son making money and excellent workmen available for her to build churches on these sites with the help of the church historian Eusebius, who supervised all the plans under her direction.

They built eight churches in or near Jerusalem, pulling down old ones, indeed not only replacing old with new but at times effacing old pagan buildings. Three were built over caves, long used by pious men and, no doubt, all manner of beasts before that. Soon afterwards the pilgrimages started, with people coming from far and wide to see the Holy places of both the Old and New Testaments.

The three friends travelled to see the cave in Bethlehem where the Lord Jesus was born. Teilo stood there in appalled amazement as he entered it, for it was so awful. As they stood there Teilo turned to Dewi:

"It's enough to make you lose your faith, isn't it," he said, "to think the Lord of all the Universe should choose to be born in such a wretched place!"

Dewi nodded his head as they stood there silently. "And yet" thought Teilo, "doesn't it just show how much God loved us to do such a hopeless thing!" From then on he felt he needed just to be alone and to think about it. All the power of the cosmos in just that little cave! Teilo slipped off to the nearest quiet place which turned out to be the adjacent cave where St Jerome had spent forty years of his life making the Vulgate version of the Bible. Here he tried to come to terms with the enormity of it all. And a sense of the importance to God of each human life began here and never left him.

Teilo found that Church services at this time were based on the Jerusalem liturgy and the Armenian lectionary, which included the reforms of Cyril of Jerusalem in 348. Sunday Eucharist was attended by all the clergy and laity of the city. The sermons were unusually long - extremely long sometimes, first from the presbyter and afterwards the Bishop - and were greeted by the congregation with applause and groans not by any means necessarily in that order! 'So that the people could constantly hear about the Bible and the love of God.'

Throughout Sunday there was a succession of services, fewer but longer than the weekday ones. During the week they started at cockcrow, the next at first light, then full daylight, followed by 9am, 11am, noon, 3pm and 4pm, with fasting twice a week on Wednesday and Friday. Lent started eight weeks before Easter and lasted until Holy week. Easter went on for seven more weeks with the feast of Pentecost on the fortieth day. The many saints days were marked by a celebration of a Eucharist, but Christmas was not yet celebrated.

At Jerusalem there was a boys' choir, so that there was some practised singing but, as there were no books for the congregation, hymns and psalms would be led by a solo singer, the rest of the congregation responding in unison or just repeating a verse. The psalms were sung in groups of three called 'globala' consisting of one psalm followed by two more sung in unison.

The friends were not there for Easter, but it was all explained to them by their guide who gestured volubly if interrupted by passers-by. Candidates for baptism presented themselves before the bishops and presbyters on the first day of Lent, together with their godparents. They were examined as to character, while the godparents acted as their witnesses. If they passed the examination, they were accepted as 'electi', for they were adults not infants (infants in Christ that is, or newly born into Christ).

For the first five weeks of Lent they received three hours instruction from the bishop. In the sixth and seventh weeks he taught them the Creed, which was explained both literally and spiritually and which they had to repeat to him individually on the last day of their instruction, the Saturday before Palm Sunday.

Throughout the seven weeks of Lent the candidates were exorcised daily by special clergy ordained for the purpose.

Any lay people who wanted could listen to the lessons including instructions to both candidates and godparents. But this was not enough to cleanse them. Only when they had been finally purified by washing at baptism was the deeper Mystery revealed, which included the explanation of Baptism itself, the Holy Chrism and the Eucharist. Because Baptism is one of the sacred mysteries, it was not performed in public but privately, in a separate baptistry set apart from the main church, where the candidates also celebrated their first communion. To help in this there were lectures on the 'Mysteries' every day.

At each place of Biblical interest they visited they were led by a priest in private devotion; if it happened that the commemoration of that place was being celebrated that very day, the appropriate lessons and psalms became part of the service, giving an historical quality to the liturgy - a very moving experience for all pilgrims, for it brought the past to life for them.

The Jerusalem liturgy and Cyril's reforms were responsible for 'The Holy Fire', symbolic of the resurrection bringing light down into darkness, commemorated in the Paschal vigil at Jerusalem, in the Palm Sunday procession and also in the veneration of the Cross on Good Friday. The Armenian liturgy also reflected Jerusalem's liturgical life.

Before they left for the next stage of their journey, they were presented with gifts. Dewi was given an altar; for Padarn with his beautiful singing voice there was a staff and a choral cope; for Teilo a bell, 'Bangui', not large or handsome, but sweet-sounding and to be greatly venerated, for later it was to heal the sick. At one time it was also used to record the hours of the day, just as the church bell has been rung down the centuries in country districts by the priest, for the benefit of those working in the fields, thereby regulating their day. If people took a false oath on Teilo's bell, it condemned them; this and other powers it was later to lose, when polluted hands held it. Dewi took with him one other special gift from Jerusalem to the Church in Britain - a very large sapphire.

They visited Galilee and had many discussions with friends at Jerusalem, trying to decide on the places they should see from amongst the many they wanted to see in the time available. At last they set sail for Hippo on the north coast of Africa; with many tears of farewell especially from the friends with whom they had stayed but from the many others they had also come to know whilst in Jerusalem.

A freak storm blew up as they were sailing west across the Mediterranean sea; the cargo was well lashed to the boat but great waves crashed across it, drenching the decks and even terrifying the crew; Teilo and his friends were very sick but grimly hung on, praying they would arrive safely. At last the storm blew itself out and the cold waves calmed, as they continued the journey. The sailors pulled hard on the oars, thankful it was all over as the hot sun beat down on them again, the boat hugged the north coast of Africa, until they reached the port of Hippo. It came into view as a long range of cliffs, lapped by a brilliant azure sea; the three friends knew of it as one of the largest ports of Africa; it had existed for over a thousand years, the civilisations of Phoenicia and Rome both having left their mark. As the friends disembarked, they set out on foot for the Christian quarter, passing the gracious villas of the rich in the residential suburbs overlooking the harbour. They were still feeling distinctly queasy from the journey and their legs were a bit wobbly but they soon recovered.

The Coptic Church received them with honour. They knew of their work in Wales; many contacts had been formed via the seaways, but it was a matter of great importance for both churches that these three young men, who were forging such a great work for God in Wales, had now come themselves to make their own personal contact with the church they had so closely followed. There were many similarities in their Christian approach, but Dewi particularly represented the extreme asceticism of the Celtic Church. He, it was known, would stand for long periods up to his waist in a river, reciting psalms and praying to God. His food remained simple and contained no meat or fish; he still drank only water - and would never use animals to do his manual labour, but both he and his monks must carry out all such work themselves, being yoked to the plough just like the oxen.

Teilo's holiness was loved by all, though he was never a man for excess. His gentleness encouraged the more timid to approach with their problems, yet his quick brain could fast detect humbug and excuses. With those who would waste his time he could be firm and direct - no one dared to stand in the way of his dedicated purpose to serve God, for the gentleness was really a sign of his strength and a deep self-control. The motivation for his life was his deep sense of the goodness of God; even in his worst moments of personal temptation or of feelings of futility, he had learnt to struggle out of moods of depression and to think clearly; he was then able to contemplate the great love of God in sending Jesus to die for us, an act which must have appeared totally futile at the time. The test of faith is always rigorous; it is always easier to see the way things look at the present moment, than to understand what God's purpose behind the present moment could be. But Teilo's experience had taught him to believe in this purpose, so that he had learnt how it was possible to praise God with all his being, regardless of the way things looked - and to rest in this knowledge with faith. The result in his life was very basic security which could overcome personal misfortunes or any depression of the moment, so that everyone he met was attracted by his joy.

But Teilo found all the time that there were new things about the Christian life he had to learn, a process which would never stop throughout his mortal life. Augustine's writing was a great challenge to him, for the puzzle to the Christian has always been to find some way of living one's present mortal existence, even whilst reaching for the heavenly city, of continually being brought low by one's inability to measure up to those highest standards within oneself. A duality is born - one far from comfortable to live with.

Teilo, Dewi and Padarn had all been brought up since childhood in that same school of monasticism and were therefore feeling quite at home with all that the Coptic Church had to tell them of their Christian faith and teaching. They were shown the precious Books of the Church, illuminated manuscripts with designs and motifs related more to Byzantium than to Rome. As in Jerusalem the three men talked at length with the Patriarchs about the Faith. Here they were able to question them about those early founders of monasticism - St.Anthony, St Jerome and St. Augustine - and about their writings on the Christian life. "The Heavenly City outshines Rome," St Augustine had said, "beyond comparison. There, instead of victory, is truth, instead of rank, holiness, instead of peace, felicity, instead of life, eternity."

Their discussion centred a great deal on this St Augustine of Hippo, who had founded his community in Africa just over a hundred years before in 390. But before committing himself to the life of a monk, Augustine also had to go through agonising conflicts as regards honours, wealth and marriage; he also had a son whom he dearly loved. It was really too close for Teilo's comfort, when they started to discuss the Pelagian heresy which had led Augustine into heated argument with his contemporary, another Celt living in Rome named Pelagius.

"As I understand it", said Teilo turning to Dewi, "It's all about humility before the Grace of God; we have been given free will to exercise as we think fit. Yet because of our weakness we do not always do what is right. So it is vitally necessary to call on God for help, an act which demands that we are humble enough to ask for and accept that help."

"That's not quite the way I see it", replied Dewi. "I believe that we have to learn to master ourselves by stern discipline. You can't expect God to go round helping all those too weak and feeble to restrain themselves. I tend to agree with Pelagius, that we are expected to take strong measures for our own salvation."

Padarn butted in "You have missed the point both of you. It isn't a question of God's Grace helping us to avoid sin or not - according to His divine intervention in our dilemmas. 'Truly the gift of God is to love God'. He loved us from the beginning and we were born to love Him in return. Our self-will, whatever you call it, self-centredness or sin, warps us and weakens us; we are then unable to love Him or anyone else for that matter, except from our own selfish point of view; our perspective has been thoroughly distorted by putting ourselves in the centre of the picture the place of God. This is what free will is about. We didn't love Him first; He first loved us. Ours is a response to what He has done."

Teilo looked uncomfortable. "There really is no compromise I suppose. If God has really called us to do something for Him, this must come first. He has promised to see us through to the end and He wont let us down. "His mind as ever filled with the commission to build his monastery in Wales when he returned, Teilo was to peruse carefully Augustine's plan for the ideal monastery and those great writings on the 'City of God' - ' the city which has justice for its law and love for its citizenship'.

In St Augustine's lifetime, Pelagius had come from Britain to live in Rome in the first quarter of the fifth century, that period of the later Roman Empire, when Roman refugees were fleeing to north Africa from brutal purges and assassinations. Augustine was by this time an old man, gentle and understanding of human frailty, whereas Pelagius found himself daily standing in a group of that noble class where debate thrived. His idealism and preaching were harsh. He could not come to terms with the thought of original sin. The idea that man was sinful from birth was to him both ridiculous and distasteful. "Since perfection is possible for man, it is obligatory," was the basis of his beliefs. The idea that original sin could make man incapable of not sinning ever, struck him as absurd. Augustine and Pelagius nearly met at Hippo in the year 411, but Pelagius sailed instead to the Holy Land and the controversy was carried on by correspondence. Pelagius's influential body of supporters in Rome spread the belief that by his own effort anyone could and should maintain high standards and good values; in the midst of conventional life, at a time when Christianity and morality generally had become nominal in Roman social life, the Pelagians said that man is both free and fully responsible for his every action, indeed that sin is a deliberate act of contempt for God.

The gentle old bishop was quite a psychologist, quickly recognising that fallen human nature could hardly bear such a cross. He was concerned with the inner tensions of the individual; for example, in advocating continence to a rich widow, he had humbly to admit that there could be a hidden danger "I have often observed this fact in human behaviour; with certain people, when sexuality is repressed, avarice seems to grow in its place."

Augustine was also of course a theologian and much concerned with the relationship between man and God - that of the child to his father, dependent and involved - whereas Pelagius felt that when a son grew up he should become fully independent; and he wanted to be a part of a reforming church. He was convinced that man was created good by the Creator and that man's nature did not need to change. Augustine on the other hand preached that even the baptised Christian throughout his life constantly needed healing and transformation, itself a gradual process requiring an attitude of dependence on God. He understood human frailty and accepted humanity with love, whereas Pelagius judged people with an unattainable yardstick.

It was here too at Hippo that St Augustine had written those five monumental books on the 'City of God'. What fascinated Augustine about history was that 'It could be seen as a stretch of time in which the new-born oust the dying.' 'A great river slipping towards death', interspersed by God speaking in prophetic sayings until the coming again of Christ. He traced this progression throughout his three books, in order to show his readers that the whole history of the human race pointed to a division between the earthly and the heavenly city. He had stressed this tension again, beginning with Cain and Abel and working through prophetic history.

He described two groups of humanity, visualised in his terms as two cities - those who had the capacity to long for something different and those for whom the present sufficed, that is those often engulfed by the present. It concerned each man's capacity to love, the quality of that love and therefore what he loves. We are all temporary residents on earth - 'resident aliens', pilgrims, and yet by necessity accepting our present life as having a purpose - to do some good, to improve some situation, to avoid some greater evil in our common mortal life. The theme of the book is about being otherworldly in this world. It is about love, "Order me in my love," said Augustine, who ever believed in the essential goodness of created things, but believing that goodness to be in fact the gift of the Good God.

All this added to Teilo's unrest - he knew the supreme act of love that God had shown was in His Son's death on the Cross, to bring us back to Him, released from sin and death by His own death in our place; Teilo's unrest increased because he became convinced that he must reject Ygrain forever and fight instead for the Gospel, especially now that he had been made a bishop. Britain was in danger of turning its back on the real message and even Dewi had almost misunderstood the subtlety of Pelagianism. It was more insidious than the threat of the Saxons.

Direct contact between the churches of the eastern Mediterranean and the Celtic west was continuous over these busy seaways - even more so at this time when there was so much strife and havoc on the mainland of Europe. The British church was to be cut off from Rome for quite a period; instead the Patriarchs of Jerusalem and Constantinople were to be in much fuller contact with those 'Islands of the Seas', by which phrase many believe Isaiah was alluding to the British Isles. It was for this reason that Dewi, Teilo and Padarn were consecrated to the episcopate in Jerusalem and not by the Pope in Rome. It seemed to them as they left Jerusalem that they had shaken the dust of the world off their feet. Here they had come to worship with many other pilgrims who loved the Lord Jesus; they would always have a great nostalgia for the place where such variety of colour of fruit, clothing and people mingled and where so many smells of the aromatic east could mix so easily with the scent of incense on the altars.

The seaways at this time were being used for a wide variety of purposes - for trade, for exploration and even as escape routes for slaves - like St Patrick - to freedom from their tyrannical masters. Many had come by sea from eastern countries to the west, often bringing their skills and knowledge of eastern culture with them. The three friends were well aware, for instance, the legend of St Joseph of Arimathea, which claimed that he was a wealthy tin-merchant and owner of a fleet of ships. The legend goes that his fleet sailed west and north as far as Cornwall, bringing with it a wide range of manufactured goods and taking on return Cornish tin back to the Mediterranean. Whether the legend was true after 500 hundred years of telling, none could be sure, but Joseph, it was claimed, was the younger brother of the father of the Virgin Mary and, when Christ was a young man, this great uncle had brought him on one of these trading expeditions.

A later legend told that after the Crucifixion and during the persecutions in Jerusalem, Joseph, now head of Jesus' family, together with Mary and nine others, were cast out to sea by the Sanhedrin in a boat without oars; the boat finally came ashore at Marseilles at the seaside town of Deux Maries-Sur-Mer, near Arles, which was to become the senior church in Gaul. Here, later, the contemporary of St Augustine, John Cassian, came from the eremetical solitude of Egypt and the Holy Land, to found a monastic community. His teachings marked out the future path of western monasticism, his writings becoming the inspiration of St Benedict.

Teilo and his friends were anxious to make the return journey by a route similar to that alleged to have been taken by Joseph. Having deepened and enriched their faith during their pilgrimage in Jerusalem and also by contact with the desert fathers of north Africa, they again embarked, this time for Marseilles. Here they were to learn many tales from those Christian descendants of the remnant who had escaped the early persecutions in Jerusalem, now already settled for hundreds of years in the area. They would include the re-telling of the old story of how Joseph and his company set out from Marseilles for Britain in AD 39 at the invitation of the Silures, who lived in Glamorganshire and on both sides of the Severn estuary. On islands a little way inland Joseph was said to have built his wattle church and worshipped Christ. So that when the Romans under Agricola arrived in Britain ten years later, they found Christianity already indigenous there on the island of Glastonbury (Ynis Witrin). Many of Dewi and

Teilo's contemporaries believed this story and chose to be buried at Glastonbury.

The three friends were now on the last lap of their journey home, Dewi carrying with him that precious sapphire which he planned to give to this same church on the island. They all disembarked at a harbour on the south-east bank of the Severn estuary and made their final pilgrimage to the little settlement at Glastonbury. Here they stayed and recounted the highlights of their journey and here also Dewi, filled with so many memories, had a dream. He dreamt that he was to build a west chapel for the existing church there, but he must not build on the site of the ancient church, for that land was already hallowed. Dewi did as he was bid and made his gift to Glastonbury of the priceless sapphire, which he laid on the altar.

Here then the friends parted, Dewi staying a while to complete his business and Padarn setting out by boat for Moridinum; Teilo sailed from the island of Glastonbury up the Severn to the mouth of the river Wye which he followed till he reached Dubricius' centre at Henllan, to consult with his master. Several of the most famous Celtic saints were magistri under Dubricius at this monastic school, Iltud and Prince Budic amongst them. The school was situated near the ancient Roman city of Ariconium, just four miles north-west of Ross; it thronged with great numbers of pupils eager to learn.

Dubricius' influence extended over the whole of South Wales and Devon and Cornwall as well. Ariconium was very likely the centre of the Welsh Christian movement of the fifth and sixth centuries; it was in the Celtic kingdom of Erging, not very far from Brecon, itself named after Dubricius's grandfather Brychan.

This area around Ariconium, known as Archenfeld, remained essentially Welsh although later surrounded by Saxon land; the area has indeed seemed to remain 'stilled in time', while it has always had its own laws and customs, privileges and obligations.

Christianity had gained much ground in romanised parts of Britain, but the real conversion of the tribesmen came with Dubricius' ministry in the late fifth century. Apart from the strife in northern Europe, the Saxons in Britain had also cut off Christians in Wales from the continent, causing the Celtic Church to become even more independent of Rome; Christianity and the Celtic language were therefore of increasing importance and became the major factors uniting scattered groups in all parts of the Celtic west. But the church was not yet organised; it had a weak diocesan structure in those early times, but now the monasticism which had first appeared in the late fifth century was increasing in importance and an the administrative structure based on the monastery was beginning to replace even that weak old diocesan framework.

The first known monastic settlement was at Glastonbury, after which monasticism spread before 500 along the coastal regions of Wales, and later during the sixth century to Ireland and back to the north-west coast of Britain in the latter half of the sixth century. It was the spread of this monasticism which could be said to have crystallised the special nature of the church in Britain.

Be that as it may it was the next generation, Teilo and his contemporaries, who were to consolidate the monastic work inland; the saints would obtain the permission of the local rulers to set up monastic settlements in these pagan areas. Just as soon as they had gained enough converts, the monastery would be founded, an island of Christianity amid a pagan society, where monks could preach and teach, serving the district around. Teilo was more fortunate than most in that King Aircol was already a Christian king and fully supported his work; for many saints, although related often to princely stock, it was necessary first to convert the ruler or prince before any favour or support was possible.

Dubricius greeted Teilo openly and warmly, anxious to hear all Teilo could tell him; they soon retreated to Dubricius' private apartment and talked. "I have long had it in mind to appoint you, Teilo, as my successor. and now it seems appropriate to discuss these plans", he said when they were alone; in fact Teilo was to stay quite a while with his holy master. They discussed how Teilo would accompany Dubricius in his work and so get to know something of the responsibilities it entailed; this was how it would be. And so, promising to return when his mission had been achieved, Teilo took his leave of Dubricius. Crossing the gentle hills between the Wye and the Usk, he not only felt that he had made the right decision as regards Ygrain, but he knew also that one day he would return to set up further churches there near Henllan. First however he must return to Castell Argol.

MAP 2 (below) according to Michael Mountney

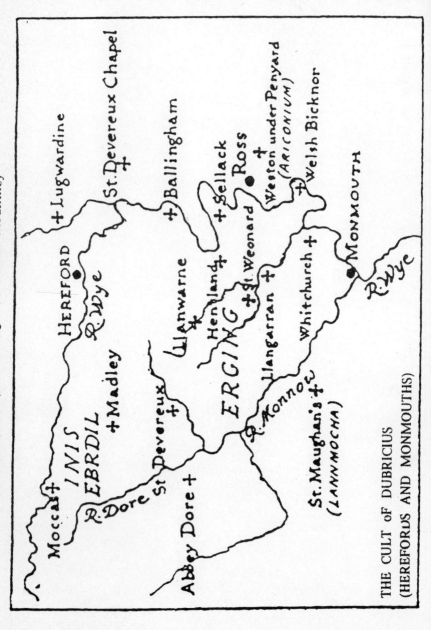

THE CULT OF DUBRICIUS
(HEREFORDS AND MONMOUTHS)

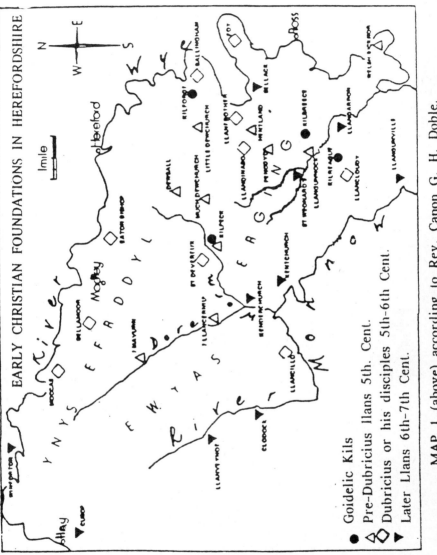

EARLY CHRISTIAN FOUNDATIONS IN HEREFORDSHIRE

1mile

● Goidelic Kils
◇ Pre-Dubricius llans 5th. Cent.
⬦ Dubricius or his disciples 5th-6th Cent.
▼ Later Llans 6th-7th Cent.

MAP 1 (above) according to Rev. Canon G. H. Doble.
GLOUCESTER, HEREFORD AND MONMOUTH AREA.

Chapter Seven

THE BUILDING OF LLANDEILO FAWR.

Padarn arrived at Argol before Teilo. As a protégé of Cadfan, he was naturally keen to tell all the news, before going to his own mission in Ceredigion. So, when Teilo reached Castel Argol, news had already spread of their visit to Jerusalem. Teilo was greeted with warmth and excitement. King Aircol listened to all he had to say with much eagerness and rejoiced with him that the journey had been so successful.

"Now we must discuss the plans for your new monastery" the King said at last, sitting back with some satisfaction. "This your own monastic city!"

So without delay Teilo set out the plans before him, the position of his church, the bank to enclose it, the preaching cross and the dwellings, the whole to be surrounded of course by a further bank with gates at the four cardinal points.

And so the work was put in hand and, as promised, King Aircol instructed his son Erbin, who had a hill-fort close to the site of the new monastery, to give a certain number of his warriors the task of constructing this new monastic city.

Teilo had had a good opportunity to visit many churches both in Jerusalem and at Hippo as well as many in the country around. They had talked much of this perfect design for a monastic city - including the one to be built of stone in Serbia by the Emperor Justinian, to be called Justinia Prima, where the acropolis was to cover the whole extent of the hill-top, which they had heard was to be enclosed by a wall with fortified towers and to contain churches and a large cathedral, with baptistry and a town alongside; in Egypt too they had

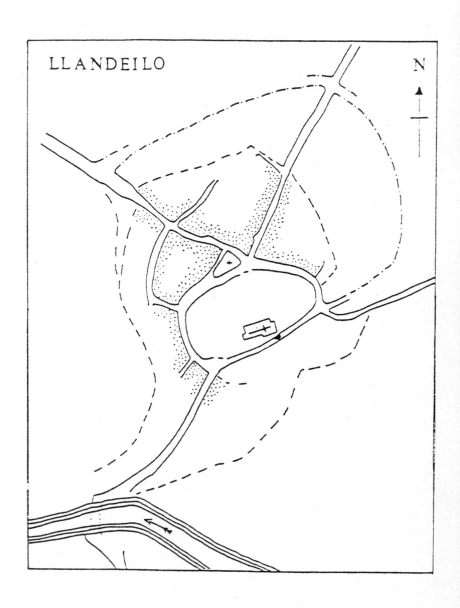

LLANDEILO

N

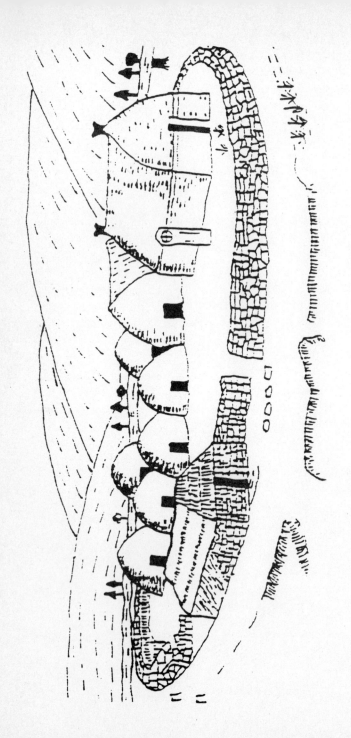

A TYPICAL CELTIC MONASTERY

found the famed mud-brick monasteries in the desert, where the monks were able to live lives of prayer and solitude away from society.

Local churches naturally used local building materials. The Romans had built churches of stone, but these were now decaying in the urban areas of Britain; likewise the Irish monastery style was well known to Teilo - the church built of sawn oak with a rush roof and usually surrounded by small beehive cells for the monks, some in stone, but mostly of wattle and mud. One monk per cell was the rule, the whole surrounded by an earthen bank as an enclosure and protection for all the buildings, in which was also a large wooden cross and an area for the monks' burial. This was then the type of monastery with which Teilo was familiar.

Since the Romans had left, the local people had once again gathered for protection in the old Iron Age forts on hill-tops with their steeply banked fortifications - so very different to those walled cities of the East with their bustle and narrow streets which Teilo had so recently experienced.

The idealised plan now for the west was a circular enclosure, three concentric walls enclosing three areas of sanctity: within the bank at the centre was to be the monastery and the baptistry; the next bank would enclose the market cross and village settlements, while the outerbank would enclose an area of sanctuary for the traveller, with chapels and crosses at various gates, where pilgrims could give thanks for their safe journey to the city. As regards the street plan, the ideal city was to contain roads radiating outwards from the centre, with gates at the four cardinal points. In practice, of course, there was no rule as to how a monastery should be built - each was to have its own individuality.

Dewi's monastery at Mynyw (in the marshland of the valley Rosina, close to the sea port) was at a key point for vessels from the Mediterranean and the East, from Cornwall and Brittany, and also a junction for ships setting off for the northern and western coasts of Britain, the Isle of Man and the other western Isles; he certainly had chapels near the gates, where travellers came to give thanks for their safe journey; he loved children also and made special provision for their training and education.

St Cadoc at Llancarvan, Glamorgan, never ceased to rule as a prince, so that his monastery reflected the style of a rich ruler. Here he daily fed many hundreds of the poor. Not far away from Llancarvan, at LlanIlltud Fawr or Llantwit as it was later called, Illtud presided over a large teaching monastery and, being in close proximity to the sea, welcomed travellers from the continent and western Britain; but many monasteries would have such accommodation for travellers, where a special welcome and hospitality would be the rule. Padarn, with his deep love of music and art and having taken a special interest in the illuminated manuscripts of the Coptic Churches and those at Jerusalem, was to take back with him a determination to set up a miniature scriptorium within his main monastery - a special cell being provided for a monk talented in this art; indeed in later years his monastery was to become famous for books produced there; this was also true of several Irish monasteries, where learning and manuscript work became famous throughout the known world.

A well marked path, leading from Urien's stronghold on the rock above the Cennen river, led across the valley to a ford on the Tywi and thence up the hill to where Teilo was constructing his monastery. It was known as Heol Rheged. Below this hill, boats from Moridinum would unload, the cargo having to be carried up the steep hillside to a point where the workmen could use the supplies.

The earthen banks were becoming solid and high now around the monastery site; great ramparts with the large wattle-and-mud church alongside were growing apace, now almost complete. The stream to be used for baptism spurted as a spring outside the east end of the church and slightly to the north of it, a position which Teilo had chosen for his baptistry, to flow on down the steep side of the hill into the Tywi river at its foot. Smaller wattle huts now surrounded the church building, where the monks would retire to sleep at the end of the day. They were all well used to hard manual labour, which was built into the rhythm of their lives.

The monastic enclosure was surrounded by a town with its own bank; here lived the workmen who were assisting the monks. In addition to this labour force, Erbin, Aircol's eldest son, would daily send a considerable band of men from his fort nearby on the other side of the hill towards Argol. Thus the work progressed quite quickly and within a matter of months Teilo's monastic centre was becoming a thriving community. Roads radiated from the centre, along which local farmers would come daily from the countryside to supply the workmen with fresh food; a tiny town was beginning to grow to the north, with the monastic area and the great church along the river side to the south. The well-worn exits to this oval- shaped enclosure were at those positions which the Druids of an earlier period may well have marked as summer and winter solstices, although there is no direct evidence that this was previously a Druidical site.

In the excitement and bustle it was not difficult to become part of the heaving crowd almost immediately; Teilo was determined to finish his project by summer and when the roof was complete the main building for worship could be consecrated.

He had plunged straight into the work; he had already taken so much time off for the visit, he could hardly ask for more until the monastery was well underway. It had all been so hectic and exciting, daily the king had come to watch the work progressing and now whilst the last details were being completed, Teilo decided that the time had again to visit Vortipor's camp to see his friends there, hopefully bringing them back to Llandeilo Fawr for the consecration.

Ygrain must have heard by now that he had returned and, although he was longing to see her, he was also dreading the thought of how he could possibly explain his decision; in a sense he had almost put it off, unable to face her. But now, since two or three months had already passed by, the King's court was due for session and he was expected to attend, before he could return to his centre for the consecration by Dubricius.

It was now the time of year when King Aircol and his court would move to the main centre of administration at Arberth, leaving only the permanent staff at Castel Argol. Aircol rode out and down the valley with his chief warriors and men of the court. Teilo followed soon after; this time instead of his usual method by foot and boat, he rode across the high ridge of hills, visiting three churches on the way, those at Trelech, Brechfa and Llanpumpsaint. The monks he had placed in charge were always anxious to talk over their latest problems and to meet with Teilo in prayer, but this time he carried with him news of his journey to Jerusalem and this was to be a particular thrill and inspiration to them all - including the camp followers.

But there were also the local problems that took up much time; many had to contend with special local difficulties - unbelieving neighbours could make life very difficult; they were usually only petty quarrels, but sometimes these could lead to serious fighting, so that the monks had to be constantly on guard to protect and lead their little groups of believers: Teilo with his warm smile, his words of wisdom and encouragement could allay their fears, talking over the problems whilst working alongside them in the fields.

Teilo was in a hurry to get to Penally. Bound to see to his churches on the way, he was at last free to get down there. Still bronzed after his journey, he strode down towards his home, to be greeted by his mother who looked considerably older.

"I thought you would never come", she scolded as Teilo approached. "Such a lot has happened since we last saw you. Did you hear that Annauved and King Budic are leaving us to return to Brittany? I was afraid that they would leave before you got back, and now she has two little ones and another on the way, and poor Ygrain has gone as thin as a wraith and pale too. She has been helping Annauved with the boys and derived a little comfort from that I think."

His mother was prattling on mostly to herself, not really looking at Teilo. In her distress she had not noticed how white he had turned beneath his tan.

He slipped outside and seeing his father there approached him quickly, giving him a great hug, then stepping back to look at him. Ensic did indeed look worn as he started to explain that everything seemed to be happening at once.

"Don't worry about your mother", he said as he looked up at Teilo with weary eyes. "She's just upset, that's all. It has been a bit of a shock to hear that Annauved and her little family are going so soon".

Although there were plenty of servants they had always been a close family and Annauved was bringing her children up in the same way.

Teilo said a quick farewell to his father and found Ygrain at Erbin's main fort of the fishes - Dinbych y Pysgod, close by. She was sitting on a rock close to the seashore looking out to sea, her mind far away, not expecting Teilo. He stood and watched her for some time until at last he moved towards her, and the sound of his footsteps roused her. Looking up from her reverie, their eyes met, and already hers filled with tears as if she knew what he was going to say. Words were superfluous as they held each other for a very long time. At last she spoke.

"When did you arrive? I thought you would never come, and now Annauved has asked me to accompany her to Brittany. Have you heard about King Budic's decision?"

"Yes, I know", Teilo said staring at her helplessly. It seemed as if he had no words to say at this moment, just as if all initiative had left him.

They started to walk along the cliff, and as they did so they began to talk, he telling of his adventures, she listening with more than just intelligence, her whole being tuned in to all he was saying and not saying. At last he started telling her about Pelagianism and the effect that the discussions had had on him. They stopped for a while as she looked at him uncomprehending, while he tried to explain the motives and the reasons for his total commitment to Christ. Then, with a little cry she took in what he was trying to convey of the exclusive call he felt - to serve God.

She went as pale as death as he explained. The more he tried, the more painful it became for both, until at last she broke her silence and cried out, "But you are a Pelagian yourself! You are such a hypocrite about all this. Can't you see? You talk of your mission as though you were indispensable to God, as though you believe us and our love to be expendable. Do you really believe that God cannot manage without you? Or that He gave us our love, only for His gift to be rejected? I believe that you claim too exalted a place for yourself, Teilo; you imagine that you are the only one He can use and that you alone have to do whatever it is all on your own. Our joint efforts would be worth a lot more surely, Pelagian or not!"

She broke down in bitter sobs and all Teilo could do was to stand helplessly by. He never felt more distraught and helpless. Could she not understand? He had a job of work to do for God in which she had no part - and he felt very strongly that he had been called by God to do it. How could he refuse? It was out of the question but why couldn't she try to understand? ...yet...maybe there was something in what she said ... it worried him ... could she be right about being a helpmate for him? He stood there appalled at his own ambivalence and her pleas from the heart.. In his distress he tried to explain once more.

"Beloved Ygrain, believe me I have prayed about this in deep anguish and I truly believe that this is God's answer for us. We could never be happy for I have to be free to obey God's commands and it would make for a very painful and impossible life together. I believe that God has called me to be celibate in order to fulfil His plans. It pains me beyond measure to have to say all this. Please wont you try and make it easy for me".

But that she could not do and it was a bitter parting for them both. He stumbled down the cliff, head hung low and shoulders hunched, a dejected figure, Ygrain quite unable to let him go. She felt she would rather die.

He dragged himself to his monastery in Penally - to make his promised visit to the camp of Vortipor at Lydstep. But it was simply no good going there until he had had a chance to get over the pain of the afternoon. The heartache he had caused Ygrain was something he would carry with him for ever.

The next day however he could put the visit off no longer. The open land leading to the coast was warm and hazy in the summer sun - a very different day to that of his previous visit. As he approached the camp the scar-faced youth came out to greet him - no longer menacing, his spear held lightly and his manner friendly. Teilo thus knew that the dedication of his friend Iouill and the other monks had had an impact during their months of faithful work; they had talked to the warriors and lived alongside them, though it had been difficult and dangerous at times: their love, prayer and general demeanour had been of real influence. The monks had shown the warriors at one level how to till the ground, while at the other the stability of their lives had been recognised by many. Teilo was well pleased that he would be able to report such progress to King Aircol when he attended the court at Narberth; Vortipor had in fact already been summoned by the King, so that at last the three monks were able to take their leave and go their way together.

Teilo and his two friends set out for the court at Narberth and, when they reached it, found it full of excitement. Teilo knew that his family would be there with all the local nobles when the court sat and was prepared for the news that peace had been restored in Brittany in the region of Cornouaille, from which its rightful ruler King Budic had earlier been forced to flee. He had sought sanctuary in the court of King Aircol for many years now. Later, by marrying Annauved, Budic had become part of life in Demetia. However everyone knew that this was only a temporary state of affairs and that one day he must return to his own land in Brittany. Now the preparations were being made for the family to leave.

Teilo's parents, reconciled now to their departure and happy to see Teilo, greeted him warmly with tears of joy, longing to hear all the news of Jerusalem and the east, but tearful too that their daughter and her little sons, Ishmael and Teifi, must soon leave them perhaps never to return. It was an emotional time for them all - with so much to say and the time drawing near when they could neither see each other nor talk.

King Aircol summoned his brilliant and trusted friend Theodoric, the mercenary Goth who captained Aircol's Demetian fleet. Theodoric had commanded that the fleet be made ready to sail with arms and men, to help King Budic return to his own land. The fleet could be ready to sail within a few weeks and now last-minute questions arose and final details had to be settled.

Theodoric had helped Aircol to establish himself as King in Demetia, by driving out the Irish from the coasts and installing Aircol as the new ruler. He had also driven back the Irish from the coasts of Cornwall, where he was later to be given a permanent lordship near

Padstow, St Ives and Falmouth. Now this great hulk of a man, rough and strong as an ox, stood before Aircol in the court, as they discussed the situation in Brittany.

King Budic sat with his head resting on his hand, as he tried to trace the sequence of events which must follow. His brother Maxentius had expelled him from his rightful inheritance, which they held in equal shares from their father Daniel. The land was in the region of south-western Brittany with its capital at Quimper, which they had conquered together, killing Marcellus and then dividing the kingdom between them. But through this brother Maxentius's treachery, Budic had been tricked of his share in the kingdom and forced to flee to Wales. Now he had gathered enough forces to return and with Theodoric's skilful help hoped to recover his rightful half of the kingdom.

Teilo looked at his sister Annauved, resting beside her husband. They had with them their two little sons, Ishmael and Teifi, and it was Ishmael who ran to his uncle Teilo, as soon as he saw him in the court. Annauved was expecting another baby and Teilo's natural fears for her safety on the voyage and on arrival in Brittany were obvious. Behind her stood her close friend Ygrain, looking pale and drawn, with her eyes lowered. The sight of her distress was unbearable, he could not look at her. There was no comfort for Teilo. He hoped that Annauved would comfort Ygrain somehow - perhaps this was part of God's plan for her that she should be going with her to Brittany. And it was a great comfort too to think that Ygrain would be beside Annauved throughout the journey and when she settled and made her home in a foreign land. Excitement at seeing them all again, only to lose them all so soon however, made this a poignant time for all.

Theodoric had come to Britain and served Arthur as an ordinary soldier, when Arthur was established ruler in Britain. He was a mercenary, a strong and reliable captain, and Aircol was pleased to send him on this mission to take Budic's family in safety, back to Brittany. He knew the seaways like the back of his hand and as a well-trained soldier could be relied upon to support the family and help them to establish themselves again in western Brittany.

100

There were of course other matters for the court at Narberth to attend to in this present session, many local disputes of various kinds. A rich man named Tutuc, whose corn was ravaged by pigs belonging to a man from Penally, had killed an infant named Typhei with a lance. As the disaster had happened on Teilo's family land the King asked Teilo to adjudicate. The man knelt cowering before Teilo, begging forgiveness. Knowing the aggrieved family so well and their desolation at the loss of the beautiful child, Teilo found it very difficult to pronounce judgement and on the King's advice took Tutuc's two villas of Cil Tutuc and Pennclecir for the church.

Vortipor however was quite unable to keep silence at this pronouncement and turning on Teilo he swore at him:

"You stinking prig, standing there with that pious expression on your face; given half a chance you would accept everyone's land to augment your wretched church; you curry favour with my father, but slyly snatch another piece of land from his Kingdom of Dyfed in the name of your church. You are nothing but a grasping materialist".

"Be silent", thundered King Aircol .

Now the King turned to the final business on the agenda, as he faced his son Vortipor and demanded to know how things had fared at Lydstep in his stronghold. Somewhat ill at ease, Vortipor turned to Teilo again, suggesting that he speak for him. When Teilo gave his report and told of the work of his two brother monks in the camp, the King rejoiced that things had so altered, that no more murders had occurred and that the former drunken orgies had ceased. The King now turned to Teilo, this time with tears in his eyes, and asked if he would accept yet more gifts of land on behalf of the church.. Vortipor's face was by now purple with rage; the humiliation of being hauled up before the entire court and then to hear of Dyfed being diminished even further in favour of the church was outrageous; he swore to himself that he would one day take his revenge on this manipulative priest; but he held his tongue; his day would come.

"And now Teilo", the King continued, "what more can I say? The court has not heard yet of your travels and the honour bestowed on you by the Patriarch in Jerusalem, making you, Dewi and Padarn bishops amongst us: what is it that we can do to honour you?"

"My Lord King", said Teilo, "there is a matter which lies close to all our hearts and that is the dedication of the great church at Llandeilo Fawr. I would hope that as my sister and King Budic are to depart so soon, we should be able to celebrate this great day whilst they are still with us; that their departure should not be all sadness at their loss, but that we should have something great to celebrate also".

The whole court murmured assent at this; there was general outburst of cheering and excitement as the King declared the day when they should all gather at Llandeilo. Teilo stumbled out of the court room into the brilliant sunshine outside. He felt torn in shreds by it all - and the pain that he had caused Ygrain was still gnawing at his heart - but he must get back to Llandeilo and see to the preparations for the dedication of the church. With the need to channel all his energies into the work, he must somehow try to forget the pain he had caused her.

THE DEDICATION. The great day for establishing Teilo's work had come. King Aircol and all his court were in attendance. Teilo's family, together with King Budic and Teilo's many friends, sat close by the altar. The great church was packed with monks and all who had helped to build it. With the populace from the surrounding countryside they crowded into the building, filling not only the church and the churchyard beyond, but overflowing also into the monastic city of Llandeilo itself.

The church was a long low building of sawn oak with a rush roof, it would have been very dark inside but for the many candles which lit the interior with a warm bright glow. As the great crowd raised the song of praise to God, the dedication of His church was under way; there was rain on the wind which gently blew the large clump of trees on the hill above the church, but the rain mercifully held off. Teilo stood in their midst with his head bowed as the service began. Father Dubricius was old and becoming frail now, his white hair flowing over his shoulders, his venerable old face aglow with joy and praise. His work for Wales had been that of a tough visionary, training and teaching the future leaders; Teilo, the man who would fill his place, was fulfilling all the early promise he had shown as a youngster. Dubricius was truly happy that things were going just as he had planned. He looked at Teilo, as he stood there young and strong, with that glow of joy still about him, that made everyone who met him feel better for having been with him. Strong in mind and body and at the height of his powers, he had a brilliant mind totally dedicated to his God and to the work of the Kingdom of Heaven.

Ygrain was also watching the service from her place a little behind the family. Her heart was still and her thoughts calm as she witnessed the moving scene, which would be forever etched on her mind. The voices raised around her in full song reflected the warmth and glow of the candle light. The altar was set for celebration of the Lord's supper and near it the spring of pure water for baptism; the love that flowed out to Teilo from all his friends and loved ones in the congregation mixed with her own feelings - standing - almost a spectator to the scene. Teilo stood behind the altar, over which hung the censor, just as did the incense which suggested prayers going up to God in the church at Jerusalem. He raised his hands to the Father in heaven and, as he blessed the celebration, Ygrain continued to watch, fascinated as though in a trance; she could see the scene being played out before her and her only part still was as an onlooker. This was her turning point; from here on something in her heart froze, as her reason told her, almost with a jolt, that Teilo could never be part of her life.

The service continued with communion but as she stood there unable to move, unable to go forward or retreat, she knew that her heart would not allow her to be such a hypocrite as to accept communion with all the rebellion she felt against God welling up inside her. So she continued to stand rooted to the spot as Teilo and his flock dedicated their work to God - here on the hill in this beautiful valley; the future of his church was standing in history, but surging forward for the timeless work of saving souls, the stream of blessing and cleansing issuing out from the Baptistry beside the church as the water gushed out into the valley below. Old Dubricius, Dyfrig the water bearer, the bringer of faith to the nation, dedicated the flowing spring. The valley was both a kingdom and a city - a whole place - a holy place - with the church at its head. History was reaching out for an ideal, the past and future realising it to be something that is always there - earth and legend as one - for they are truly one - a dream world - the valley as it must and should be. All this Teilo saw in a moment - the natural geography as the womb, the valley's many aspects functions and activities standing as a microcosm of the world, with the king's place - Argol - at the centre.

King Aircol turned to look at Teilo, whose radiant face revealed this great inspiration that had captured him, and Aircol, himself a strong and holy man, understood. The greatness of the moment seized them both and they threw back their heads and sang out their praises and poured out their hearts to God; indeed echoes of that great dedication ring about the place still, for those who have ears to hear.

Teilo preached on Pelagianism, "St Augustine declared that there were two cities, the city of God where the love of God reigned and each man put service of his neighbour and the well-being of society first - the city of the just - the Heavenly city; and the other city where the love of self reigns. He had a great pessimism about human nature. But I pray that from this place Christ will always be preached. Let me try to explain the way I see it".

Teilo went on, telling the people that they had a choice, "You may think that all that God requires is for us to do our best, to live a good life, to improve ourselves and the lot of others, in short to leave the world a better place than it was before. Do you agree?" there were roars of assent as everyone thought this was just what they were supposed to do.

"Well I am telling you that by believing that it is so easy to become good, you are actually lowering God's standards and pushing Christ further away. You see it is not as simple as you suppose, for behaving in this way you are proclaiming that His life and death are irrelevant to you, just an optional extra, a pretty story. But I am telling you that the issues are a matter of life and death.

We all have to die, this is something inevitable and however much we think we are doing good, our moral condition remains the same". A sick twinge gripped Teilo as he said this, he could not look at Ygrain, though he knew she was there in the crowd listening. He paused a long time trying to pull himself together - he must continue the message God had given him to preach - somehow he must go on.

104

"If we examine our hearts" he said, " we know that however much we try, we have not the power to overcome our bias towards selfishness. We would all love to do what we want to do; our nature is selfish. Even if we believe we are totally committed to helping others, we naturally want to suit ourselves. But, however much we think we are spending our practical lives 'doing good', we are not tackling our own internal predicament. For this we need something extra - beyond ourselves - this is the Grace which God has offered us in Christ. It is Christ I preach to you today. He died so that we could have this offer of a new nature; not our old nature but a nature in communion with God over which death has no power. You can live in this communion now, if you wish. It is freely available through what Christ did for us on the Cross, Christ is risen from death, His tomb empty, He is here with us now, He has broken the power of death. Break out of the tombs of your own lives and live with Him today. We can learn to live in this Heavenly city now, to do His will and not our own, to fulfil what He wants us to do in this life, which may be very different from what we want or expect".

This was Teilo's message, to which he was true all his life, but the cost was real enough and he never forgot that for a moment; he was shaken to the core by his own personal dilemma. As for Ygrain, she was not convinced. The whole thing left her sad and bewildered.

BUDIC'S RETURN TO BRITTANY. The feasting and rejoicing continued for half the night. Castel Argol was alive with bustle and noise. The service the previous day had taken place at noon, after which all the guests had returned to Argol to celebrate. Every house in the neighbourhood was full and Cadfan especially was highly excited and involved with the celebrations. From his settlement near Argol he was able to entertain many of the guests, putting them up for a few nights. His servants were busily occupied with all the arrangements, both here and at Argol. Both he and King Budic had much to talk about; they were both natives of Brittany and, though Cadfan's area was to the north of Budic's kingdom, there was a great deal of common interest.

Far too soon the time came for Budic's departure and there were many who followed the company down river to the sea port of Moridinum.

Aircol accompanied the family, led by Teilo, to the bay. It was not a long journey down the Tywi in small boats to the fleet waiting at the sea port of Moridunum. Suddenly the company had grown quiet. Somehow on occasions like this, Teilo thought, there is so much to say and yet one is quite unable to say it, except in trivialities. He sat in one of the boats accompanying the family. Ensic and Gwenhaf were huddled together close to Annauved, with Teilo on her other side; his brother Mabon held little Teifi, whose large round eyes were full of excitement and who with Ishmael had hardly slept a wink since the party had arrived in Llandeilo. The memories and experiences their little minds took in at the service, combined with the feast and promise of a sea voyage, would make them very drowsy once aboard, but not now, while with Teifi on his lap, their uncle told them of his adventures on the trip to Jerusalem; Ygrain was close at hand, ready to hold Teifi if the excitement became too much or he were sick!

When they finally rounded the last bend in the river and the fleet came in sight, the children started laughing, pointing and chattering all at once; Teilo had to take a firm hold of little Teifi lest he should fall overboard. They could now see the calm blue ocean in the distance and the points of sunlight flickering on the water, whilst the masts of the fleet ahead rocked and dipped above the bobbing waves. King Budic stepped ashore at the harbour and was greeted by Theodoric, who saluted him with a broad smile. The combined force of King Budic's fleet and that of the Demetians made quite a formidable array. Everyone stumbled ashore and those returning prepared themselves to board the ships almost immediately, for the winds were set fair and the tide was about to turn, so that there should be little delay.

Soon the company was ready to sail. Teilo stood on the shore with his arms about Ensic and Gwenhaf, who stood proud but tear-stained, to wave off their daughter and her young family. Mabon shouted a few last messages as the ships pulled away, and many others of the party found it difficult to swallow back their tears. Theodoric looked huge, as he stood astride the poop of the largest boat, giving orders to his men as they unfurled the sails, while the gentle breezes increased the speed of the boats through the water. They would fade out of sight all too soon. Not a word passed as the wind took the sails and the party on the shore gazed at the departing ships. King Budic stood erect on the deck with his arm around his wife and with Ygrain quite close, holding the hands of Ishmael and Teifi, both waving with excitement and quite unconscious of the long parting ahead.

Annauved's words rang in Teilo's head as he watched - "Teilo" she had said, "when my baby is born, I will dedicate him to you and your work for God in Wales. Pray for us."

As the ships grew smaller in the distance and faded to little flecks, the company stood on the shore, unable to move, until the fleet was quite out of sight; they then broke into little groups and stumbled slowly and quietly away.

Theodoric's plan was to hug the coast of north Devon and follow it down to the Isles of Scilly, some of which were still attached to the mainland in those days. The dangers were the little rocks and islands on the way, so that he had to keep well clear, whilst keeping the land in sight. Rounding the Scillies, the fleet was out in the open sea and, taking advantage of a following wind, made straight across that channel between Brittany and Britain, heading in a south - westerly direction.

It was already rough enough for the passengers, although there was not too much of a swell, but coming within sight of the Brittany coast, Theodoric had to go carefully. He must not head straight in, for fear of the rocky islands, which constituted a hazard to all shipping in those parts. Meanwhile Ygrain spent many hours standing on the ship's poop, watching the sea. Her feelings seemed to be echoed by a shoal of dolphins escorting the boat, with the plankton on the surface of the water, luminous in the evening light. As they dived playfully under the prow of the boat, they threw up sharp slivers of spray like daggers of light shooting across the prow. The diving dolphins and the flying spray seared her very soul with a swift penetration of pain. The loneliness she felt in her heart was somehow assuaged by the

107

fascination of the water, constantly changing yet ever the same. On calmer days she watched, hoping almost desperately for a change of mood, as the colours varied from grey to blue, to violet to green and as she caught the perpetual rhythmic beat of the waves on the side of the ship, lapping here and there with white foam and spray. Somehow it all had a soothing effect on her broken heart, while it was interesting to see Theodoric's expert handling of his busy crew, constantly at work controlling the ship.

Now they were closing in to the shore and navigating that comparatively narrow passage through the small islands of the west coast. Theodoric clearly knew the passage well, for when with a sudden rush the boats were carried by fast-flowing tidal currents at a terrific pace through the channel and into the bay of Douarnenez, he remained in control and they flowed in confidently and without mishap. The journey had taken several days and a few very cramped and uncomfortable nights and the passengers and crew were tired and ready to rest. Theodoric therefore gave orders to anchor the fleet and they took shelter to the north of the bay. They had been fortunate that both wind and sea had been kind to them, but they were in no shape to disembark, until they had a calm harbour in which to recover.

King Budic and Theodoric also needed the time to make their plans. They had not lost a man nor a ship on the voyage, but the soldiers were not all used to sea voyages and had to be prepared to fight, for although King Budic had been assured that the country was prepared and ready to welcome him, it was just possible that not all his countrymen were friendly; this they would soon find out for the fleet could be seen from all points round this enormous bay of Douarnenez. He knew however he had many friends on the mainland and his first concern was to establish a base, where he could safely leave the family and press on ahead with the military force to regain Keeper(Quimper),the old capital of his kingdom. For the time being they could stay aboard, until a bridgehead had been established; he had sent out his spies and decided that the only element of surprise he could offer was attack by night, but perhaps he was worrying unnecessarily for he could have a most joyful welcome; this again they would soon find out.

As it was, the fighting continued for several days. A few bloody skirmishes took place, but the casualties were minimal for Budic's brother was now dead and the Bretons were anxious for a stable kingdom. Budic's men thrust into the wooded country but encountered little resistance, the chief danger being from bears and other wild animals; they were reassured that the country would soon be theirs with King Budic established in the kingdom of his father Daniel and grandfather Riothamus. Meanwhile the women and children were becoming restive, lying so close to the shore; when at last a relief force was sent back to arrange for them to disembark by night, they were quick to clamber up the sandy shore to a safe place on dry land.

Annauved's time was now approaching and she was glad to be safely on shore. They brought her and her party up the hill to the north of the bay into very high country - remote and safe from the usual routes, where they could wait until it was time to live openly in safety. Annauved, feeling homesick, stayed in this mountain stronghold until her child was born. The other women of the party stayed with her with a well- armed body of soldiers guarding them. The place she called 'Argol', as it is today, in memory of her beloved homeland; here they all waited until peace was established in the kingdom and here little Docco was born. He was named Oudoceus and he was dedicated to Christ and to His work back at home in the land of their fathers.

Chapter Eight

THE SYNOD OF LLANDDEWI BREFI.

The height of the summer was over, when the Synod was called in the hills near the old Roman fort of Llanio. For most of the western Welsh and the profusion of religious leaders and their followers, interested in the big movement going on in Wales, this was a good central meeting place. The synod had been called mainly to deal with the controversy that Pelagius had set in motion over a century before. Dubricius had invited Teilo to speak, but after all those accusations from Ygrain that he behaved like a Pelagian, Teilo felt he could not take part and refused to attend the synod.

In Llandeilo Fawr a monastery rhythm was now set in motion; youths of all ages were being sent to the monks for training and education. More houses were required for the growing population and for those needed to support them. They were exciting times, but in the evenings when the monks retired to their rude shelters, they had a chance to talk about the coming synod and would chat quietly, before falling back exhausted for the night's sleep, rising again at dawn to continue the work.

The evenings had an autumn chill now; the smell of the leaves and sticks burning in the monks' compound and the sound of voices of those still awake, breaking the night's stillness, mingled with the little breeze which stirred the trees on the summit of the hill to the west of the monastery; indeed the same special sound of that wind in those trees still murmurs today. The daily workmen had returned to their homes while those who sold food and produce in the market were back in their homesteads; Erbin's men had long since gone over the hill to their camp, to return in the early dawn light for another day's toil. Mabon's mind was busy with the latest news that had come to their camp from Dewi, who had travelled up to Llandeilo Fawr to visit Teilo, to lend a hand with the work and to continue his journey up the valley to Crug-y-bar, where he planned to stay with his friend and teacher, old Paulinus.

Dewi and Teilo had worked in unison for many years now; Teilo had even helped Dewi to build his monastery. But the friends were so different and, as the work increased, they tended to polarise, Dewi finding himself more and more involved with his thriving monastery and the demands of organising it as he wanted. He was very much a Welshman, whereas Teilo much more represented the Roman past, so that they appealed to different sorts of people; leading eventually to a different outreach for their work. Dewi had been discussing with Teilo that night the ever-growing threat of the teaching of Pelagius, which was spreading over from the Mediterranean throughout Wales and especially amongst those in contact with the seaways. Dewi's monastery, being close to one of the busiest ports in Britain, was bound to hear news from travellers; they came to his monastery to rest after their arduous ocean voyage, before continuing their journey north or to Ireland, a country with which Dewi was in close touch.

"What is this teaching of Pelagius?", asked Mabon of Iouill, who shared his wattle shelter. "It seems to be having a pretty devastating effect on the work of the churches in the east and they say it is now becoming a bit of a threat to our own".

The sounds of the camp were low but Mabon, none too clear at the best of times himself about such erudite subjects, deemed it wiser to put the question to Iouill privately to try to work out what exactly the threat was; it didn't seem too far from the aim of many Christians.

"After all," said Mabon, "Pelagius was only trying to stir up the slackers in the Christian faith - those who were settling back, maybe easy-going Christians, not taking their practical obligations too seriously - and there were more than a few of these in Rome a few generations ago. What is all the fuss about? Wasn't he just encouraging them to have a stricter obedience to the teaching of the Christian Church and to excel in zeal for Christianity".

"No Mabon, oh Mabon you've got it all wrong", said Iouill; "this is the very danger that St Augustine was complaining about. Can't you

111

see that, while Pelagius was encouraging his followers to become self-sufficient, to strengthen their own will and self-dependence, by his very over-emphasis on the ease by which one could become good, he was actually lowering the standard of that Christian virtue".

Young Mabon realised that he was getting a little out of his depth and it was all a bit late for this kind of talk! He was thoroughly sleepy by this time, and yawned.

"Well I do see that; if man is thought capable of striving for improvement on his own, it does rather leave out the role of God in his life".

"That's just it", said Iouill "if Christianity is just a competitive way of life, in which some do better than others until the Divine standard is reached, then Pelagius was probably right; but what happens when its late at night and you're tired, not thinking quite so clearly, it's dark and why bother anyway? What then?"

"Well" continued Mabon , - for the moment more alert - "Do you remember that scar-faced boy in Vortipor's camp and how hard he tried to overcome his desire to steal things which he 'just happened to see'? What an obvious difference we saw straight away, when he broke down, after trying and being tempted yet again - when he asked the Lord to come into his life to help him - so much so that he did not even want to steal. That was Grace - a result of the living Lord having a real relationship with the boy - which not only stopped him wanting to steal, but also had a profound effect on his whole outlook and nature - he became a loving glowing person, out to help others - it was clear for all those around to see".

"Yes", said Iouill, now in deep thought, "it was lovely to see the change. Although probably it was his own will which took the first step, it was the grace of Jesus, which took him over and changed his whole personality".

But two monks were by now overcome with sleep - Pelagius would have to wait for another day. A quiet peace spread over the camp, broken only by the occasional spark from the fire, and the breeze continuing to stir the trees in the wood on the side of the hill.

The next day it was time for Dewi to move on up the valley into the hill country near Caio. Many memories stirred him, as he followed the path to the hut shelter of his old master, Paulinus, now blind and not really able to care too well for himself unaided. His many years of faithful work in the area had not gone unrewarded, for the church there had prospered (and there are farms today near Crug-y-bar called 'Ynys' or 'island', meaning an island for Christ in a pagan sea).Paulinus and his brother Urthwal were still teaching daily in the monastery at Pant-y-Polion, now known as Maes Llanwrthwl after his brother. Paulinus was expected at the Synod at Llanio any day now but, hampered by the blindness, he was thinking twice about making the journey.

Dewi took the path to Paulinus's settlement and, as he approached, old Paulinus was seated at the door of his wattle church waiting for him; a monk standing beside him bent down and told the old man of Dewi's arrival and helped Paulinus to his feet; he took his stick to start down the path to greet him, his long, flowing-white hair giving him a venerable appearance; Dewi with his light swift step was there to hold him as he stumbled down the path. With what joy the old man led Dewi indoors! There was so much he wanted to know, so much about the work; how had it progressed and, yes, the trip to Jerusalem, so many months before; Paulinus wanted to know all about it. And so they chatted until well past dark; the embers burnt low in the centre of the hut and eventually Paulinus's happy conversational tone took on a low urgent note.

Dewi was listening acutely, as Paulinus turned to him and said, "The Synod is to be held nearby shortly; I urge you to attend it, Dewi. I realise the heavy workload you always bear, but with your recent knowledge of the issues in the church you are the man to go to the Synod and speak of what you know to be the truth on this matter of Pelagius, which is tearing the people of Wales apart. Over-emphasis on anything always leads to distortion; it unbalances the whole - and our Gospel of the Lord Jesus is a whole Gospel; it encompasses all the rich teaching of Christ. The situation here is becoming critical; heresy leads to schism and our church will become divided - no longer one whole rich Church of Christ".

The fire crackled a little and Dewi who was sitting at his old master's feet looked up to see Paulinus's brother, Urthwal, standing at the entrance. How long Urthwal had been there, neither knew, so engrossed were they in their discussion. Urthwal was Paulinus's constant companion, for Paulinus being blind needed someone all the time to guide and help him. David, remembering the old man's strength and dynamism in the old days, was very sad to see the two brothers thus hampered in their work. It meant a lessening of all they could plan and achieve, but they had taken the blow in a spirit of humility, not complaining, simply getting on in the best way they could.

Urthwal now wanted to join this topical discussion. "The trouble with Pelagius", he said, "was that he overlooked man's bias towards self-will from the beginning. To say that new-born children are in the same condition as Adam before the fall can only mean that Pelagius's contact with small children was pretty limited. From the beginning a new-born child cries for and demands what it wants in the way of food or attention and is very compelling in its demands, usually bawling until it gets what it wants. It takes superhuman energy at any age to change and to conform to the will of the Holy Spirit. Worse than that, if one really thinks that Adam's sin or selfishness only affected Adam himself, one has not really thought through the fact that what we do or fail to do - however small - affects other people for good or ill. The evil of sin was underestimated by Pelagius and the thought that all that was needed was for man to strive on his own for improvement, is a fallacy. We all need guidance, teaching and grace to fulfil the best in ourselves".

Urthwal was quite worked up as he held forth on this subject. Dewi, still sitting on the floor of the shelter was gazing into the embers of the fire, remembering all he had learnt on the journey, of St Augustine's dispute with Pelagius and how even Pelagius had been troubled by St Augustine's words about continence. "I have no hope at all but in Thy great mercy. Thou dost enjoin on us continence and when I knew that none could be continent, except God gave it, this also was itself a part of wisdom, to know whose gift it was". Pelagius's assertion on the one hand that a man can be without sin, if he chose, on the other Augustine's prayer to God, "O Charity, my

114

God enkindle me! Thou commandest continence. Grant what Thou commandest and command what Thou wilt", seemed to Dewi arguments that were poles apart.

It was time now to turn in for the night. Urthwal guided his brother Paul to his bed, and Dewi slipped away to the cell prepared for him that night. He slept very little as his mind turned over the arguments raised. As dawn broke, he was out in the countryside walking round some of his favourite haunts, remembered from the time of his pupilage with Paulinus. When he returned to the camp, Paulinus, Urthwal and their companions were already breakfasting. Dewi was soon chatting and eating alongside his friends. For Dewi it as always it was frugal fare - bread and water - whatever was necessary to keep body and soul together - but he would never touch any animal food; he always kept his body in severe restraint.

Their time together had been very precious, Urthwal accompanying Paulinus as usual. Dewi knelt down with them to pray before leaving; he wanted to impress on his mind all those things wise old Paulinus had told him. After the prayer the three men rose to say goodbye and Paulinus turned to Dewi saying, "My son, will you now give me your blessing; soon I shall be setting out for the synod and this is a difficult journey for me to undertake".

So Dewi turned and stretching out his hands put both on Paulinus's forehead, covering his eyes with his hands; he pronounced a special blessing for his health and strength, with thanks to God for all that Paulinus had meant to him as a teacher and a follower of Christ. Dewi then made the sign of the cross on his old master's eyes and, as he took his hands away, to his amazement Paulinus opened his eyes and looked Dewi full in the face. The three men were speechless, until Paulinus with a cry of praise raised his voice saying,

"I can see; my eyes have been opened!"

Hearing such a cry come up from the camp, monks came rushing from all parts to see what the rumpus was about, but all fell silent, as amazed they watched their master with his arms raised to heaven, giving great praise to God for the recovery of his sight.

Dewi stood back in humility, realising that this was not from him, but simply the Grace of God through him. A great feeling of joy broke out in his being at the thought that God had healed his beloved master. Paulinus, then turned to Dewi and blessed him with all those blessings that are written in both the Old Testament and the New; at length Dewi took his leave and climbed the hill to Caio, where he and Teilo had jointly founded a church near the Roman station at Louentium. As he made for the sheltered hollow of the hills, he thought again of this miracle that God had performed and wondered what a Pelagian would make of it. It was presumably an act which a Pelagian would not wish to consider too deeply.

THE SYNOD. Many of the older and experienced men were already gathered, chief amongst them Dubricius, whose master Germanus of Auxerre had led the church against Pelagianism in Britain so many years before; there were Bishop Paulinus and his brother Urthwal, Bishop Guistilianus and all the notables in Welsh religious life; any others who could be spared from their work including those learned in the Scriptures and the teachers in the church. Thus a wide range of leaders gathered at this time, when the Celtic Church could still not claim to be formally organised as a church, though Dubricius was beginning to place it on a more formal footing.

For some time the discussions waged around one topic or another, until the great debate itself on Pelagianism was broached. This subject was wreaking havoc both with the new Christians and with people generally; twice in the previous century the Pope had been obliged to send St Germanus of Auxerre to put this heresy down in the church in Britain. He had been ordered by the Pope to Britain in 429 and also 447, in Vortigern's time, for the same reason. Now the whole issue was being re-opened a third time; the controversy had waged since the period of the late Roman Empire; it had been fairly successfully repressed by the Bishops and early ascetics of the late fifth century, but these men were now ageing and handing over the pressure of Christian work to the new generation of Dewi and Teilo and their companions; the heresy was looming large in another generation.

Paulinus stood up; "Brothers", said the old Bishop, "There is one who has not yet appeared at our Synod, an eloquent man, approved in religion". The old Bishop continued to describe Dewi, explaining that he had formerly read under him in his school at Ty Gwyn and it was obvious for all to see the miracle performed by him recently. "My advice is that you invite him to join us. There was a great murmur of assent as old Bishop Guistilianus supported Paulinus's words, giving the Synod a word or two about Dewi's early life at his school at Hen Fynyw near the coast of Ceredigion. The people already knew his father, their King, and that Dewi was fifth in descent from Vortigern who had had much trouble with the same controversy (Vortigern had also found himself in a hopeless situation - he would offend Christian Europe, if he supported Pelagianism, but would offend an influential section of his own people, if he did not). Bishop Paulinus knew that Dewi would still be at Caio, so Dubricius ordered that a messenger be sent with all speed to fetch him, Meanwhile the Synod carried on with other matters for debate.

The old Sarn Elen road led from Llandovery over a range of hills, passing by Caio on its way west. It was this road that Dewi was now to follow to the Synod with the messenger. It was two days' journey at least and the hill country was becoming higher and more remote from the settlements all the while. After travelling along the route and making as good speed as they could, at last they ascended the high ridge above from where they could see Llanio below, down in the valley. They paused to regain their breath, for the valley seemed a long way down; it was here that the messenger boy had his fatal fall on the pathway when miraculously Dewi is said to have revived him. Descending the steep path as quickly as they could, Dewi and the messenger arrived at last at the Synod.

The crowds gathered noisily on what turned out to be a mild sunny day. There was no hope of all being accommodated even within the largest assembly building, a wattle shelter used by the Synod for debate until now. So the crowds gathered out in the open. One speaker after another was heard by the crowd, his ideas being greeted with applause or disagreement. The general hubbub grew, as more and more of the crowd joined in with asides to their neighbours, until things became quite out of hand; disagreements led to argument, to abuse and eventually to physical blows, when the whole meeting broke up in disorder.

At last Dewi raised his voice which came ringing, clear as a bell, over the din of the crowd. "Men, brothers, friends, let us be still a moment and listen to what God has to tell us. Let us pray to our Father in heaven to give us His grace and peace in our hearts. May we have the humility just to stand quietly and listen to His voice, for anger is clouding our minds and we alone are not able to clear them."

A hush descended on the crowd and all stood silent, their heads bowed, until all that could be heard in this natural amphitheatre were trees gently shaking in the breeze and the occasional bleating of sheep from the hillside. After what seemed a long interval, the crowd began to raise their faces again; they turned towards David and saw that he was standing on a mound from which he was preparing to address them; many of them whispered that they could not remember the ground there being raised like that before, while others murmured that they had offered their cloaks heaped up in a pile for Dewi to stand on; however there were no complaints, since at least his lithe frame could now be seen, for he was not very tall and they could now better hear what he had to say.

Slight he may have been, certainly not as tall as many of his contemporaries, but as Dewi stood there staff in hand, his woollen cloak draped about his shoulders, bare feet shod only in sandals, he still had great dignity and presence as befitted a King's son and; as he stood quite still, gazing across the heads of the crowd, he began to speak, at first quietly and then with gathering assurance; the people fell silent and became deeply attentive.

Dewi told of the circumstances in which Pelagius had been teaching around 400 AD; a Celtic monk he had found his way to Rome, where his influence had grown among those young men of noble family, who were there to train for careers in law or as bureaucrats in Imperial Rome. He was now able to graphically describe the conditions, for he had been there himself.

"Pelagius was trying to stir those lax, easy-going Christians in Rome," said Dewi, "and his motives were of the highest - he wanted a stricter obedience and he told people that, if they wished and if their will was strong enough, they could change themselves and avoid sin;

they needed to grow up and exert their freedom of will and assume the manhood of God's children.

- 'It's not your strength', Pelagius had said, 'it is your will'.

"Hear, hear," shouted one of the crowd; "I like to be in control of my own life; I'm not having anyone else tell me what to do".

"Right", said another, "and then there's this nonsense about 'original sin'; take a little baby; who could believe a helpless little one like that was a sinner? Rubbish, I say; new-born children are in the same condition as Adam in the garden of Eden, before he disobeyed."

"Well, Pelagius would agree with you", Dewi said, taking command of the situation again. "He believed that Adam only injured himself, when he sinned - not the whole human race - and that Adam would have died, even if he had not sinned. He believed that it was a matter of will- power and that if they chose they could avoid sin".

"Hear, hear," shouted a few of the crowd.

Dewi paused awhile, allowing the commotion to settle, and then he addressed them. "My brothers and sisters, we are surely agreed that men have been given free-will, but if a man is ignorant of God, who is to say that his free choice may not lead him to any wrong conclusion so that, acting like a natural man, he may do evil and thus sin. Even if the way of truth is made plain to him, he may still of his free will choose to do the selfish act instead of the more difficult unselfish one, if love is not his motive. It is quite easy to misuse free-will; but this is not the point. Can you not see that by fostering our own independence we put the soul further away from Christ who restores us from moral death? Shall I tell you the story told in the Scriptures about the rich young ruler who came to Christ, asking what to do to obtain eternal life?"

"Yes," they all shouted, the crowd loved to hear a good story; their native tongue - being early Welsh -the Scriptures being written in the educated language of the day, namely Latin, such stories were only accessible to those who had been schooled; so Dewi read to them from his Bible, translating as he went along.

"And as He was setting out on his journey, a man ran up to Him, and asked Him 'Good Teacher, what must I do to inherit eternal life?' And

Jesus said to him, 'Why do you call me good? No one is good but God alone. You know the commandments: Do not kill, do not commit adultery, do not steal, do not bear false witness, do not defraud, honour your father and mother'. And he said to Him, 'Teacher, all these I have observed from my youth'. And Jesus looking upon him loved him". Dewi continued to address the crowd, "The young man was acting as a Pelagian would and Jesus loved him for it. But the young man knew in his heart that this was not enough. He had followed God's commandments scrupulously and had discovered it to be a good but negative and sterile way of living - he was a very good Pelagian and he was not satisfied. What quality had he seen in Jesus which had made him dissatisfied with his own quality of life?"

Dewi paused for a response from the crowd, but they remained silent. He returned to the Book for the answer. "'You lack one thing; go, sell what you have and give to the poor and come, follow me'. At that saying his countenance fell and he went away sorrowful; for he had great possessions. Jesus said ' How hard it is to enter the kingdom of God!" ... the disciples said to him 'Who then can be saved?' ... He replied to them, 'With men it is impossible, but not with God; for all things are possible with God' ".

Dewi paused; he was silent for a while, waiting for the crowd to take in fully what he had just read. At last a man from the middle of the crowd broke the silence. "What was the answer to the young man then? How could the young man be saved?"

"Yes", they all murmured to each other, "what happens next; how does the Gospel continue?"

After a moment or two Dewi lifted up the Book again and continued reading from St Mark's Gospel, Chapter 10, until he came to the words "For the Son of Man also came not to be served but to serve, and to give his life as a ransom for many". He closed the Book and looked around him; there were some bewildered faces still, so Dewi explained the passage again.

"Pelagianism or Humanism can only go part of the way, in a spiritual world. Pelagius said that both the laws and the Gospel lead to the Kingdom of Heaven. In this passage Jesus was saying that the law does not go far enough; He had come specifically to show the only way."

"What was that way?" shouted a man from the crowd.

"Ours is not a dry gospel. It is a Gospel of love. God's love towards us from the beginning. God giving all the time. He gives us a beautiful world of His creation and yet we go our own way, we spoil it, we pollute it and worst of all we do not love each other; instead, by using our God-given free-will, we take advantage of each other; we are unkind; we thieve, murder and get lost, wandering aimlessly far away from paradise.

Pelagius was deeply troubled about this situation and told people that they must make a determined effort to change their ways and scrupulously to follow God's commandments - there was nothing wrong with this - Jesus loved the rich young ruler for doing just that, but that young man knew in his heart that that was not enough to save him; so we read in St Mark's Gospel Chapter 10 that the young man still felt there was something lacking. 'Good Teacher, what must I do to inherit eternal life?' and he was told that nothing less than the total abandonment of himself to follow Christ was the answer; this was unfortunately for him 'and he went away sorrowful'. Would you like me to continue with the Gospel story?"

To a man they all answered that they would.

"Listen closely then. The Gospel goes on to say what happened next on the road up to Jerusalem. 'Jesus was walking ahead of them; and they were amazed, and those who followed were afraid. And taking the twelve again, He began to tell them what was to happen to Him saying, 'Behold, we are going up to Jerusalem; and the Son of man will be delivered to the chief priests and the scribes, and they will condemn him to death and deliver him to the Gentiles; and they will mock him and spit upon him and scourge him and kill him; and after three days he will rise '. Doesn't it seem strange to you that the Gospel talks of Jesus' death, immediately after the story of eternal life only being made possible by God? This was the supreme act of Love".

Dewi continued, "The young man and the disciples were then told that they must be prepared to follow Jesus, not only by observing God's commandments but even having to continue to identify with

121

His death, undergoing daily death of self-will; such death leads to eternal life; mortal death cannot be avoided, but it is only physical; if we follow Him, such physical death is immaterial; if our spirit dies in accepting the death of Jesus, it goes with Him through death and out again into paradise for ever. Pelagius was denying this; he was denying that it is through Christ that the whole human race is able to die, nor through the resurrection of Christ that the whole human race rises again".

"But" shouted another from the crowd; it was Gwyther, a man of short stature, one of the great competitors in 'The Games'; it was he who had competed for many years in both the Decathlon and the chariot-racing with considerable success; a Welshman who could compete with any Roman! "I have no wish to lose my self-will", he shouted; "I'll take on anyone as regards endurance or integrity", he said. "I wasn't born to give up my free-will or my independence. You're asking me to give away my pride, it fairly gives me the creeps. I'll remain a Pelagian through and through and all the better for it too". He turned away red in the face with indignation, his red hair and his brawny arms emphasising his outrage; but he was soon back again.

"What you are asking me to do is to surrender my strength, my individuality and all that is good in me to an unseen power, engendered by a man that died on a cross. I'm a Christian and I believe he died to save me all right, but he was not lily-livered; he never denied himself nor his right to live his life as he considered best; I do more good for others here than many of these I see standing around; once you tell me to give myself up for anyone's sake, I'm lost; I've surrendered all that was best of me - what for? for a myth as likely as not. I don't accept your interpretation. Pelagius believes in Christ as the Way, the Truth and the Life, but not at the expense of himself - and we are all born in the image of God with equal opportunities to prove it. You can enjoy the pleasures of this life without becoming effete. The Lord talks to me directly in my prayer; I do not need the word of the Lord interpreted to me by any other man, be he a bishop or a council of other mortals; in this way does one man claim to have almighty power over others; this was the claim of the Druid priest and a similar claim was made by Rome.

I can set my own standards in the best traditions of Christianity without losing myself completely. We do not all have to become idle, self-seeking and egotistical, as you say the Romans had become; Pelagius shows us the way - that is by good hard work, recognition of our Saviour and application of his ideals and way of life in our own lives. I see no need to lose myself or to follow any such misguided principle. In fact, more than that, it goes quite against the grain; God did not make me unique (nor anyone else for that matter) to give it all away- to throw in the towel - that is to treat our God-given attributes with complete disrespect; it smacks of blasphemy. To lose oneself in order to find oneself is nonsense in any language and coming from you, someone for whom I had much respect before, I find it quite distasteful or worse than that, heretical to all that I've been taught!"

Dewi however was not to be dissuaded. "You are so right, Gwyther my friend. That is exactly what Pelagius was saying. That we can do it all on our own - we do not need His help - we can do it alone. In practice however we know what such human effort can achieve alone - death. What do you think God's view of sin is? What do you think God expects of man? Total independence? Christ did not die just as an example; he was the Way to God and in Him we have Life. Pelagius is denying the creative living experience of the Holy Spirit, renewing and revitalising men day by day, if and only if we are prepared to accept this Grace. God knows that when we are in the right mood, physically and mentally fit, in the right company, when the country thrives and is flourishing, when the weather and elements are kind, man can do quite well; but what happens when one or more, even all these factors are against us? What of man then? We need help - even at times total help or we go under. God is not saying you lose your identity, but that you will find your real identity, when you have found Him; His saving Grace will give you limitless power to be yourself through Him without enormous weakness, manifold errors of judgement and numerous sinful paths leading away from your first intent. What does God expect of man? That we work in this world to bring the knowledge of this saving Love to all the earth.

But my brothers these earnest Pelagians have a very serious time trying hard to make merit, in order to earn salvation for themselves; it is an impossible standard which they are endeavouring to reach, whereas we are the 'Resurrection people'; our lives should shine out with the joy of living; freely God gave us our lives; we are just temporary residents passing through; we can take nothing from this world with us; nothing is ours; we are just tenants holding everything in trust for the generations which follow; all that we can leave behind is the example of our faith, so that our loved ones will be able to join us in the world to come. We are discussing no less than the loss of this precious legacy, a golden thread which leads from here to eternity; follow that joyful thread my brothers, that shaft of sunlight, which Christ sent to lead us into eternity. Do not lose sight of that light; accept the Grace of the Son of God.

By this time there was an uproar in the crowd. Dewi had stopped preaching but was still standing facing the crowd; having delivered his argument as fully as he could, he was exhausted. But the crowd was exultant. They raised him on their shoulders and a procession formed, as they carried him with shouts and cheers to the meeting house nearby; but the church leaders had also gathered and told the crowd to sit down. It was quite clear that Dewi had persuaded them of his ability, not only to lead and minister to them as a great evangelist, but also as a king's son to command their love and respect. That day did not end before they had agreed to make him their leader as bishop over all.

This was the turning point that Dubricius had been seeking for a long time. When Dewi, Teilo and Padarn had made their visit to the Patriarch in Jerusalem and been blessed as bishops for the Celtic church, they had represented south Wales between them. Padarn from mid-Wales, Dewi essentially based in the south-west and Teilo's also in the south, but to the east of Dyfed, could all now develop.

The learned men at the Synod held a private discussion before the Synod broke up. It was agreed that they should gradually hand over to the younger men who had proved themselves worthy to carry the Gospel into the generation ahead. With this in mind Dubricius made his way from the Synod towards Llandeilo Fawr, where he expected to see Teilo and perhaps stay for a while at the monastery. His old bones ached with rheumatism as the moist autumn air penetrated to his joints. He mustn't complain, but he had travelled so many miles over the countryside preaching and teaching that now he would be glad to take things a little more easily and watch his protege Teilo get the bit between his teeth. He had always liked Teilo who had more than fulfilled his early promise.

Teilo gently greeted Dubricius as the old man arrived at his monastery, to rest after the Synod and refresh himself before returning to Henllan. In fact, conscious of the fact that Dubricius was becoming frail he encouraged him to stay on, making him as comfortable as he could in his monastery on the hill. Deiniol also made it his business to keep Dubricius's cell warm and see to it that he had materials at hand to write his future plans for the church.

The monastery overlooked the valley and the hills where his grandfather, Brychan, was born and had raised his large family. The story tellers spoke of his hot temper and deeds of prowess. It was a good place for Dubricius to stay and take stock. He had kept faith with the family, but his work was not over yet; these days brought Dubricius many happy memories. In the evenings, when Teilo's duties allowed it, and until the spring when they would travel together to Henllan, they could have important discussions about the future. By that time Dubricius would have regained his strength and they could look forward to a few happy years working together, before Dubricius' final retirement to the island of Bardsey (Ynys Enlli).

During this time Dewi visited Llandeilo Fawr, whenever he could get away from his own monastery. It was an important time for them all and the discussions were deep and detailed, for Dubricius had the backing of the Synod to resign in favour of Dewi, who wished to be based in St David's. This wish had to be agreed, so that Dewi would have to hold another Synod to discuss it and to sanction important canons. (This is not to say that Dewi did not use Caerleon as an important centre just as Dubricius had done). But the Irish had been sending many men to Dewi for training at his monastery for some time now Dewi , Cadoc, Gildas and Cybi had all been engaged in training men, such as Finian (later of Clonard) and Brendan from

Ireland, at the monastery in St Davids; access was easy and communications were good, but it was not until the late 560s that the Welsh influence on the Irish monasteries was to begin in real earnest.

The winter passed quickly, the frozen earth thawed and the early snowdrops brought fresh hope for the new year. Dubricius recovered and now both he and Teilo were to travel together; a new chapter was opening in the story of the church. As the earth warmed and the deer became bolder, stags began to round up the does; the bleating of new lambs could be heard crying from hill to hill; and old black crows were calling to each other in the trees above Llandeilo and early primroses were opening to the sun, as Teilo and Dubricius mounted, to set out slowly with their small group of monks, up past the old familiar haunts through the beloved valley.

Just outside Llandeilo, a little stream bubbled over the stones, a tributary of the Dulas beside the Talley road, named 'Erddyl' after Dubricius's mother, known also as Erbdyll or Efryddyl in Herefordshire and daughter of King Pepiau of Archenfeld (Weston under Penyard) and Erging. A large area south of Hereford - Ynys Efrddyl- (her island) is also named after her - she always seems to have been associated with water like Dubricius whose Norman name Devereux and the Celtic equivalent, Dyfrig, which is derived from the word water, after the legend of his birth. It goes like this: '

One day as the King returned from hunting, while his daughter was washing her hair, he noticed that she was pregnant; he was so angry that he ordered that she be put in a sack and drowned. But the river Wye washed her onto a sandbank. The King ordered that she be burnt and she was duly placed on a pyre, but she would not burn. The next day he found her nursing her baby, Dubricius'. The truth is harder to establish, but Brychan's son Brynach was Dubricius's father and Dubricius was born at Madley near the river Wye in Ynys Efrddyl. When his work at Henllan had grown too big he founded a settlement at Mochros, which translated means 'swine moor' and is now called Moccos near Madley, at that time 'well wooded and abounding in fish'.

Be that as it may, they were now following the Roman road, as had Dubricius' grandfather Brychan before him, turning off at Llangadog, past Cadoc's church (afterwards to become associated with Dewi) climbing up the road past Llandeusant and the Roman camps, until it dropped down again alongside the river Usk. As he shivered in the chill spring air, Teilo pursed his lips, hoping the journey would be over before the weather turned again to rain, as happened so often on those mountains; if they pressed on briskly, it would not take them more than two days. The ponies steamed and snorted, their warm breath clouding the clear air, but they were enjoying the ride after a long winter of idleness. The journey through the Black Mountains soon ended, as they saw the Golden Valley of the Wye spread out before them, and Dubricius and his companions made for the familiar monastery of Henllan.

Invigorated by the fresh air from the mountains, Dubricius was delighted to find that his strength had returned to him. Henceforth the two men continued to travel together; it was a tremendous period for them both; they established two churches adjoining each another in Erging, the one at Llan Guern(or Llanwarne) and the other alongside the shared cemetery at Henllan. Dubricius already had foundations in Dumnonia at Porlock in north Somerset; his Welsh foundations included one at Caldey island, where his faithful old servant had always kept his dwelling sweet and fresh for him to return to during his missions. A stone with the inscription on it commemorating his tonsured servant stands at Caldey as a monument to him forever. He also had a church at the second century foundation of Llandaff. He had been constantly on the move, for which reason his influence encompassed the whole of the south west and, though Teilo was to take charge of the expanding Welsh section, where he may have replaced Dubricius's influence at Carmarthen, he did not do so in Gwent. North Gwent and Erging always remained heavily stamped with Dubricius' influence. Dubricius's churches (said to be twenty-four in all in this area), together with his Bishopric at Llanarth, made up his chief responsibilities between the rivers Usk and Wye. As though time has stood still, this area has throughout the ages maintained its old customs, privileges and laws; though politically in England, ecclesiastical it has remained Welsh. Dubricius's famous college, attended by so many great men, was on the site of the present day farm of Llanfrother (church of the brothers) with its wide view from the end of this ridge, over magnificent country spread out below. At the other end of this ridge, down in a hollow, can be found a little church on the edge of an earlier Celtic village, before the altar of which, on the pavement, lies a tiled cross, a reminder that the Celtic monks habitually lay prone on the ground with arms outstretched to pray.

In this same valley forgotten by time, Dubricius and Teilo taught the timeless truths of the Gospel. Two thousand monks would train here for seven years, before leaving for their missionary work. Teilo also found Aidan, his childhood friend (not Aidan of Ferns), supporting Dubricius here. At Llandaff, Dubricius is named as the first bishop, though not the founder of the See; Teilo is named as the second bishop. Though it was not a bishopric until the tenth century.

Holy Dubricius at last felt the time had come for his retirement and prepared to depart for Bardsey island. His loss to Henllan must have been enormous , for the support and friendship he had given to so many ·dedicated men in his time had been immense. And yet how he must have longed for a settled place, after all those years of wandering and solid hard work! What memories the old man must have held there on the island, and, although no doubt ready to lose those reins, how eagerly he must have longed for news of Teilo's continuing work on the mainland. Teilo must have communicated with him so many times, before he was laid to rest. Many saints retired to Bardsey, twenty thousand bodies of saints lie buried there, but Dubricius is specially venerated, although the records seem to have been lost during hostile raids on the coasts - no doubt they were burned.

One of the legends of the island was that no one could die. The same legend was maintained in Landevennec in Brittany, where Winwaloe rebuilt the abbey; shortly afterwards the oldest monk died and others followed, but in order of age;" this was long the rule in the monastery and has only just been changed", says one writer much later - when they stopped dying in the right order presumably! When Cadfan died at Bardsey, Teilo was asked to regulate the affairs of this monastery; in his absence Doclydwy, who with Cynon and many others travelled with him from Brittany many years previously, and who had accompanied Cadfan to Bardsey, used to take care of it; later Teilo was to appoint Lleuddad ab Alan to be in charge.

Chapter Nine

CIVIL WAR. c537

In the same year that Saint Dubricius died, Arthur's son, Mordred, by his half-sister Morgan le fay, raised an army against Arthur.

News of civil war was brought to Demetia by messengers riding in relays across the country. As one of the Emperor Arthur's bodyguard, Vortipor set off at once to Arthur's defence with a large band of mounted warriors. They rode hard, their faces grim and their expressions set. The thud of the horses' hooves were like drum beats, the beating thud of their own hearts making the accompaniment, while flying banners trailed in line with the horses' manes. Clods of earth were thrown up on their sweating horses hides as they rode, fearful that they would not reach the battle in time.

With not far to travel, Urien Rheged, ruler of Strathclyde and husband of Arthur's half-sister Margaret, also hastened to Arthur's support. In spite of all this aid there were such large Saxon hordes (including Mordred's malcontents) now ranged against Arthur, that the battle was an unequal contest, a bloody civil war. By the time the noble Aircol arrived, it was too late; indeed Aircol was himself to sustain a wound in the fight, from which he would never recover. He was carried from the battlefield by the men of Dyfed. Then followed the long depressing march home to Wales.

Arthur's last battle was at Gueith cam lann; this battle of Camlann is recorded in the Annales Cambriae of 537, under the entry:- 'The battle of Camlann, in which Arthur and Medraut perished and there was a plague in Britain and in Ireland'. The exact location of Camlann is of course unknown; there has been speculation that it was the old Roman fort of Camboglanna on Hadrian's wall (Birdoswald today); it may have been in the south -west near Glastonbury on the river Camel; certainly no one knows where Arthur died or was buried, indeed this is the strength of the legend, that he was mortally wounded in the battle but escaped. For many years it was said 'Arthur will come again', as though he had not died but had disappeared until his wounds had healed. Such a legend no doubt assuaged the despair of the British although he was never to return.

Medraut or Mordred was both Arthur's son and nephew by his sister Morgan le fay, who one night tricked him into bed with her - (she later married King Lot of the Orkneys). Mordred was the leader of the revolt against Arthur, then probably in his sixties, at which time younger rivals would be hoping to take his place; in consequence any discontent or ambitious in his own army or that of the invading Saxon kings rallied to support Mordred. As it was, both Mordred and Arthur were no doubt mortally wounded in the battle, Arthur's army was destroyed and the old fellowship broken and scattered. Bedevere was amongst those who helped Arthur from the battlefield and he was taken by boat to be healed of his wounds. He may have been taken back to Glastonbury to be buried; whatever the facts, in the confusion he disappeared.

Deiniol, one of Dubricius's monks, had a brother Cynwal who was the last of Arthur's warriors to see him alive; Cynwal escaped to Wales to become Abbot of Caio on the death of old Paulinus, carrying with him those precious relics, prized from ancient times. A stone found in a field called Pant-y-polion at Maes Llanwrthwl bears this inscription: 'Guardian of the Faith and Lover of his Land, here Paulinus lies, liegeman of justice..' (SERVATVR FIDAEI PATRIAEQUE SEMPER AMATOR HIC PAVLINVS IACIT CVLTOR PIENTISIMVS AEQVI). This is no memorial stone for a Christian saint, but it could well have been an inscription ordered by a soldier such as Cynwal who, having left Arthur's service, could think of nothing more appropriate for the great Paulinus.

King Aircol was growing old by now, he could look back on a life which had seen many changes in his own country. As a young man he had fought to establish a new dynasty in Dyfed, where lived by now a bilingual people speaking both Goidelic (Irish) and the Brythonic (British) tongue. He had knitted these folk of Irish and Welsh origin together, whilst at the same time fighting off piratical

Irish from his shores. One of the descendants of Elen and Magnus Maximus, he had proudly taken the Roman name of Agricola in his campaigns, anxious to establish, like Arthur, all that was best in Roman rule - that old rule of law with its civilising influence of learning, which by the end of his reign was again flourishing throughout the kingdom of Dyfed. Amongst his titles was that of 'Protector' (to the Emperor Arthur), a title held by his son Vortipor as well. But Gildas, writing of Aircol, said that his principal quality was of 'a good Christian King', one who gave much of his hard-fought land to St Dubricius for the church. He had now sustained his final battle wound, which at times was causing him a great deal of pain. But the worst pain of all was the loss of his old companions, divided and slain by civil war. Such a short while ago everything seemed so secure; they had had many years in which to cultivate the land and build peaceful co-existence - the whole lifetime in fact of this generation, all due to the strong rule of Arthur; now all that was shattered.

Towards the end of Aircol's days he spent more and more of his time at Argol and he may have died there. One can imagine him on beautiful days, gazing up the valley at the Black Mountains, watching that constant kaleidoscope of colour, as clouds change the landscape from blue and green to purple and grey and back to green and yellow, in endless variety before one's eyes. From here he could just see the stronghold where his fighting companion Urien was based across a range of hills. Though Urien was a good deal younger than Aircol, they had much in common. Of late Urien had sent over one of the bards from the training school on the hill opposite Carreg Cennen; Aircol had taken great delight in this music and poetry, which told of heroic deeds of war and extolled the bravery of the warriors, many of whom Aircol himself had known; he was also encouraged that, when he was gone, there would be strong warriors to defend the land against all-comers. Urien's territory was across the river Tywi, which flowed past the base of Argol; his land stretched from the Gower peninsula with the old Roman station of Leucarum at its estuary, up between the Tywi and the Tawe, whence his compatriot Cunedda before him had also driven out the marauding Irish. Gower had been part of Aircol's territory for a long time, but he had given much of it

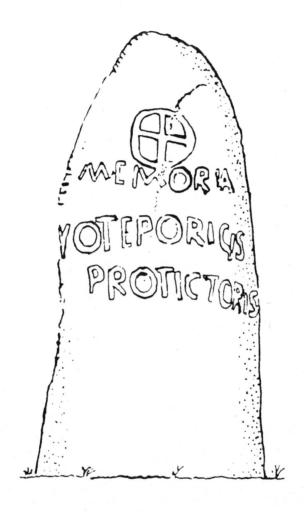

The Vorteporix stone

to the church, to Dubricius, to Iltud, to Teilo and to several others to set up their own churches: now he was older it was a great relief to see Urien Rheged patrolling the land south of the Tywi river - a real protection for the southern boundaries of Demetia.

Mid-way between his warrior camp high on Grongar hill(as it is known today) and Castell Argol(Dryslwyn), Aircol built a small summer camp for himself, known as Cwm Argol. The slope of the hill caught the evening sun and, as the sun set, he could look down the valley toward the mouth of the river Tywi and the sea. Castell Argol had become a steep climb for him in his old age and yet he would be in no other spot. When he desired to go up to the stronghold, to hold court or for any other special reason, his men would lay him on a litter and carry him up the steepest part. On the South-east corner of Castell Argol he had built a little chapel, where the court could gather regularly for prayer and to sing praise to their Creator. At Cwm Argol he was cared for by one of his daughters; she would have the dwelling as her own after his day; a little further down the slope a path led to Sarn Argol where another of his daughters lived; both were devoted to their father and many pleasant hours were spent here in his company.

And between sleeping and waking he would muse on his early life, when as a strong warrior, of the dynasty of great Triphune, he also took a Roman name, that of Agricola, leading a band of men in support of Arthur to defend his land of Demetia from all and sundry. How they had thundered through the green hills all around, cutting down the invaders and establishing strong stations on the coast as well as inland - at Nevern, Lydstep and the old Roman bases at Loughor and Moridinum. He dreamt of old companions now long dead, of faithful horses he had loved and owned, horses which had carried him across west Wales, hunting boar or bear or stag with the dogs baying for the kill; or bravely riding into battle against fierce foes. A myriad sounds would echo through his head in dreams such as these and then he would welcome the soft harp and singing of the bard which soothed his old tired brain. And the bard would sing of many famous deeds and praise the valour of his many friends.

More poignant still than this, at times he would ponder on the future of his native land. All that he could do to make the Gospel known throughout his realm he had done; he had made Argol his great mission centre from where bands of men were supported in prayer and where all the great plans for the mission had been formulated. How would this be after he was dead and the next generation had taken their place? What of those values then? He had seen how it was with Arthur. Would the future bring the disintegration of the vision they had held so dear? Who knows! He had no power now to influence that unknown future; his work was done for good or ill.

Then came the day for Aircol to go the way of his fathers. A great procession formed up in the round camp above and moved out of the southern entrance; Aircol's daughters watched the white oxen with their long horns being led down the steep path, pulling the funeral bier behind them. As the warriors poured down the hill in solemn order, the great horn was blown to salute their king - such a wild note, but yet sweet and mellow, an eerie sound echoing down the centuries, as they laid their king to rest in the place he loved best beside the bank of his beloved river. In due course, as the years passed, they were to lay his daughters unpretentiously one on each side in this unmarked grave.

With the death of Aircol all hell broke loose in Demetia. Vortipor had only been biding his chance; now he was ready to strike. His father had been a strong king and he dared not do anything to prejudice his chances whilst he was still alive, but his preparations had been made and, returning from a major war up in the north with a great warrior band, he took his brother Erbin by surprise. In a savage and bloody but brief skirmish Vortipor fought his battle with Erbin's men at their camp between Argol and Llandeilo Fawr, murdering his brother with his own hands. Now he was King.

Vortipor had no use for Argol; he liked to be where the action was, down near the coast where the ships were continually calling with cargoes from foreign parts. So, leaving his father's grave without mark or sign, he rode down again to his own palace, now at Narberth. Henceforth a very different rule of law held sway, the people being kept in constant fear for themselves and their property.

Teilo and Dewi however did not intend to pass over the matter lightly. They conferred together at a spot near Argol, Dewi's Clas church of Llanarthney , where they decided to hold a small memorial service for their old king Aircol and his son Erbin. The land thereabouts had been hallowed ground for generations; Isernius had founded a little church there, just across the river at Llanegwad (now just a pile of stones at Llanhirnin, but one of the oldest foundations in the country). Meanwhile a large service of remembrance was to be held at Narberth, where Vortipor was to be declared King.

Problems were to increase for both Teilo and Dewi. Vortipor was not at all disposed to give any of his land to the church; he felt it had taken over too much of his kingdom already. There was therefore no room for expansion. Dewi was very much taken up with his new responsibilities. Dubricius had used Caerleon as a central base for Glamorgan and for the next ten years Dewi concentrated on making a profound impact in the area of South Wales in general, as well as on his plans for continued training in his monastery for those Irish monks who would eventually would go back to their own country; St Patrick's work needed representation in the present generation.

To the east of Dyfed however, from the banks of the Tywi river, Teilo found sympathetic help from Urien Rheged; he therefore expanded from now on in this direction, setting up a church at Llandybie and another further west at Pontardulais which he called Llandeilo Talybont, near the river crossing. This church was also known as Llandeilo Fach, 'little' in contrast with Llandeilo Fawr, the 'great'. On the Gower peninsula at Llandeilo Ferwallt he founded a great church at Bishopston (Bishop's town), while he was to divide his time between the Bishoprics of Henllan, Llanarth and Llandeilo Fawr. .

Sadly, after the death of Aircol there was constant fighting amongst the lesser kings of Demetia, and the Saxons took advantage of the situation and moved westwards into Wales. Never did the country have unity again, as reflected in the writings of Gildas. Off the shore at this time, possibly on Flat Holm island, Gildas, sick with dismay, wrote his tract on 'The Ruin of Britain, with all the spleen he could muster. In it he exposes with graphic epithets the wickedness of the five Welsh Kings, including Vortipor.

Although Gildas does not mince his words to these Kings, he tends to strike a tender note when trying to make them see the error of their ways. Posterity does at least have another picture of the Kings with whom Dewi and Teilo were dealing during this decade.

There was a sudden large scale growth of monasteries around the 540s, when Dewi and Cadoc trained Irish for the ministry at St Davids. Gildas too is mentioned in this connection, teaching the Irish at St Davids and preaching with 'burning revival energy'. There was continuous preaching every Sunday and although Gildas is known to have thought that Dewi's asceticism was too extreme, no doubt he came to accept it, for their cause was the same. Gildas is also remembered for his work in Ireland preaching and teaching there; certainly after his outspoken book 'The Ruin of Britain' he would have had good reason to seek a more comfortable life in Ireland rather than live under the rule of Vortipor or any other of those kings he had criticised! Among the monks who benefited from the training were Brendan, founder of Clonfert who took himself to Gildas for more advanced training, and Finian who founded Moville and was a disciple at St Davids from the age of thirteen.(It was another Finian who founded the monastery of Clonard which began the new monastic revival in Ireland; he died in 549.) Kieran founder of Clonmacnois was the master of Columbanus who many years later led missionaries into Gaul. Teilo and Dewi were initiating a new age in Britain with Garmon and Padarn in central Wales and Daniel in the north, using Gildas's book no doubt in part as propaganda to stimulate the inner spiritual life.

However all these new schemes were to be rudely interrupted, for the bubonic plague was followed by the Yellow pestilence from Europe. Dewi and Teilo made contingency plans about this, arranging that, should it ravage their island home, Dewi would stay and Teilo leave with as many as he could, in order to save a remnant of the British. Dewi was adamant that Teilo must perform this duty and if necessary take up the reins in the church on his return.

Chapter Ten

THE YELLOW PESTILENCE.

Teilo awoke before the cold dawn and, as he became conscious, could feel someone shaking his shoulder and pulling at his cloak. He sat up with a sudden lurch, to find a dirty tousle - haired youth, huddled and shivering on the floor beside him, snivelling and shaking in the cold, obviously afraid.

"What is it boy?" Teilo said, as he turned with some misgiving and dragged himself up from his straw bedding on the floor, his feet prickled by the straw and the cold air waking him.

The boy was obviously unwell, as he also stood and tried to explain to Teilo that his family needed him at once; he reeled a bit with dizziness. He led Teilo into the village where his home, a little wattle shack, was propped up against the earthen defence bank. Looking through the doorway, Teilo saw with horror that the family were indeed in a bad way. The mother appeared to be dead - sprawled across a table. A little child sitting on the straw in the middle of the room was reaching out with both hands to an elder sister, who stood above her looking distraught, her right forearm pushing her hair back and sweat pouring down her face. In her left arm she held a toddler who was crying incessantly.

Teilo knew the yellow plague had already reached the Welsh shores from the continent and now realised to his dismay that it had travelled as far as his own area. Nothing could be done; it meant sudden and horrible death for whole communities. He and Dewi had heard of its spread from Persia and had feared that it would be spread by travellers coming by sea; it would soon devastate their own land. By now the baby was silent; cold beads of sweat on its forehead, a waxen pallor and froth forming in its mouth confirmed the fading signs of life. The older sister stared at it with dark horror in her eyes,

137

and, as her own cheeks became drained of that pink flush of fever, she laid her baby gently in the straw and sank into a little heap herself beside the baby and the child. All three were quite unaware of Teilo's presence, while the boy too was near to death; he let out a scream as silence fell on his little home and rushed in to cling to his dying sister, too weak to lift her or assist in any way. There was nothing Teilo could do. As he dropped the hide curtain which hung about the doorway, a fierce flush of fear and disgust almost made him sick. He propped himself against a tree to recover, whilst his eyes filled with hot tears, his mind racing - to forge a plan of rescue for others from this horror. It might already be too late.

"What was it Dewi had said?" Teilo muttered to himself. It was hard to be clear about anything just now.

"If this thing happens, we have to work fast. It is no good attending to communities already affected; gather up those at a distance, those who are so far clear, and take them to safety; flee with them, not to the usual harbours, but away from normal commerce, to the coast at Ceredigion. I will arrange for King Gerennius to have a small fleet of boats ready to sail at short notice. Flee across Ceredigion and escape from Din Gerran to Brittany taking whom you can with you. I will stay here as bishop for the flock left behind; you must care for those - many hundreds we hope - who can get away! If I do not survive this emergency, you must return, but not until your are absolutely sure it is over, and take my place in Wales".

The words had appeared almost unreal before, but now, horror of horrors, the dreaded pestilence was here.

Teilo was in Moridunum at Llandeulyddog, the abbey named after his follower Teulyddog, close to the water front. He sent word to Dewi by a messenger on horseback and left the town in an easterly direction, following the river towards Argol. Once clear of the town, coming upon the first communities, he passed them word that they must leave everything and follow him up the valley to Llandeilo Fawr. He rang his bell, 'Bangu', as he came to a little group of dwellings; the inhabitants had begun to move about, waking from the night's sleep, rubbing their eyes as he approached.

few followed him, many did not, for they had their cattle to see to or old folk to care for, so that most of his following were young, with promises from others to follow as soon as they could.

At last Teilo reached Llandeilo Fawr, hot and his mind still racing, as he turned over the various last-minute matters to be sorted out. By this time he had quite a following, a motley collection of people of all ages, all more than a little startled, some hungry and most dishevelled. Here townsfolk opened their homes to the hungry followers and welcomed them in, to wash and to rest, whilst food was prepared. But Teilo went straight to his monastery, where he hastily summoned all his monks together for a meeting, to discuss what should be done.

Clearly so many people could not be accommodated in such a small community for longer than was necessary, nor could time be wasted in getting them to the coast. So it was agreed that a few monks should travel with the people, whilst others would stay behind to carry on the business of the community, to nurse the sick and to keep groups isolated as far as possible. Those who were afraid departed ; those who felt obliged to stay were prepared to face the consequences.

The following morning, now rested and able to continue their journey, the travellers set out across country for Ceredigion and the coast. Teilo was to follow them, for he had many plans to make and directions to give to those he had to leave behind. Lovingly he said goodbye to his monastery - for he was very loathe to leave and would far prefer to have stayed and helped those at home. The brothers prayed fervently, but felt still that Teilo must go with the party to ensure their safe journey, get them settled on the Armorican shore and bring them safely back again after the emergency was past.

His sister Annauved had sent messages to Teilo for many months, telling him that her husband King Budic owned land which he offered to any who might wish to settle in his country, should the need arise. Now Teilo was to be the one to take up this offer and see that people were made welcome and enabled to build homes in safety there.

By this time Dewi had arrived at Llandeilo Fawr. Teilo was still not convinced that he should go - he would have far rathered Dewi took

139

the emigration - how could he ever face Ygrain again? He hated himself for what he had done to her so many years before. They were by now in their forties, all the best years of his life he had ceaselessly toiled in God's cause, not sparing himself in caring for the people who had come to know and love God, he had spent himself going round the countryside doing good to all he met and now he would rather die here with them in the country he loved. He had built up his thriving centre at Llandeilo Fawr, a teaching monastery, training monks to travel all over the country. How could he leave all this work?

Dewi found Teilo in tears in his little room at the monastery.

"What is it old friend"? asked Dewi.

"I can't possibly go to Brittany" was Teilo's reply.

He told Dewi all that he was feeling and to his utter surprise

Dewi said that he understood.

"Padarn and I knew all those years ago on the trip to Jerusalem, how you were battling with yourself about Ygrain" Dewi said. "It was only too obvious to us who were so close to you, yet we had no intention of trying to influence you in any way. We prayed about it often, for we knew that it would break you if you refused God's call, knowing also that by making a decision against Ygrain, you might also not be able to endure the pain".

Dewi put his arms around Teilo's sobbing shoulders as he continued.

"My dear old friend, do you not see that it is precisely your capacity to care about people which has made you such a true pastor to your flock all these years; the way you have been able to enter into the feelings of those who needed you, though it cost you dear, helped them to grow in the faith, and enabled the work of God to be so powerful in our land. You have not spared yourself and the people know it, they have seen what true holiness is about. God has called you to walk the dangerous path of love - only he who loves can be hurt - and it is God's will that you are both loving and able to be hurt".

Teilo looked at Dewi in unbelieving astonishment.

"How on earth did you see what I was going through all these years and say nothing"? he questioned, his exhausted face hiding nothing of what he felt at this moment.

"We who love you know you well" replied Dewi "and it because of these very qualities in you that you must lead the refugees, they trust you and will follow you whatever the perils of the way through which you must lead them. Padarn will probably go shortly after you, of course he will be returning to his native land, I expect that many of the Breton contingent will accompany him also".

"But Dewi, how can I leave you here"? Teilo remonstrated.

"Can't you see that all my life has led up to this? God has called me to live a life of personal austerity and frugal discipline, I know that you also are able to live in this way, but my austerity has always been extreme, a laughing stock to some people, I know! You must be the shepherd of the flock now, I can endure whatever God demands of me in these difficult and dangerous times. I am sending my mother over with you for your protection and I will visit her if I get the chance, but I will not stay. My place is here".

Teilo saw that Dewi was right. "But how will I ever face Ygrain again" he said, turning to Dewi.

"See how God will lead you when the time comes" said Dewi.

Meanwhile, many more were adding to the numbers of those fleeing across the hills. As they did so, terrible tales of the yellow pestilence came with them, augmented each time they were retold. Men said it "was like a watery cloud passing overhead, beginning to cover the whole region. Everything it touched with its pestilential breath either died straight away or became sick unto death". People called it "the Yellow Pestilence" because it made everyone it attacked yellow and bloodless. "None were spared, neither men, nor animals, nor reptiles".

By the time Teilo had caught up with the fleeing people and his small party of monks, he found that a number had set sail for Ireland already. King Gerennius welcomed him, saying that, although he himself was desperately afraid, he had to remain in the country; he was afraid for his own life and felt that he would never live to see

Teilo's return again. However Teilo prayed with him and, giving him the sacraments, promised that he would not see death before he saw Teilo returned from the continent and once more able to give him Holy Communion.

They received true hospitality from King Gerennius; he had filled their boats with provisions and had looked after these terrified people with every courtesy and help; Teilo was deeply touched by him. However, it was time to embark and the tides carried them out into the choppy Irish sea, whence they set sail for Brittany. This was always the most hazardous route. Most travellers elected to go as far as they could by land, to avoid those treacherous islands off the south-west tip of Cornwall. But the circumstances were unusual and as they rounded St David's head, a number of little boats pushed out to sea to join them. Teilo called the ship's captain to hold back and Goronwy, this captain, ordered the sails again to be lowered. He scowled a bit as he watched the boats approach and muttered an oath when one of them pulled alongside, allowing a messenger to be pulled aboard his boat. The messenger went straight to Teilo, unbinding a jacket heavily wrapped in oiled skin and strapped to his body. He advised Teilo also to strap it to himself, for it contained the archiepiscopal pall from Dewi to be sent with Teilo for safe keeping in Brittany. Again hot tears welled in Teilo's eyes as he considered the plight of his country and the uncertainty which Dewi must be feeling to force him to such extreme measures.

Goronwy unfurled the sails again and the boat headed out into the ocean, the winds stronger and the seas even rougher now; many of the people were very sick. The thought that they were leaving their native shores perhaps for ever was affecting them and sobbing could be heard here and there in the boats -until Teilo started the singing. It began quietly at first, but then, as the monks and the whole ship's company joined in, the sound of singing filled the waves; the splash of the spray from the oars punctuated the sound, but soon the lull of the waves became regular and rhythmic and, as the boats sailed further and further, the coasts disappeared from view.

By evening the storm was upon them, the wind screaming overhead, as the men fought at their tasks, straining every muscle. They gritted their teeth as the rush and roar of the next great wave approached from behind, a deep- rooted worm of fear in their bowels as the ship, lurching sickeningly in the trough, was at once caught. It slapped against her timbers and, moaning, surged forward once again, mad, frightening, the ship scudding out of control as the men fought for their lives, bent over breaking oars, spray swirling from spinning crests.By then water and froth swashed about the decks, the women and children clinging to each other; another wave crashed overhead, threatening to wash them into that great foaming void around them. The Captain hung helplessly to the helm, visibility with the dimming light no more than a few score yards, while spray and confusion filled the air; Teilo was by his side gripping the helm with all his might and muttering a silent prayer. Neither the Captain nor Teilo had time to turn to see what lay behind, as suddenly the wave was upon them.

It crashed over the entire ship. Teilo and the Captain were sent sprawling , stunned but with dimmed mind taking in the horrific scene amidships. The wave had smashed most of the oars on the starboard side, the oarsmen being swept from their benches; they lay broken-winded, gasping for air, the water surging around them. The port rail was shattered and through the gap a torrent poured away overboard, taking with it three people, two of them children, their mothers screaming as they went. The confusion of tangled spars, ropes and rigging, people and provisions, made rescue attempts futile. Stung again by yet another wave, the ship lumbered forward before the northerly gale, no longer light and buoyant but sluggish and rudderless, with bruised, saturated bodies, timbers soaked to the core.... and still more water came aboard.

Never had a night seemed so long. Exhausted and haggard, Teilo was able to look around as the dawn light began to illuminate the seascape. The wind was abating but the sea still ran away from them, and both sea and sky had the cold grey pallor of a dying man. The proud ship had been clean, hard and sound, but the storm had taken its toll; it was chaotic with pieces of broken oars and timbers, bedraggled people and packages strewn about haphazardly. The ship now bloated, wallowed drunkenly in a swollen sea. Casting his eye once more around the horizon, Teilo began to realise the full effect of the havoc wreaked. Yet of the score of ships and craft which had set out the previous morning, with real relief he was able to count the great majority still in sight; although all were well blown off course, amazingly few appeared to be lost.

He helped the men bale out, as women and children sat around shivering or wringing out their clothes. Their own position also was well off course, for they spotted the Cornish coastline to the east, whilst, lying ahead, low in the water on the starboard bow, they could pick out the Scillies, sparsely populated and rarely visited by passing shipping. It was here that they decided to pull in for cover and before dark the battered timbers of those little ships were lying on the soft sand of a sheltered inlet.

This was indeed a wretched start for his frightened people and Teilo quickly gathered together his monks for discussion on the best plan to salvage the remaining food and belongings and to calm the émigrés. It was clear that they needed some help and a small boat was sent to the mainland, but it would take days before assistance could reach them. One of the boats was indeed missing, as the monks found when they took their tally amongst the people. Perhaps however they had been washed ashore on the mainland. Meanwhile fires must be lit, food was needed and shelters had to be built. Soon every able-bodied man, woman and child was straining away to achieve this under the efficient care of the monks.

Goronwy made an inspection of the damaged craft. Some of the boats were after the Irish pattern, long and narrow and used for transporting cattle and sheep if necessary. They had fine curved, sheer, long-lifting bows which enabled them to rise and ride over almost any sea and with a good following wind could accomplish ninety miles a day, but no boat could survive for long in such a gale and fury at sea. There was many days' work ahead to refit them.

After dark, Teilo went a little apart from the party to pray. As he looked into the night sky - calm now the wind had dropped, as had the temperature - he was aware of that other world out there beyond the stars. His people were frightened and demoralised, they felt they had lost everything. 'O, God', he thought,' what have we left? Some have lost family and friends, even their few poor possessions have been washed away; and yet I know in my heart of Your Love. Help me to show them this Love in spite of everything. Poverty is hard enough to bear, though You alone know how little they had; now all we have is each other and our will each to help the other, washed up as we are on this little island. You know how the people feel; some fear that the repairs will take too long and we will run out of food. Help me to reassure them and to comfort them, that they may come to see Your loving hand even in this apparent disaster!'

There was plenty of natural spring water; vegetation was plentiful, and there were berries to be gathered, but very little in the way of meat, though some fish were caught and shared. Teilo and his men were tough; they were well used to privation and to improvisation on their constant missionary journeys. Some people however had been badly bruised and injured in the storm and others still very shaken. They needed comfort, and younger children were ailing and sick. There was no sign of the yellow fever however; thankfully the monks began to set a rhythm to the day and the party gained strength from their example and began to follow this rhythm for themselves, some even joining in the praise to God and worship. Teilo felt that God was blessing the party in an unexpected way as the people joined together and fell into this pattern of the monks - manual work on the land, food gathering, shelter building and all the other necessary tasks interspersed with prayer and praise. All this welded the people into a community, caring for each other's needs, no longer concerned so much with their own wants.

At last boats which had been sent out to help those still at sea returned, but not alone, for the missing boat returned with them, together with a few others which they did not recognise. As they pulled in to shore, the people cheered and shouted their greetings. Captain Goronwy strode out into the water to hail them. Already in high esteem he had now made a good job of the boat repairs, his battered old face blown around with grey frizzy hair. His broad hairy chest had been seen in the thick of it, shouting commands to the crew in a hoarse old voice. His boats had ridden many a storm, but never had one had such damaging effects; it had been a bad time before dawn had broken and the land of Lyonesse appeared ahead; total disaster had only just been averted, but his weathered old face with its nose more like a large carbuncle appeared as visible proof of his ability to ride just such a storm. He would have stayed in port a day or two longer, but most of his passengers were pressing to escape from Din Gerran and the fever, so he had left against his better judgement. However now that everything was seaworthy again, they should lose no time, for the autumn tides would be upon them all too soon. They had stayed on the land long enough. And so with a westerly wind behind them and a fine clear day ahead , everyone bundled what remained of their belongings back onto the boats and the

fleet set out once more for the coast of Brittany.

With a day and a night of calm weather behind them, the people awoke thankfully to a new pink dawn spreading across the sea. Teilo was nudged awake by the lapping on the sides and opened his eyes to see the Breton coast straight ahead. But what a disappointment! It appeared totally unapproachable. The cliffs were rugged and austere with jagged rocks protruding high out of the water. Goronwy set course along the coastline but it continued forbidding. For a full day they travelled east along the coast, past creeks and coves and sandy bays and a few inlets where a river opened into the sea, but they were not to land on any of these. They were making for Dol and Teilo's old friend Samson, who as soon as he heard of their approach prepared to greet them and to make them welcome. On their way they circumnavigated one or two islands , passing close to Paul Aurelian's retreat on Batz and, although they saw no sign from the sea, Teilo made a mental note that he would return when the opportunity arose.

The people were chattering quietly as the day progressed, when suddenly Ilud, a blond-haired twelve year old, pointed excitedly to the sea ahead. 'Look over there!' he cried. Everyone strained to see what had caught his attention; they could make out a commotion below the waves when, all at once and over a considerable area, about a hundred or so porpoises rose to the surface. They were encircling a shoal of mackerel which, like a boiling cauldron, were being rounded up for a meal.

By late afternoon they arrived at that part of the coast nearest Dol. Rounding the headland they came scudding into a large sheltered bay, in the centre of which was a small island standing in marshes surrounded by the dense forest of Scissy; Teilo sent up a prayer of thanks to God for preserving them through the storm, he had a feeling that God was keeping him safe for something special - but what - "Is it Ygrain?" he asked himself.

Their turning into that spacious bay marked the end of the voyage and a cheer rose up spontaneously from all the boats. Now in the gentle evening light they came close by the shore and across the shallow water they could see Samson standing in the midst of his followers, all of whom must have been waiting for hours to greet the exiles. Neither those on shore nor those in the boats were able to say anything for the moment, but as the boats came closer it was the children who raised great shouts of joy and anticipation. This broke the tension and indeed everyone started chattering; some were in tears, others loud with their greeting, as all slowly clambered up the shore. Only Teilo and Samson remained silent. They had last met in very different circumstance, never really expecting to see each other again. Now they were here together, brothers on a foreign shore, both speaking the same language, both with so many shared memories of Dubricius, of Caldey, of Argol, of teachers and of early friends and family. A silent embrace was all they could manage in what looked like a situation of total disaster for their country back in Wales. However they must not give way.

"Well", said Iouill, the monk, "What next?"

Indeed greetings over, they all set about making plans.

"First, brothers and sisters, may I welcome you to the shores of Brittany". Samson's broad smile and his group of helpers soon dispelled their fears of the strange country indeed the guests felt strangely at home already, but Samson's greeting in their own tongue quickly strengthened this feeling. Any apprehension they might have had melted away and, as they followed their hosts up the beach away from that enormous bay, they marvelled at the countryside, so similar to the land they had left behind.

Dol lay only a mile or two inland and the sun would not set for some time yet. So they followed their hosts along the route leading to the compact little settlement which would become home for some of them for many years to come. Others would eventually travel much further inland, some to make permanent homes in Brittany, many like émigrés the world over to name their settlements after their birth place in Wales. So their new country became almost a mirror image of their old - with 'the Black Mountains' across the centre, Pen-ar-bed or Finisterre (and in Wales Pembroke the equivalent to Lands End) to the west and many more Welsh and Cornish place-names to become dotted throughout the map of Brittany.

All autumn they worked together to settle the newcomers and to help them build their homes before the chill of winter. A number of the people moved further inland, to clear the waste ground and to start little farms of their own. The country was well wooded and many wild animals inhabited the forests. Bear and boar, wild oxen and deer and everywhere a rich bird life, plenty of streams and rivers and a warmer gentler climate than the one they had left behind. The land too was rich and fertile with wild flowers filling the meadows, and the growing was easy. But the first year would be a hard one, for they had arrived in the wrong season and would have to depend on what they could forage.

Samson certainly had plenty of work to give them. He showed Teilo all that had been achieved in the area since he arrived several years before. Now they decided to plant an enormous orchard together. They drew up a plan of the proposed plantation. It was to stretch from Dol to Cai, a great grove of fruit-bearing trees three miles long. Ever since it has been called the orchard of Teilo and Samson. At Cai, Teilo found a fountain of water, which has since always had health-giving properties for the sick; it was also credited with helping sailors waiting for a favourable wind, for by cleaning out the fountain their prayers would be answered with an appropriate wind. It was clear to Teilo that he and many of those he had brought with him could be usefully employed helping Samson. So he also agreed to stay with him, at least for the time being, until all the folk were settled.

On arrival at Dol, Teilo had much to tell of events in Wales since Samson had left. Firstly they unrolled the carefully wrapped stole which Dewi had entrusted to Teilo to give Samson for safekeeping. Since it had not been spoiled by the sea nor during the journey, and they decided to put it secretly away while the plague raged in Wales until it was safe to return it there. (As events turned out it never was returned and in centuries to come the Pope in Rome could find no record of it ever having existed, itself not surprising since the Celtic church was at that time out of contact with Rome .The barbarians had overrun the city of Rome and much of western Europe, so that the Celtic church was affiliated more by sea to the church in Jerusalem and to the east. Although Dubricius had consecrated Samson as bishop in Wales, Dol was not a Bishopric in Samson's time; it only became such during the period 1076 - 1143. Eventually there were to be five Dumnonian sees in Brittany: Treguier, St Brieuc another old friend of Teilo, St Malo, Dol and St Pol de Leon, founded by Paul Aurelian).

THE THREE CELTIC PENINSULARS
(Mirror image maps of Brittany, Cornwall, S.Wales)
Finistère, Land's End, Pembroke
(Land's end in three languages)

(a).

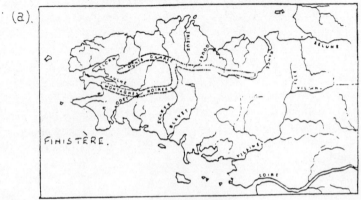

1,BRITTANY

(b).

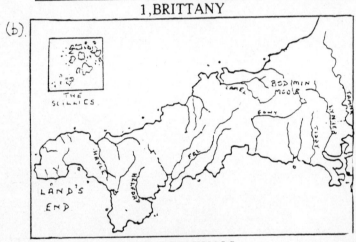

2,CORNWALL

(c).

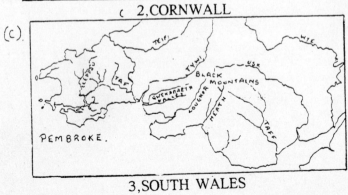

3,SOUTH WALES

CELTIC MONASTICISM

FOUNDATIONS OF DYFRIG AND TEILO

Dedications to Dyfrig and Teilo
Dyfrig dedications indicated thus | Henllan |

(e)

THE 'DEWI' (OR DAVID) CHURCHES

Dewi.

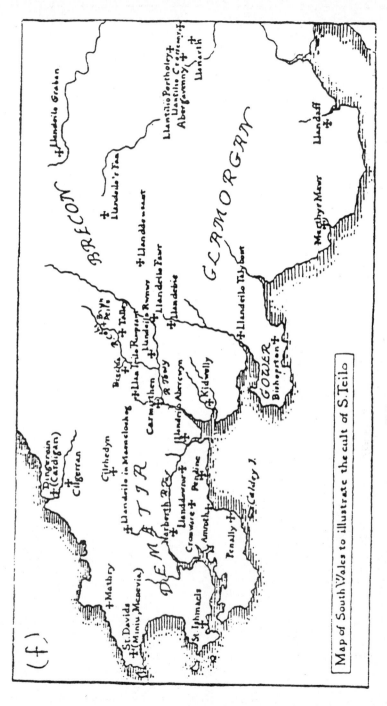

(f.)

Map of South Wales to illustrate the cult of S. Teilo

THE FOUNDATINS OF TEILO

CELTIC MONASTICISM(contd)
MAIN CENTERS OF GILDAS, PAULAURELIAN, SAMSON AND TEILO
MONASTIC SETTLEMENTS IN CORNWALL

(9).

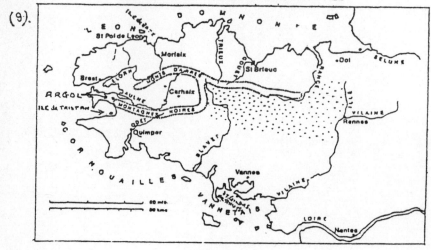

BRITTANY
(ARMORICA)

(h).

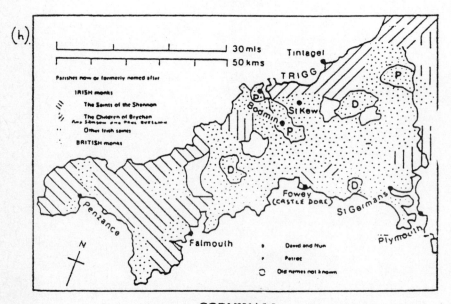

CORNWALL
(DUMNONIA)

i).

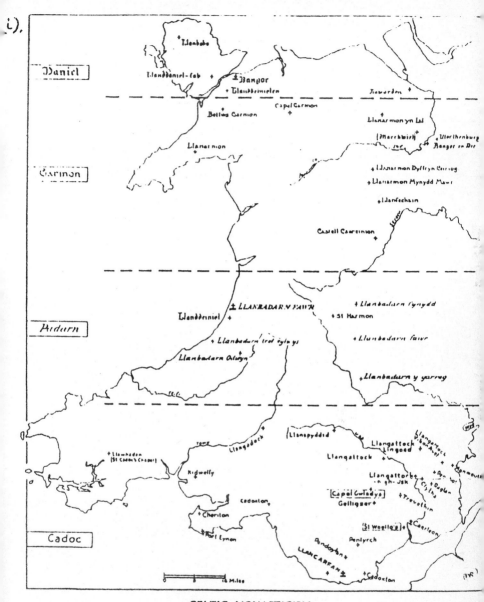

CELTIC MONASTICISM :
THE CADOC, PADARN, GARMON AND DEINIOL FOUNDATIONS

Chapter Eleven

THE FOUNDING OF LANDELEAU

Brittany (Armorica) 547-555 AD. 'Seven years and seven months' was the total period of the Welsh émigrés' stay in the country of Brittany.

The grove was going to take more than one winter to complete giving Samson and Teilo time to catch up with all that had happened. As they sat in the evening after a hard day in the fields, they would reminisce. Teilo told Samson how Dubricius, their beloved master, had retired to the island of Bardsey (Ynys Enli) and how he had died there.

"You must have missed him more than anyone" said Samson.

"He taught me as a child, of course, then later I followed his ministry until I took over" Teilo mused, "but it was what he gave me that dictated my future life, for due to him I became a lover of God from an early age. I caught it from him, it was an infectious holiness that he carried around with him". He smiled as he thought of the many scenes he'd witnessed of Dubricius at work. "When I became interested in his teaching, I found the love of God becoming a reality to me as well".

"You wouldn't recognise Demetia now Aircol is dead". He continued, "Vortipor's rule is ruthless as you might expect. Gildas has written a tract on the five wicked kings in Britain he will never be able to show his face there again! It all started with the civil war in the north. Vortipor and old King Aircol travelled up there to give Arthur their support and Aircol suffered a mortal blow, as did Arthur of course".

Samson interrupted:

"Yes and now news reaches us of Maelgwn Gwynedd, king in Gwynedd since his father Caswallon died, when we were young, now being elected 'King of the Britons'! So that he is now ruling not only north Wales but a much greater area as well. His general tyranny in Wales is a scandal". Samson remembered being at school with him at Llantwit Major, when Maelgwn was one of the unruly ones, headstrong and tough; he was not surprised to hear how he had turned out.

But Teilo was upset at leaving Dewi alone to face the Yellow pestilence and Samson tried to help him to come to terms with his feelings.

"You mustn't upset yourself so much about it Teilo, Dewi's whole life has led up to this, from a child he loved God. He is strong in heart and mind - if he hadn't cracked the whip and forced you to go, everyone you have rescued here would have died. He has great simplicity, or complexity, whichever way you look at it! He's hardly human - more like a biblical Jeremiah or Elijah figure. He'll really come alive under this pressure - whilst you are called to be a pastor to all these lost and homeless souls. You must not fail them now. You can exorcise your own personal demon by getting stuck into the work demanded of you now."

It was during the following summer that Teilo, parched with thirst, stopped for a drink and digging around discovered a spring from which the fountain of Cai first appeared.

At another time, he was sitting wearily on a boulder in the shade of some saplings, chatting to Samson of their future plans. "I would like to travel south", he said, "to the court of Budic, now that the people seem more settled".

"Why don't you go while the summer heat is with us", Samson had replied. "Nothing much can be done here now that the crops are growing. The people are quite capable of harvesting and you are due for a break".

It seemed good advice, so Teilo packed up a few belongings and set off by way of the coast and the island of Batz, for he thought that he would take the opportunity to see Paul Aurelian before cutting down south to the Kingdom of Quimper. Paul had now spent many years building up the foundation at Pol de Leon, dividing his time between there and Batz. His cousin there, Count Withurs was very old, but delighted to welcome Teilo, saying that Paul was not on the island, but on the mainland. They settled down for a chat and the Count recounted the tale of Paul's arrival in Brittany, joking about Paul's unworldliness.

"The problem was that if Paul wanted to wander off again and set up somewhere else, he might get into trouble with a less sympathetic landowner! I therefore counselled Paul to take upon himself the office of Bishop, so that in that position he would have authority to teach the people and instruct the clergy. Paul did not want any worldly honour for himself and was extremely reluctant to take my advice".

He chuckled to himself as he recounted to Teilo how he did it.

"I had therefore to fall back upon stratagem, since all the population was clamouring to be instructed by Paul! I decided to approach Paul with a request that he take a sealed letter to the King of the country, King Childebert. I told Paul that my own rule was under the authority of the King and that, owing to distance and lack of means of transport, I had had no communication with him since my appointment. Paul agreed to take the letters. In one letter I informed the king that I was sending Paul, a man of God, that he might ordain him Bishop (even against his will), for he had refused to be ordained many times although most worthy of the office and Paul promised to return with the reply".

Count Withurs continued. "He set out on the arduous journey to Paris, where King Childebert ruled, and was called to the presence of the King, who, having read that letter reproached Paul for hiding his talent. He then sent for three bishops and before a multitude of witnesses Paul was consecrated to the episcopate. He was given lands with exemption from taxes for ever, to form a perpetual diocese, and documents of proof with boundaries stated. Paul was ordered to found a church for Christ at every place he stopped for the night, being called for many discussions about the detail of the work during his stay in Paris. Paul was thereby able to found many churches and every time he passed by a temple for the worship of demons, he changed it to Christian worship".

Teilo was considerably amused by this story and afterwards took his farewell of the Count who sent him in the monastery boat back to the mainland where he walked the few miles to Leon to visit Paul. The local ruler by this time was Teilo's nephew Meliau, King Budic's son. He was King of Leon, and married to the daughter of Riwal a chief from west Dumnonia (Devon) who had also fled from the plague. Now in Brittany he had become overlord of the recent immigrants in the area. His headquarters were established at St Brieuc, with the river Gouet to the north, on an estate of modest size surrounded by woodland and brambles where Teilo stayed for a while and where he was told the local story.

Riwal's neighbour Francan challenged him to a horse race, over a measured course, to which everyone in the neighbourhood came. Boys, small and light, specially trained for racing, quickly mounted; Francan's horse went into the lead, but the boy could not hold it and was thrown among sharp stones and killed. However Francan's son Winaloe performed a miracle; he raised the boy to life at a place now called Plou-Fragan.

Teilo stayed with Paul as long as he could. Paul in turn took him to see the work he was doing, which covered a wide area of Finisterre, with his centre at Pol de Leon. Close by was the aged Brioc, born in Ceredigion, but educated with Iltud at Germanus's school in Paris before it was overrun by the Goths. Just as Brioc and Illtud had prayed together with him in Brittany for the work in Wales many years before, now Teilo had the painful task of telling Brioc about the decimation and havoc caused by the yellow fever in Wales. But the work in Brittany was impressive. The old deserted Roman towns were being rebuilt and in the countryside Paul in his gentle way not only tamed the wild animals he encountered, but was turning the people to God.

Teilo had to tear himself away from this district, for he had not yet visited the home of his sister Annauved, although she herself had made the long journey to see him shortly after he arrived at Dol. He was anxious also to find out how the family were at King Budic's court to the south, their children all grown now. Teilo tried to remember how long it was since they had set sail to Brittany; his mind was hazy; so much had happened, but he must delay the visit no longer.

Budic's court was at Quimper, quite a way down south. He had to leave the coastal region of sandy beaches with their cliffs of red granite to strike out into the lowland region of Finisterre, just avoiding the mountain range; this meant that he was making for the mouth of the river Aulne. By now, another spring was bringing the countryside alive. Small animals and birds scurried excitedly about their business, calling to each other or, like the squirrel, playing their crazy games. Teilo's spirits were high as he rode past fields full of wild flower, the yellow mimosa dancing lightly in the breeze. Every now and then he would have a sparkling glimpse of the sun, dazzling on a very blue sea, as it had been from time immemorial - yet every day was fresh and new, alongside those stark reminders of the past, standing stones here and there and chambered tombs of civilisations much older than Teilo's, now being lapped by waves on a warm sea shore. At the mouth of the Aulne, he was close to Argol, where Budic and Annauved had first made camp on their return from Wales.

Teilo kept moving south and soon, peering down, he could see Budic's chief town, Quimper, capital of the region of Cornouaille, nestling at the base of the steep hill on the banks of the river Odet. Budic had built a powerful western Kingdom. His son Meliau was king of Leon, and married to the daughter of Riwal. His daughter had married King Mark Conomorus, who was living on the bay of Douarnenez after the tragic death of his previous wife Iseult.

Teilo had long wondered how it would be, this home of Annauved in the south; he clopped along the streets on his horse, looking at the buildings on either side; the warm stone seemed welcoming, the town comfortable and friendly. It did not take him long to reach the King's palace where he became the centre of attention, as Annauved hugged him and introduced her grown-up sons, Ishmael, Teifi and Docco whom she had dedicated to Teilo's work before he was born. These three young men begged to be allowed to help Teilo as monks in his church. King Budic at length rescued Teilo from all this embrace and drew him aside to a courtyard where a cool fountain trickled and splashed refreshingly; they had matters to discuss.

They talked quietly of many things, until the veil of day dropped to reveal the night. Stars gleamed above them in the courtyard; still the water at the fountain continued to splash and spill; Teilo had dropped into a drowsy sleep. Suddenly he was awake - or was he dreaming? He seemed to hear the swish of skirts and patter of slippers under the verandah across the courtyard; opening his eyes he looked in the direction of the sound. Standing there in the shadows was Ygrain, a lovely golden tan on her cheek, which had never glowed there when she lived in Wales. He glimpsed her for a moment, then she was gone. Fully awake now, Teilo jumped up and stared into the shadowed corner and, moving in that direction, stared again - but he could see nothing. He shivered a little, for the night air was cooler now. Wondering how long he had been asleep, he turned and went indoors.

Later, at dinner, he asked his sister what had happened to Ygrain - was she no longer at court? Annauved looked at him long and hard.

"I thought I saw her here this evening in the courtyard", Teilo said under his breath and Annauved very tenderly replied,

"Would you like to see her? She has changed a lot you know. It's many years since you last met and she left with me to Brittany in a huff after the way you behaved. She spent many years pining away".

Teilo did dearly want to see her, so Annauved agreed to arrange it, if Ygrain gave her consent.

He met her in the cool courtyard where he had had the vision of her the night he arrived. Considering the time since they last met, Teilo thought she had remained much the same. It was not until he started speaking to her that he realised that Annauved was right; this was a very different Ygrain. The last time they spoke, she had called him a hypocrite, accusing him of trying to be perfect by his own efforts. That accusation still rang in his ears and he had to confess that he was apprehensive about meeting her again.

But she stood there looking cool and relaxed. It was obvious that all those years she had had a guilty feeling about her accusation to him; for as he entered the garden she moved towards him and looking him full in the face said "Eliud, how bad I have often felt at saying those things to you. Will you let me now say I am sorry; I didn't understand it all at the time. I wronged you. Will you forgive me?"

He smiled and now moving slowly towards her relaxed as he gazed at her open face, taking in her every nuance as he did so. Suddenly he realised that they were for the first time at one and he felt exultantly happy. He had only to look at her to realise that she had found God in a new way. Before, as a girl, she had become a believing Christian, but now through all that she had suffered, her faith had deepened and she realised for herself how utterly loveable God is and that it was indeed possible to follow Teilo's path for good motives.

But there was something else, she had changed towards him too. Unexpectedly Teilo felt a twinge of disappointment, almost as if he still expected her to be just as she was before.

"Teilo, I see now that what you said all those years ago is true - we could never have been happy together, we would always have been pulling ourselves apart in different directions. I would have watched you unhappily, constantly hankering after God's work, and all the time you would have been unhappy too - tied down and unable to throw yourself into it all fully. Did you know that Dewi was my confessor and true friend? He knew quite well how you would feel. He couldn't understand how you could ever have allowed a woman to make you so unhappy and to dominate your thoughts. He helped me to face the situation".

As always they talked freely with each other; they talked and talked until nightfall, when they had to join Annauved and Budic for the evening meal. Deeply they still felt for each other, but they agreed together to be brother and sister instead for the sake of God's work.

At supper Budic broke the spell by pulling Teilo's thoughts back to the present emergency:

"How are you going to settle the large number of refugees from Wales?" Budic asked, anxious to help Teilo. "It should be done as quickly as possible; there is no telling how long this plague will take to play itself out".

They were now in their second year in Armorica and the number of refugees had been increased by more shiploads from Wales. During the following days the discussion revolved around this problem, for many were still at Dol and the small community there was doing its best to accommodate them. Naturally the discord and frustration caused by having no settled place could not be allowed to fester longer than was necessary and, now spring had come, both Teilo and his people needed a place they could at least temporarily call their own.

"Dol could hardly be farther from us here", Annauved remarked: "Why, it is diagonally across the country with mountain ranges, thickly wooded and full of wild animals in between - not suitable at all for casual journeys. Teilo, why don't you set up in the middle of the country, on the river Aulne? There you would have transport in both directions, north towards Dol and west to the bay of Douarnenez".

Teilo's colleague and friend, Padarn, had by now returned to his homeland of Brittany with many of his flock from Ceredigion and re-established himself at Vannes. Padarn had arrived in Britain in 516 and spent some time at Illtyd's monastery before he founded his church at Llanbadarn, in Ceredigion, where he had presided for over twenty-one years before the Yellow plague attacked the country. Now it was good to know Padarn was in such close proximity again, although just then the political situation was dangerously confused around Vannes, to the south east of Budic's kingdom.

Eventually this area was to be ruled peacefully for a time by Macliavus, but just now he was being murderously pursued by Conan of Vannes, his brother, who had already killed three brothers. Macliavus was protected by Mark Conomorus who hid him in a tomb in Carhaix, pretending that he was a corpse. Macliavus then had himself tonsured, was consecrated bishop in his brother's kingdom and on the death of Conan made lay ruler of the area. Budic understandably made an agreement with Macliavus that when either of them died the other would protect their son.

Another old friend, Cadoc, was also highly venerated in Vannes and in Finisterre as well as in many other places in Brittany. especially on the Ile de S.Cadou near Belz where he fled from the Yellow Pestilence with a large party of monks. Here Gildas stayed with his old friend Cadoc for a while. But he eventually settled on the southern coast in the area of Vannes on the peninsula of Ruys. He brought with him a companion, Biezy. They built their cells on the right bank of the river Blauet and although solitude and discipline were severe for them, they were surrounded by a land rich in wine, forests with excellent wood, wool, flax, butter, honey, fruit fish and game, on the edge of the sparkling blue sea. In many ways it was a paradise, a perfect situation for the monks to concentrate on worship and praise and contemplation of God, but their first concern was care and love for their fellow man. Men of action, they were deeply committed to the concerns of the people. It was to these issues that these people now addressed themselves and their lives showed how deeply they became involved. Gildas founded the church of St Gildas de Ruys which, six centuries later was ruled by the monk Abelard, whose love for Heloise was to ruin his brilliant career.

During the seven years of their exile Gildas, Teilo and others had many important discussions on the future strategy for Britain. But not yet, Teilo must first find a place in which to settle and to make a temporary home for his people.

The founding of Landeleau

Eventually Budic sent Teilo with an escort across country to see for himself. His sons accompanied Teilo: Ishmael, Teifi and young Oudoceus, Annauved saying that she would follow later. The forest was thick with plenty of wild boar - and game abounding everywhere. Teilo's affinity with animals meant that he was never afraid of sounds by night, but he could well imagine how the more timid of his party might feel at night when the wolves howled. As he passed through small clearings and hamlets, he came across many familiar names of those who had been there before him.

Brioc had another sizeable settlement and, in close proximity was an older one which had been founded by Edern, Vortigern's son, whom St Germanus had rescued and brought to Brittany for safety from Wales; a few miles away was another familiar name, that of Hernin (Isernius, commemorated in Wales by Capel Hernin near his native Argol). Perhaps the same Isernius had travelled here also? They were now miles from the haunting smell of the shore with pine woods close by the beach; they were almost at the centre point of the country, as they came upon the twisting, turning river Aulne, with the hill above it. How like his homeland! This is where he would build his church with the river winding at its foot; he would call it after Llandeilo Fawr. And so it was, later to be known as 'Landeleau'.

And so throughout all the land of Brittany the Welsh people were made welcome. Wherever they made their little settlements they would often name them after that place in Wales whence they came. The well-known longing of the Welsh for their homeland was thus a little assuaged, that longing which they call 'hiraeth'.

This was the third major emigration of the British from their homeland to the land of Armorica, to be known as Brittany or 'little Britain'. The first had come with the settlement of Cynan Meriadau - Elen's brother; the second under Riothamus during Vortigern's time (Elen's son - in - law), when there was that inrush of Saxons on the eastern side of Britain; and the third at this time, caused be the panic of yellow fever around 547 AD. However there was also a constant trickle of people moving in both directions and settling, especially that earlier major concentration of missionary monks who travelled to west Wales. Teilo stayed in Brittany with his people for seven years and seven months.

Before he could build a church on his chosen spot, he first had to seek the permission of the landlord. He stayed for a long time in the forest of Pohez, intending to build his church there from standing stones with a flat stone roof at a place called Menez Glace. However since the frogs in the marsh nearby made such a terrible noise, he moved on and built it elsewhere.

Local people pass down an amusing legend! 'His sister had come to keep house for him, and was very keen for him to build on land near Menez Glace, and when she heard that he had found a place elsewhere to build his church, she pretended to be full of joy, but was really upset. He had asked the seigneur at the local Castel Gall if he might have some land. The seigneur had readily agreed on condition that he only used land which he could cover from sunset to cock crow - that is, in one night.

Teilo stood at the door of his house and began to whistle, when out of the wood came a wild stag which knelt at his feet; Teilo mounted it to

159

traverse his domain. The animal galloped along with all speed, but when they passed Castel Gall the owners set their dogs on to him. Teilo just had time to jump into an oak tree, while the stag hid itself in a wood until they were gone. Without doubt Teilo would have made up this delay if it had not been for his sister, who had also prepared a ruse - one could hardly believe this sister to be Annauved!

She took a cock from the chicken-run and pushed it up the chimney; then in the hearth she lit a faggot of dead wood; the cock, trying to escape the smoke, beat its wings desperately and crowed, waking up all the chickens in the village and the crowing of the cocks spread from chicken-run to chicken-run, stopping Teilo, who was bound to his promise. Undoubtedly without this trick, his parish would have stretched from Collorec on one side to Cleden on the other!'

St Teilo is depicted in Brittany mounted on a stag!, not necessarily because the legend is true, but to show that special affinity that the saints were said to have with wild animals, a gift of authority over the animals which we have too often lost along with our desire to submit ourselves to God. The stag is an early symbol of Christ; in Christian symbolism the stag has been depicted as drinking from a chalice, to represent the soul's thirst for God. The inference made by Teilo's statue must be to show his total dependence on Christ.

King Mark (Conomorus) or Marcus, as he was variously known, became chief at about this time of the region of Poher in which St Teilo's church of Landeleau is cited at the confluence of the rivers Aulne and Hyeres. The power-hungry Conomorus had now worked his way inland from Douarnenez, to establish himself in the romanised fort at Poher under the patronage of Budic, overall King of the area, married as he now was to Budic's daughter (Teilo's niece). At Budic's expense he desired to increase his power over the whole region of Brittany, first dispossessing all those petty kings surrounding him. Thwarted in his personal life, he became more and more reprehensible in his political life; he is depicted as a venomous , winged serpent. He was reputed to have killed many people, eventually some third of the population in Brittany! He became for the people an evil monster, but the power of the saint, it was believed, was enough even to overcome this, so that whilst Teilo lived and worked in the area, he acted as a brake on Conomorus's worst inclinations.

Extending his kingdom into the centre of Brittany, Conomorus was protected by the mountains of Aree to the north and the Black mountains to the south, with the river Aulne flowing through the middle. Like Paul Aurelian he too came originally from the Llandovery region of South Wales, perhaps from the area of the Villa Bannedos at the triple mountain refuge now known as Tre-Bannau, Banc tre-bannau and Bwlch tre-bannau. In this case one can understand his knowledge of Paul Aurelian's work in the Llandovery area and his need to have him at his stronghold of Castle Dore, after the tragic end to the love affair between Tristan and his own bride-to-be Iseult, the daughter of an Irish King.

The story is well-known, but must have a place here. Because of his love for his father's bride-to-be, Tristan, as we saw earlier, had been exiled by Mark to Brittany, where he landed with a fleet in the Bay of Douarnenez on the island since known as Ile Tristran. Later King Mark had followed Tristan, bent on escaping from the yellow pestilence. Meanwhile Tristan had married another princess, also called Iseult, but it was an unhappy marriage. When he heard that Mark was fleeing the yellow pestilence and bringing his former love with him, Tristan sent word to the first Iseult that if she came in love she was to order that white sails be hoisted on the ship's mast; if she sailed with black sails then her love for Tristan had died. Tristan was very ill and as he lay dying Conomorus's fleet sailed into sight in the bay. (Now the second Iseult had intercepted the message from Tristan to his former love.) As Tristan asked from his sickbed what colour were the sails, the second Iseult lied and said that the sails on Iseult's boat were black. On hearing this, as the fleet sailed up the harbour, Tristan lay back and died. Rushing from the ship to Tristan's bedside, Iseult, King Mark's wife, found Tristan dead, whereupon she fell into a swoon and died in his arms. His grave is at Castle Dore near Fowey, where there is a stone beside the road with the inscription 'DRUSTANUS HIC IACET CUNOMORI FILIUS.'

King Mark had his palace built at Plomarc'hs on this very spot in Douarnenez at the mouth of the Pouldavid estuary. After the death of

Iseult, Conomorus married Budic's daughter Trephine and in due course a son was born to them; this son's name was Tremeur. But Conomorus, as we know, was a very violent man who abused his wife and Trephine's life became a living hell.

With the help of his three nephews Ishmael, Teifi and Oudoceus Teilo continued to lead his people and from his own foundation at Landeleau he built a church which was to last for over a thousand years. He will always be remembered there by the people, for annually they proceed round his parish in their famous tromenie, from 7am till 5pm, following the course he took. They stop at S.Elau's tree, where a sermon is preached, and as they process they sing a Breton hymn about Teilo. The parish remembers him in several ways. There is a dolmen there, called 'Ty Sant Heleau', two fields known as 'Parc Sant Elau-bras' and '-bihan' and there is 'Goarem Sant Elau', while at the door of the church is a stone sarcophagus in which Teilo lay to do his penance. Teilo certainly seems firmly based in Brittany to judge by his dedications there.

During Teilo's time in Brittany there was an enormous influx of immigrants from Britain. These brought their problems with them. They did not suddenly become different people when they landed on the other shore. The monks also continued their work in the same way, while the people who were used to tilling the soil found new land to cultivate and those who were tyrants continued to be tyrants in a foreign land. Never did most of them imagine for one moment that their stay in Brittany would be a permanent one while Teilo, unlike Paul Aurelian and Samson, knew that his life's work was in Wales. Gildas knew this to be true of himself also and much preparatory planning and discussion was needed when there was a moment to spare from the day to day toil. Having become disillusioned by the decadence of the five princes on the mainland, Gildas concentrated on training men for work in Ireland. This training had been started by Dewi at his monastery of Menevia - an ideal site equipped with boats to assist in the missionary movement in Ireland. It was to these matters that Gildas's mind turned during his time in Brittany. Gildas's work lay on the Welsh west coast and in Ireland with Dewi, but Teilo knew that his main thrust must continue eastwards into Britain, so that Gildas and Teilo needed to co-ordinate their future work.

Eventually after seven years or more the yellow pestilence was declared to have left Britain and Teilo decided to return to his native land together with any of his fellow countrymen who wished to return home again. He also received news that King Gerennius of Cilgerran had been taken very sick with a painful disease and had sent for Teilo to give him final communion before his death, as Teilo had promised when they embarked seven years before.

According to the Book of Llandaff, Bishop Teilo called to himself his family and people of his country and reminding them of his promise to King Gerennius on the way to Brittany said, 'Know ye, my children, that our King Gerennius is grievously afflicted with a painful disease and will shortly depart from this life. Therefore prepare for us our ship'. King Budic and Teilo's sister Annauved brought to him their sons Ishmael, Teifi and Oudoceous, who had been earlier promised to him for the work as missionaries to Wales. With Budic was a large army, for Mark Conomorus was again troubling the area. They all knelt before Teilo and besought him to save their land from the ravages of Mark, who now ruled over a third of Brittany; they all lived in fear and terror of him and were afraid that once Teilo left, Mark's tyranny would escalate.

The Book of Llandaff continues: "The holy man came to the seaport as they were weeping and mourning on account of the departure of so great a father and, while they waited for a favourable wind, the Bretons pleaded with Samson to persuade Teilo to stay with them, for they were very afraid of Mark Conomorus.." But Teilo is adamant. He will agree to stay at Dol but only until the party of exiles are all gathered together there. After refusing the gift of one horse, another magnificent beast appears, miraculously brought by an angel to take him to the Bishopric of Dol for enthronement. The story goes that the noble horse was later presented to Budic to assist his soldiers in battle - and from that day Bretons are famous for their magnificent war horses. To this day there is certainly a chapel of St Geren in Dol cathedral.

At last the people are ready to sail after seven years and seven months in exile. Teilo commanded that a large stone sarcophagus, "which ten yoke of oxen could scarcely pull"!, should be cast into the sea and attached astern of the ships to float behind them (presumably fixed in the mode of a catamaran across two or even three smaller boats or rafts). As they were sailing home, half way across the sea, another ship met them and announced that the king was dying, but was awaiting the coming of Teilo in fulfilment of his promise. So all the ships sailed to the port of Din Gerren - the king's capital - and the stone appeared with them as the ships pulled up to the harbour!

Teilo went straight to King Gerennius and, finding him still alive, was able to administer Holy Communion before he died. He was gently laid in the sarcophagus for burial. After this "the holy man, accompanied by the clergy and people in great numbers, made his way back to his Episcopal see in Wales to abide there until the end of his life".

La Troménie : le parcours.

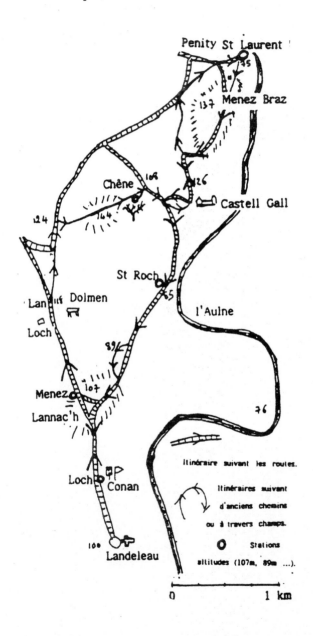

Penity St Laurent

Menez Braz

Chêne

Castell Gall

St Roch

l'Aulne

Lan Dolmen

Loch

Menez

Lannac'h

Loch Conan

Landeleau

Itinéraire suivant les routes.

Itinéraires suivant
d'anciens chemins
ou à travers champs.

Stations
altitudes (107m, 89m ...).

0   1 km

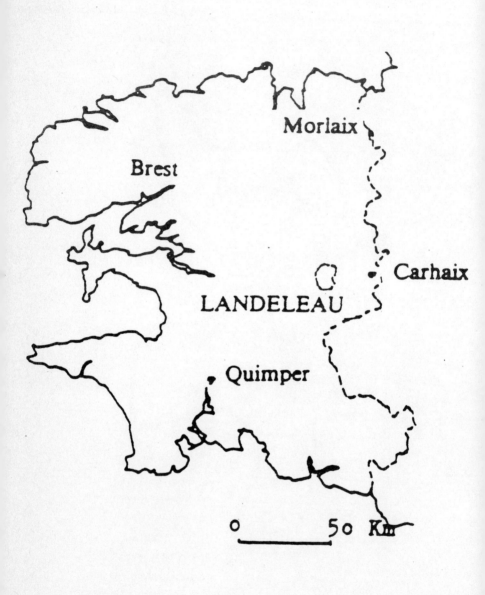

CLONMACNOISE "CROSS OF SCRIPTURES" IRELAND

Chapter Twelve.

TEILO'S RETURN TO BRITAIN.

c555 - 580s. St Teilo's life in Wales after his return from Brittany.

When Teilo landed on his home soil once more, it was to a very different country that he was returning. Dewi was gone, 'migrated to the Lord' and Teilo could not help grieving inwardly for his closest friend; nothing could ever be the same again; of course it was purely selfish to grieve, for Dewi himself was now in the closer presence of his Lord, but he missed the old familiarity, the understanding they had and the teamwork, yoked together in the Spirit as they had been Dewi's legacy to him and all future generations was a constant reminder of him however; everywhere he went in south Wales he came upon little settlements or a cell of a monk at work in the neighbourhood, witnessing to the fact that Dewi had been there imprinting his stamp for Christ.

During the Yellow Pestilence Dewi does not appear to have had much influence at Llandeilo Fawr, but he is mentioned in connection with Caeo, Llangadog and Llanarthney. Perhaps finding the central position of Llandeilo Fawr was convenient but not wishing to disturb anything that Teilo had started there; Dewi developed Llanarthney at the foot of Argol as an important mother church, which according to legend, had the custody of the mystic gifts bestowed to his father Sant for Dewi before his birth'. Teilo could well have sunk into a slough of depression at this time, if he had allowed himself to do so. They had told him that Dewi's last words to his followers were, "Be joyful, keep the faith and do the little things you saw and heard from me." These few words summed up for Teilo his best memories of a friend whose clear, uncluttered mind was able to focus on the minutiae of detail, in the same way as a child's unclouded mind can. 'No wonder that Dewi had such an affinity with and love of children', Teilo thought. There was so much to do but, had it not been for the encouragement, enthusiasm and drive of his monks and supporters all keenly awaiting his plans and directives, Teilo might first have been tempted to retire from the action. He looked around and, rousing himself, realised that he must take stock quickly and set things into motion. At least he did not have to contend with Vortipor on his return, for Vortipor had died in the plague years. A coloured stone had been raised over his burial place in the centre of Dyfed at Castell Dwyran and on it had been carved MEMORIA VOTEPORIGIS PROTECTORIS - along with Irish Ogham writing on the side.

Maybe towards the end of his life Vortipor, protector of the Emperor Arthur, had had a change of heart; maybe he had even co-operated with Dewi to help his people; no one probably will ever know, but with a cross at a later date inscribed on his stone one could be forgiven for thinking that Gildas's harsh words about him did not tell the whole story. (see appendix) The throne of Dyfed was now occupied by Cyngar (Cincar), soon to be followed by Pedyr (Peter), from whom Teilo received support and help. Maelgwyn Gwynedd had also died of the plague.

But Teilo was now almost in his sixties. As the years had passed he suffered a heavy degree of strain, bearing the buffeting of much political chaos for his people in trying to lead them faithfully through. He did this not in his own strength, but allowing God to work through him, daily relying upon his obedience to the Divine Will. The period ahead was an enormous challenge, requiring from Teilo that he dedicate himself anew to his calling. He must forget all that was behind and press on with renewed faith for the work ahead. His task from now on was to rebuild the monasteries, which over nearly eight years had fallen into disrepair, and revitalise the work to be forged from within them.

After the plague years Cadoc too left his disciple Cadwaladr in charge of his church in Brittany and returned to his monastery of Llancarvan in east Glamorgan, where he was both a secular King and a religious ruler. He was older than Teilo and like him he nerved himself for the task ahead. No doubt those years in Brittany had been used for concentrated study, prayer and much discussion between

Gildas, Cadoc, Teilo and the many others; it had been a good time for planning future strategy in Wales. What remained of the British church from Roman times was a priestly ministry with almost as many bishops as churches; bishops were but priests as were the presbyters. They were in dioceses but these had become cut off from Rome. The other division consisted of those clergy (bishops and presbyters) who had adopted the monastic life; this group, fairly insignificant before, had grown and developed fast, preserving the customs of the early Christian Church in Britain; before the plague years there was considerable tension between the two but now the Celtic church went ahead.

The special features of the Celtic church were the austerity of its discipline and its intellectual activity. The monks asked nothing for themselves, in fact they did not even want to be remembered by man, their desire being to be united with God and to be forgotten. The more extreme hermits or anchorites built their beehive cells on rocky islands surrounded by the sea, to live in the main off herbs. Others only asked for a 'Small hut in a lonesome spot', in which to live in simplicity, close to nature - 'to sit at times alone and pray in every place.' On Teilo's return he brought with him not only his nephews Ishmael, Teifi, Oudoceus and Theodoric, but also all those others who had been dispersed across Brittany and further south to the Alps, even down into Italy, so that 'the nation, decimated by the pestilence, very quickly increased in numbers'. After the funeral of King Gerennius, Teilo travelled down from Ceredigion to Llandeilo Fawr, "where he remained to the end of his life, holding supremacy over all the churches of the whole of southern Britain, according to the appointment of the fathers who consecrated him at Jerusalem.' Travelling with him were a great number of clergy, including the faithful Fidelis and Teilo's own brother Mabon. Very soon he was joined by his former disciples Iouill, Iunapeius, Gurmaet, Cynmur, Toulidauc amongst many others.

So great was the extent of his work at this time, that the Book of Llandaff continues to spell out the detail of Teilo's work at this stage thus: "Of his own counsel he consecrated many men to the episcopate, sending them throughout the country distributing parochaea to them, as was convenient for the clergy and people".

There were numerous bishops, but no mention of an archbishop. Teilo was the chief bishop. On the death of Cynog, who had taken Dewi's place, it was Teilo who consecrated Ishmael to be bishop of St Davids; Ishmael was also to found Kidwelly, Oudouceus being sent to Llandeilo 'r Fan,near Brecon; Cynmur to Llangunnor outside Carmarthen and to Bishopston in Gower (known at this time as Llandeilo Ferwallt); Toulidauc was based at the important monastery in Carmarthen, later to become one of the seven bishops' houses of Dyfed and eventually the priory of St John, but in those days just a Celtic monastery. Tyfhei was sent to found Lamphey, another of those seven bishops' houses of Dyfed, along with a little church at Llandefeisant (in Dynevor park), set beside the Roman road to Llandeilo bridge and built by him on a Roman temple. Teilo's brother Mabon continued to support the work nearby, with a number of other dedications to follow later. One could continue at length describing these many disciples of Teilo; suffice to say that a new age had begun in churches both in Britain and in Ireland, a time of great monastic expansion.

Using his main monastery as a centre for the supervision of the whole of south Wales and as a powerhouse of prayer and administration where young men were trained for the work as missionaries, teachers and scholars, he could move out to the work in other areas. Llanarth to the east, on the borders of old Dubricius's territory was another important monastery for the work on the eastern border with the Saxons, but it was situated further west than Dubricius' centre in the vulnerable area in Herefordshire. Llanarth was also a convenient point for consultation with Cadoc's monastery at Llancarvan and down into east Glamorgan, to the monastery at Llanllltud Fawr. Teilo himself had hardly a dedication in this area, apart from Teilo's well near the little ancient church on the Taff river which in later times was to become the great monastery of Llandaff.

Teilo's work at Llandeilo Fach radiated out into the churches in west Glamorgan and the Gower peninsula. Llandeilo Fach is close by Urien's castle on the earlier Roman fort of Leucarum in the valley at the mouth and junction of the Loughor and Lliw rivers, and this 'Church in the marshes' was well placed on an old river ford across this river Loughor. An important part of Teilo's work was carried on here at Llandeilo Fach known also as Llandeilo Talybont, one of the oldest and historically one of the most important churches in the Lliw valley; in later times men were to cover the walls with the largest area of medieval wall paintings known to Wales. Close to the church is an ancient Grange known as Cwrt y Carnau (court of cairns) after the monk's beehive shaped cells or cairns; there is a mound known as the Castell Du (the Black castle) nearby. Teilo's nephews, the sons of his sister Annauved and King Budic were thus very active in their mother's native land. Oudoceus is mentioned here and in Kidwelly and, on the death of Urien in the 570s, Theodoric's son Mouric not only ruled in east Glamorgan but inherited Gower, and this area of Llandeilo Fach as his territory. As Teilo's great nephew, no doubt he supported Teilo's work here, but how much of Teilo's own time was spent here is hard to say. All his life he worked closely with his brother Mabon who is remembered both in the parish of Llanfabon and also at Maenor Fabon, adjacent to Llandeilo Fawr.

We should now return to the position of the Celtic church in Teilo's day. Synods formed an important part of church life in Gaul and Samson is recorded as attending one at Paris in 560, about five years before his death. Henoc, who emigrated with Samson to Dol, dictated Samson's 'Life' to his nephew, making it the earliest known, almost a contemporary account in fact. Writing before the plague years, Gildas does not mention a synod, but we know of the synod at Llanddewi Brefi and another called 'the Victoria' in Britain, although from now on the barbarian invasions were to diminish such contact for Wales.

About 564 King Ainmire in Ireland summoned Gildas to revive the faith there. It was probably the same king who extended the invitation to Cadoc whose connections with Ireland went back to his childhood when the old Irish monk Tathan had taught him all he knew in his home in Caerwent. It is clear from Gildas's book (written before 547) and his lengthy quotations, that the Bible which he had been taught at Llanllltud was the old Latin version of the second century. Gildas shows that this ancient version, survived into the sixth century.

After the return of St Teilo to Britain, the distinct Celtic church was now evolving with the sole purpose of developing the inner spiritual life. There were no problems with doctrine. In Britain as elsewhere the same view is held. Cadoc, Gildas and Dewi are said to have been the ones who gave Ireland its form of the Mass. Ireland was still divided into a great number of petty kingdoms at this time. The Kings' houses were often surrounded by a circular rath or rampart or built on an artificial island in a lake. The monastic settlements kept secular learning alive, although not based on Roman schools, for Rome never touched Ireland. Gildas however had been trained with a thoroughly Roman outlook in Illtud's school which was based on the same lines as the municipal Graeco-Roman type as was the case on the continent. There is no mention of separation from Rome in the sense of heresy in the Celtic church; the separation was purely geographical. Just as the Saxons were cutting off Wales from the rest of Britain, so had barbarian hordes invaded and cut off the Celtic Church from the church in southern Europe, obliging it to develop along its own special lines; this included a different form of monasticsm from the later church.

Until now the second century Latin version of the Old and New Testaments of the Bible had been used, but now the Vulgate - Jerome's version which had been produced about 400 - was introduced. The Druids being supplanted by saints, druidical poet schools continued alongside the monastic schools, but now there was competition; Christian poets were writing hymns and sacred songs, probably based on songs already being sung by the people, whilst the high poets were developing bardic measure; in this way the poetry and art of the Celtic past was able to survive and become absorbed into the new learning. The old oral tradition continued to prevail on the whole during these various changes and modernisation of the language , but gradually it was written down, although the earliest written Welsh retained by posterity is late ninth century. Thus Druids no longer had priestly duties, but remained as scholars, genealogists and lawyers, being assimilated into a Christian society in those roles. The position of women in Celtic society incidentally was high and this was to continue into Christian culture.

Teilo understood the gamut of human feelings: he had realised years before that Vortipor's men were possessed by a hostile force of basic human feelings, aggression and sexual drive, but without the necessary restraint; he also understood those of very different nature those who appeared to be highly moral, having repressed their feelings and taken on a facade deriding sex, but as a result were sometimes obsessed or perverted. Desire varies, but plenty of his folk lived happy normal lives. His monks were celibate but there was no rule about this; other Celtic monks were allowed to marry, as it was recognised that the growth and development of personality throughout life, in preparation for living the fuller life of God's kingdom,is often best achieved in marriage, which can gradually teach a sacramental way of living and loving in human relationships. But the complete transformation of sexual energy, in living a celibate life, is something which Christ demonstrated and is a most positive force, not given to many people to attain. It is an evolved and full development of that special man, that the Celtic saints were working towards, in co-operation with God still, it is hoped, continuing today. Love is far more than sensual desire; the highest level of love is reached by control and mutual consideration; it can never be an individual affair. Whether married or single, one must use its power in such a way that it can never do harm to another. The Celtic saints were able to make use of their sexual nature to win from it an enrichment of life, a creative and harmonious experience, enabling them to go out and do God's work in the world - a sense of enchantment and power.

But there was freedom of choice, Gildas for instance himself being a married man with children. Monks could also be laymen, as Maelgwn Gwynedd had been. This Celtic form of monasticism was missionary and expansive. Unlike the retreat of the Desert Fathers who locked themselves away from the world, these Celtic monks often used the monastery as a powerhouse, a centre of Christianity, from which they set out into the world.

TEILO AND THE SAXON INVASIONS During Teilo's absence in 547, almost as he left in fact, Ida the Angle had landed on the shores of northern Britain, to be met by Urien Rheged and his son Owain, together with Gwallawc and Morcant. They called Ida the

'Flamebearer' (Fflamddwyn), presumably because he burnt down the homesteads of the local people - later he was to become founder of the Northumbrian dynasty; Urien's family was to fight Ida for twelve years(547-59); Glappa for one (559-60); Adda for eight (560-8); Aethelric for four (568-72); Theodoric for seven (572-9); Friduuald for six (579-85) and Hussa for seven years(585-92). This struggle was to continue for the rest of Teilo's life. In his youth Arthur had brought several decades of peace by his victory at the Battle of Badon, but even before his defeat at Camlann in 537, the Saxons had taken the Isle of Wight (530). They had resumed their steady advance north and west through the country, beginning in earnest around 550, several years before Teilo's return,and in 552 Cynric the head of the west Saxon dynasty defeated the Britons at Old Sarum (Salisbury) (to be succeeded in 560 by his son Ceawlin). Now Teilo returned to Britain about 555, after which the second Saxon revolt destroyed the remnants of the British warlords, so that the Saxon position was being consolidated on the upper Thames between 556 and 593. In 577 Cuthwaine son of Ceawlin captured Gloucester, Cirencester and Bath. The same year had seen the defeat of three British kings, Conmail, Condidan and Caranmael, at the battle of Deorham in Gloucester. Now the Britons were further cut off from each other by Saxon invaders in the Severn estuary, separating the Britons in the south west from those including Teilo to the north of the Bristol Channel.

THE BRITISH FORCES AND THEIR BARDS. In spite of these several losses the British court poets were celebrating the heroes of various campaigns,one of the most famous court poets being Taliesin, who was educated at St Illtud's school in south Glamorgan, a school fellow therefore of Maelgwn Gwynedd. Taliesin still managed to encourage and support, finding causes for celebration in battle triumphs, being known as the poet of Urien Rheged, to whom he came from service with Cynan, son of Brochmail Ystragoth (Ysgithrawg) of Powys,from the adjacent land where Cynan's sister, Sannan, was married to Maelgwn Gwynedd. When Maelgwn died of the in 552, Taliesin had gravitated to Cynan's court. It was against a background of continuing Saxon incursions that Teilo was working until his death and, as the fighting continued, it must have been abundantly clear that the British were sooner or later to lose their country. Although head of the British church, Teilo could not pre-empt this final outcome; he simply had to live a day at a time. There were many major tasks such as the rebuilding of the waste land devastated by war and the yellow pestilence, rehabilitating all those who had spent over seven years in Brittany; these were now returning with young families who had never known Wales and trying to find lost relatives. Family tragedies abounded. A young family might go to the area from which they had fled, only to find no trace or memory of the old folk, crops abandoned for many years and animals dead of the pestilence; only the wind remained to groan over this wasteland. People found great solace for their trials when they listened to the songs of the bards. If Teilo had weaknesses this was one of them; he loved the poetic genius of his countrymen and music too had always been important to him; in the old days as he walked about the hills to deliver his Gospel message, travelling on foot with only his staff for support, he would spend an inordinate amount of time composing his own tunes to the psalms. When he came to a settlement he would ring his bell, Bangu (pronounced Bangy), to let the people know of his approach and they would come out to hear what he had to say. Thus he, Dewi and Padarn came to be remembered in the Triads of Britain as 'the three benignant guests of the Isle of Britain'; they were so called because they went as guests into the houses of the nobles, the peasents, the native and the bondman, without accepting either gift or reward, food or drink; they taught the faith in Christ to all without pay or thanks, and to the poor and destitute they gave of their gold and their silver, their clothes and their provisions.

Music was not formally composed in these days; Pope Gregory the Great (540-604) was to be the great reformer of Church music in the Roman Church, but the Welsh were even then recognised for their ability at harmony and the singing of the monks made cheerful accompaniment in their travels. One can imagine Teilo crossing the countryside with Ystyffan and Gwihir! Ystyffan (Stephen) with his bubbling personality was only too happy to be in their company, taking the good news of Christ from place to place. His enthusiasm was almost electric; his church high on the mountainside in Powys still looks across a magnificent valley to the mountains on

173

the other side, mountains echoing to his singing, accompanied by the small eight-stringed harp or crwth, which he carried tied to his girdle. These Celtic chants, both sacred and secular, were also passed on by oral tradition. It was Strabo who wrote 'The bards are singers and poets, interpreters of sacrifice and natural philosophers', for they were well known to the ancient Greeks and Romans. Most of the local kings and chieftains throughout Britain kept household bards, who were rewarded by gifts for playing their elegies and reciting their proverbs and sagas, while the monasteries in later times also maintained bards as historians and genealogists to record their great events. Once more Teilo set out tirelessly on his journeys up and down the countryside, accompanied now by Fidelis and joined by these two monks, Ystyffan and Gwihir, who lightened his journeys at this time with their gifts which Teilo so much enjoyed - and so they went, singing and praising God. Being a dreamy poet, quiet and gentle, Gwihir's melodies would soothe the brothers as they sat round a fire at night,tired after a day's work, while Ystyffan in contrast was very much a live wire; there was never a dull moment when he was around. While Gwihir was to found Llysfaen in Glamorganshire, Ystyffan was founding a church on the coast at the mouth of the Tywi river at Llanstephan, near the spot where wild fowl breed in Teilo's adjoining parish of Llandeilo recalls Ystyffan and appropriately adjoins Teilo's foundation at Llandeilo Graban, both perched on adjacent steep hills on the river Wye, close to the border country. The monks trudged together across the countryside of Wales in all weather, holding their cloaks close against rain and storm, daunted neither by weather nor terrain, still finding the energy to establish a settlement for Christ on the side of the mountain and on the Saxon border.

There is a tale told in the Book of Llandaff how King Iddon was fighting the Saxons nearby, when they came to plunder his country. At that time Teilo was with his monks at Llanarth (between the Wye and the Usk). King Iddon came and begged him to pray for urgent help. Teilo went out with him to a mountain in the middle of Cressenic, near the river Trothy, and they stood there praying to Almighty God for help for their plundered people; 'and his prayer was heard, and a great victory was obtained - the enemy being put to flight and the plunder being taken from them; the King returned and granted three modii of land about that mount to St Teilo and the church, Llandeilo Cressenny, with all its inhabitants, in field and in woods, in water and in pastures'. Teilo, archbishop in all but name, was the architect of the movement in the Celtic church at this time, while the work of Gildas and Cadoc in Ireland would have been the result of discussion and planning between the saints. Teilo outlived both Gildas and Cadoc and his last days were spent in his monastery at Llandeilo Fawr, which was to become one of the biggest and most important in all Wales. Here was that valuable scriptorium for production of manuscripts by his devoted scribes; from here, too, was Teilo able to oversee the work of the Welsh church to the end. Teilo was a strong personality; it was said of him that 'such grace was upon him that from his youth he was able to unravel the mysteries of the Holy Scriptures better than any teacher could instruct him; he was set on fire by the love of learning, active and popular with kings and common people alike'. This is not to dismiss the fact that he had strong human feelings in all those ways common to man; he could be as angry as the next in situations of injustice and cruelty; he understood well how people felt when they came with their personal troubles; in fact this is just what had made him such a valuable priest. Teilo himself had that very special calling to devote his whole life to the service of God. The cost to him personally, may well have been great. Many years before his death Cadoc asked him, 'What is the greatest wisdom in man?'; his reply, *To refrain from injuring another when one has the power so to do'*.

Towards the end, the seven watermen whom Teilo had rescued as babies from drowning left their monastery of Mathri in order to minister to their beloved master in his old age, and so surrounded by many friends, Teilo died peacefully at Llandeilo Fawr. 'A city set upon a hill cannot be hid' epitomises our monastic city set on that hill in the middle of Demetia which has now withstood fourteen hundred years of fortune and decline, since it was founded and blessed by Saint Teilo, who sent hundreds of holy men out from here to cross and recross Wales to dedicate the land and people to the service and love of God. Surely one cannot pass a field, lift a stone, or follow a road in this area, which has not been blessed and offered for God's

175

service. The breath of the field, the pulse in the air, all that lives and breathes were once dedicated to God, for the spread of his Kingdom in Wales and beyond - and it was founded by Saint Teilo.

PORTRAIT OF SAINT LUKE
(PAGE 218 OF THE LICHFIELD GOSPELS)

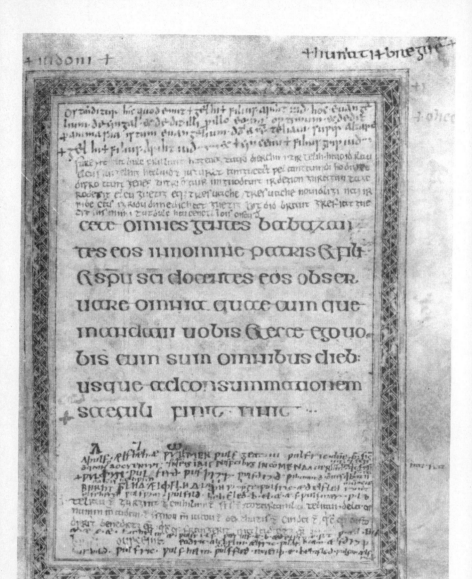

Final verse of SAINT MATTHEW'S gospel
(PAGE 141 OF THE LICHFIELD GOSPELS, WRITTEN
ABOUT 720-730 AD, WITH A NUMBER OF ADDITIONS
ENTERED ON THE SPACE OF THE ORIGINAL PAGE)

Appendix (i)
A Detective Story

'THE BOOK'

The Gospel Book variously known as 'THE LICHFIELD GOSPELS' 'THE BOOK OF ST CHAD' or 'THE GOSPEL BOOK OF ST TEILO'.

(During the following enquiry, we will need to mention another book, known as 'The Book of Llandaff' also known as 'the Liber Landavensis' which is in Llandaff Cathedral and includes a 'Life of St Teilo').

The two friends at Lichfield Cathedral had explored every available written source and other evidence from archaeology, to discover what they could about the life of St Teilo. The result of their researches had thereby become a synthesis of all they could glean from local folklore, history and the like; so little had in fact actually come down to posterity, that it seemed to them that vital information about this man, who had played such a leading part in his country during the sixth century but about whom so little was recorded, must have been deliberately suppressed.

Not content therefore with what they had already discovered, they decided to play detective once again and see if they could trace the course of the subsequent downfall of Wales. How was it that the one book which refers to Teilo, the Book of Llandaff or 'Liber Landavensis', was now at Llandaff? How could it also be that the other book - the Lichfield Gospel Book - the main subject of our enquiry, which lay on the altar at Llandeilo Fawr, making fullest mention in the margins of so many places around Llandeilo Fawr and in Welsh, was now at Lichfield Cathedral and being called the 'Chad' or the 'Lichfield Gospels'! That was what they wanted to know.

The older man thought long and hard and resumed: "It is clear to me that there is an enormous background of detail to be unravelled, before we can come up with any sensible answer to these questions.

There appear to be only three major strands, all taking place after the death of our saint, Teilo, - the first is the schism of the church in Wales from the church of Rome for a further 168 years after the rest of Britain had accepted Augustine's suggestions for bringing them back into the Roman fold; this resulted from the first bungled Conference near the Severn estuary in 601 and the second (equally indecisive as regards the Welsh churches) at Bangor-on-Dee (Chester) in 603. I intend to research the background to this aspect.

The second strand is concerned with the many battles and massacres, which followed - especially those in 615 and 616, but with those long, revengeful memories on both sides these were to last at least one hundred years. I would be grateful if you could address yourself to that strand in our research and any relevant political aspects, as regards Wales, Wessex and Mercia for the 400 years following Teilo's death.

I will also attempt to put together the third strand, namely, the religious pattern and change, which are relevant to the final destiny of the two 'Books' - not just of Rome and the Welsh Bishops, that is, but over the centuries between Llandeilo, Llandaff, Lichfield and Canterbury."

When they met next, the two friends compared notes.

"Right", said the old man, "I now have the detail behind the failure of the Pope's legate, St Augustine, in his attempts to bring the Welsh back to Papal suzerainty. Firstly he was clearly both high-handed and aloof _ lacking in the eyes of our Welsh bishops in both love and respect. Although as Gildas relates there were no doctrinal differences, there were four comparatively minor aspects of practice which they refused to change, viz: -

a) From the old Easter date, appointed by Pope Leo the Great and adopted by the British church in 453, i.e. from the Jewish/Orthodox date for Easter to the new Roman date.

b) From the long-accepted Eastern Orthodox tonsure for monks to the new shaving of the corona of the head, as adopted by Rome in 520.

c) From single to triple immersion at baptism, signifying further emphasis on the Trinity, and

d) From the long-accepted Celtic prostrate position of prayer to the new Roman kneeling posture.

It was all so futile, but Augustine further exacerbated the position by failing to understand the well-developed identity and spirituality of the British/Celtic church (since the Roman departure from Britain 200 years before), as exemplified by their zeal and fervent ideals. It was Rome who had changed her practices; Britain had maintained the traditional ways. This was to lead also to considerable suspicion that it was the Roman church which destroyed the great relics and documents of the early church - at Glastonbury.

On top of all this Augustine's criticism (and later Bede's) that they had failed to evangelise their pagan conquerors, now their Saxon neighbours, was considered to be outrageous, because in fact it was in large part untrue.

The net result of Augustine's efforts was therefore the reverse of his intent, resistance to change by the British church and the Celtic church in particular. Although King Edwin of Northumbria was to give a foothold for the Roman church at Bangor-on-Dee and his grandson King Oswy (married to Urien's great-granddaughter Rhianfellt) was to accept the Roman church at the Synod of Whitby in 664, it was to be a further 102 years before Bishop Elfodd of Gwynedd was to agree to Easter dating and the Pope as 'supremo'(768 AD). This extra resistance by the Welsh is clearly very relevant to the loss of 'the Books' from their territory".

"That's very interesting", replied the younger man at last, "for I have some specific and fascinating acts of massacre and revenge to add to it. In 615 St Augustine, furious with his failure with the British Christians generally, reaped a terrible harvest at the battle of Chester _ it was here that Selyf (Solomon) ap Cynan, the great Welsh Brochmail Ystragoth's descendant, was killed defending his territory of Powys and the valley of the Dee. But worse than this, the Saxon king Aethelfrith only three days later, tragically considering that a concourse of several thousand monks at prayer after fasting was an act of war, slaughtered 1200 of them in cold blood.

I then began to read Llywarch Hen's 'Elegy of Cynddylan' (written about 852 perhaps at Llandeilo Fawr by the monks there), which speaks of Welsh memory of that event and their revenge at Lichfield the year after in another monks' massacre (616), when the Welsh (led by Cynddylan himself) sacked the monastery, killing the monks there.

Thus a ghastly pattern of continual retaliation for several centuries was begun, including the killing of Cynddylan and his brother by the Mercians in 660, as the two brothers attempted to defend their home at Pengwern (Wroxeter) and the river Tern. There were many revenge raids by the Welsh also into Mercia during the reign of King Ethelbald and his successor Offa (757-796), who as we know was to build his dyke from about 760 onwards from Prestatyn to Chepstow, no less than 168 miles in all.

The special relevance of this is that Offa was to become the English 'supremo', promoting for all he was worth the importance of Lichfield _ as against Canterbury, which was in hostile territory and had reverted in large part to paganism. It is an extraordinary fact, not well known even today, that Lichfield became an archbishopric for twenty years and with the Archbishop of Canterbury in exile from 796-802, represented the Church of England in dealings with Rome (as much because of misrepresentation to Rome perhaps)".

"You have done well", returned the old man, "for much of what you are saying fits the pattern of my researches also, which concerns the role of Chad in our misnamed 'Gospels of Chad' _ in the context of the rise and fall of Llandeilo Fawr, Llantwit Major or Llandaff, and Lichfield.

It is noteworthy that the first half of the 7th century is much concerned with the division and separation of the Welsh from each other by the Saxon advances _ but especially the Welsh in Cornwall (at that time called 'Little Wales') from the Welsh mainland _ the maxim 'divide and rule' was already proving successful.

But it is Oswald, the son of this same Edwin that you mention, whom I find interesting, for he was trained in Iona and asked in 635 (even before that acceptance of Rome by the British at Whitby in 664) for a priest to be sent to him. It is Aidan who is sent and arrives in Lindisfarne, where great illuminated Gospels are to be produced before the end of this 7th century. And who do you think is being trained there? Our friend Chad of course! Now it is Chad who finishes as Bishop of Mercia, dying of the plague in 672, and his successor, Bishop Hedda, is to build a Saxon church to hold Chad's tomb and a further thirty-three churches dedicated to him.

Thus just at the time these Gospels are being written and illuminated in Lindisfarne and Llandeilo, Welsh power is being drastically diminished and we find Lichfield a decade later in the ascendant through the influence of the Saxon Kings and Chad himself".

"Absolutely", burst in the younger man, " and that fits perfectly with more that I have found. Lichfield grows and Llandeilo Fawr diminishes until King Maredudd of Dyfed 'one day in a fit of passion slew a man of St Teilo, in the Saint's refuge, before the altar' (according to the Book of Llandaff - 'Liber Landevensis' , in the section under 'The Life of St Teilo') and, if I may make an outline of the penance which follows, 'Gave to Llandeilo Fawr the properties of Llanegwad, Telichcloaman and Trefcannus with church, fish, water, woods etc, free of all regal service and with complete commonage for the inhabitants for ever' _ these are the last donations (about 780) to Llandeilo Fawr; henceforth Llandaff was to supercede Llandeilo almost completely and even King Maredudd himself was to be slain (again according to the Book of Llandaff) by Offa in his last attack".

"We make good progress", responded the unusually excited elder man; "there is a marginal note of the same period in the Gospel Book of Teilo here in Lichfield, which states, 'The boundaries at Loughor in the parish of Llandybie now belong to Llandaff _ that is in 800, when the Danes are beginning their attack on the coastal monasteries. It is only fourteen years later (814) that the last male line of Aircol Lawhir becomes extinct and four more years (818) before the last powerful Saxon King of Mercia, Cenwulf, dies _ and the Danes pour in to Mercia! We do not have long to wait before Bishop Nobis takes

181

over (840) at Llandeilo Fawr for thirty three years, until that is 873 _
and he is to make the last Welsh inscription in this Gospel Book of
Teilo".

"So true", countered the younger " and only one year after the famous
Rhodri Mawr became King of most of Wales (except Brycheiniog,
Dyfed, Gwent and Morgannwg) for those short five years, before it
was once again sub-divided (877) between his heirs and successors.

It strikes me more and more all the time", he continued, "What a
welter of internal feuding there was amongst the Welsh themselves
during these few centuries. It was a continual to-ing and fro-ing _
even those few county names that appear so regularly on the map like
Brycheiniog, Ceredigion, Morgannwg, Rheinwg, and Seisyllwg
represent the petty princedoms of a past age of such as Brychan,
Ceredig, Morgan, Rhein and Seisyll - and remember that Llandeilo
Fawr was included in Seisyllwg (Ceredigion). It is so rare in Welsh
history to attain the greatness of Deheubarth - or return to the great
federation of Dyfed or Powys, which existed long before this era".

"Be that as it may", retorted the elder, somewhat irritated by this
youth's presumption of his (and others') ignorance, "we now come to
another very relevant period as regards our expose of the truth. That
is the role of a relative of this Bishop Nobis of Llandeilo Fawr,
namely Asser, who was to become even more powerful, in turn as
Abbot of St David's, Bishop of Sherborne and then 'Archbishop of the
Island of Britain' _ but above all as King Alfred's teacher, courtier,
and adviser (indeed Alfred became literate because of Asser) from
880 until 910. Hywel Dda, Rhodri's grandson, was to be ruler of
much of Wales and to have great deal of contact with Asser in his
youth, which stood him in good stead when he later dealt with the
Witanagemot (or English 'parliament'); it was he who would have to
pay homage to the Mercian King, Athelstan".

"And if we look more closely at the meaning of 'homage' in this
period, the key to the puzzle becomes quite apparent", was the
haughty response of the younger sleuth. "Guess, for instance, who
pays the ransom in 915 for Bishop Cyfeiliawg of Llandaff, after he is
captured by the Vikings, Otar and Harold? No other than King
Edward, Alfred's son. Notwithstanding this, a year later in 916, we

hear of the murder of a Mercian Abbot by the Welsh - this was punished by an expedition, which captured the wife of the King of Brycheiniog at Llangorse lake.

But all this protection eventually means submission and so we find even heavier tributes soon demanded from the Welsh by this Athelstan, Edward's son. This is confirmed by that telltale comment about British dominance of the Welsh in 'those from Gwynedd and Dyfed and from the lands between Merioneth and Gower became his men'!

It is then that we find the punchlines (in Melville Richards' article in the NLW Journal XVIII on 'The Lichfield Gospels - Book of St Chad'), Athelstan 'received gifts from all over Europe, gave richly in return and especially to his followers, bishops and churches in his own land. He particularly loved to give precious books to his monasteries' - one being given to Canterbury, for example, from the Bishop of Armagh. But it is not until 1027 that comparative peace returns to south Wales with new, fixed boundaries and secular cantrefs and the re-establishment of Deheubarth".

"But", said the venerable investigator, "it is sixty years before this that we find the first name of a Lichfield Bishop inscribed on page one of 'our' Gospel Book, that is, Bishop Wynsi (963-4). The 'Gospel Book of Teilo' from Llandeilo Fawr has now truly been labelled 'the Lichfield Gospels' in 963.

'On May the 28th 934, at Winchester", writes Melville Richards, "Hywel's name along with that of Tewdwr ap Elisedd of Brycheiniog is found on a charter at the Witanagemot. First come Athelstan's name , followed by that of the Archbishops of Canterbury and York, then Hywel's followed by this Tewdwr and the Bishop of Lichfield'.

In short", said the old man, "of all the many arguments as to the exact time and place I put my money on Melville Richards, when he suggests in his article that Hywel Dda and Tewdwr, travelling from Llandeilo Fawr through Tewdwr's territory , brought the Gospel Book from Llandeilo Fawr and in the presence of Athelstan, handed it over to Aelfwine, Bishop of Lichfield, at Winchester".

(Author's note: Having now ascertained why the Book has found its way to Lichfield, fascinated by the magnificence of the Book, the men went to examine it in more detail).

The young man opened the conversation; "It is now quite clear that THE SCRIPTORIUM AT LLANDEILO FAWR PRODUCED MUCH EXCELLENT WORK UNTIL ABOUT THE YEAR 720, WHEN A SPECIAL ALTAR BOOK WAS PRODUCED WHICH OUTSHONE ALL OTHER WORK IN THE MONASTERY".

"Yes", replied the other, "for it must have taken much laborious and painstaking design and planning before it was finally produced; everyone in the district must have known about it, apart from the monk who had spent so many years of his life working on it. The design of the pages is exquisite. The text was based on St Jerome's version of the Bible, the Vulgate, but with differences, for it was Celtic and closely resembles the Breton Gospels of St Gatien of Tours; it is similar too to the Irish and also to work produced at Iona and Lindisfarne.

Although we know that the Lindisfarne Gospels were written a little earlier (in 698), the Lichfield Gospels are refreshingly original, being earlier than the Book of Kells; they are dated by most authorities to the early 700s, probably around 720. They are entirely written by the one scribe - except perhaps one line at the end of which the monk puts in a different flourish! One can only speculate as to what caused the monk to deviate from his usual writing on that day, for in the rest of his work the scribe wrote in a perfect, even hand with meticulous care, in a style known as insular majuscule, only used in special de luxe editions, not for ordinary use but ceremonial occasions - otherwise kept in a safe place by the altar".

The young man was examining the illustrations as he interrupted, "The artist was equally sophisticated, showing that he not only knew the work of Lindisfarne, but also had the capacity to understand the design of icons of Mediterranean Coptic and Byzantine origin, both in the design around the borders and more generally in the whole concept of the artistry; it has a fine geometric quality; it is reflected also in the page depicting St Luke with his crossed staff, itself very similar to Egyptian design; on the other hand it could be argued that this design was already current elsewhere, in that the border closely resembles the design down the side of the later cross-shaft of Abbot Samson at Llantwit Major".

"Look at this page", said the old man. "Here again it is like a memorial stone in the churchyard of Llandeilo Fawr, which may be dated to the ninth or early tenth century; one can find there another cross very similar to the one on the carpet page, while the monogrammed letters at the beginning of each gospel resemble Irish-Saxon work at their finest.

As for the paint itself the colours are wonderful (such as the light blue on the first page of Matthew's Gospel) and elsewhere a magnificent variety of soft reds and pink, indigo, purple and ultramarine, gold, primrose yellow and white. Unfortunately, the mixing was not expert and has badly flaked. See, there are three types of design of special interest; the first is the use of those little red dots, a Coptic device; the second", as he turned the pages, "here this animal ornament (again borrowed from Mediterranean art) showing interwoven legs and necks of birds, pelicans perhaps, in an intricately conceived, exquisite carpet page; overall a fantastic design around a cross. It resembles Lindisfarne work, especially those designs on the initial pages. Byzantine art is the third type", he continued, turning a few more pages, "here it is represented by further interlacing design, especially on these borders. And alongside the Celtic motifs and abstract designs (some of which you can see are the same as those on Celtic High crosses of the eighth and ninth centuries) we find not only Hiberno-Saxon whorls and fretwork, but also the Greek key pattern.

Again note that the style is also 'insular half-uncial', there being a gradual change to this style from the Roman after the sixth century. The monk who produced the artistry of this book was clearly a man of wide learning, who yet put much of his own originality into it; there are animals and birds in great animation with bulging eyes, contorted bodies and other unusual features. It is certainly true that a luxury article of this calibre could only be produced in a major monastery for a major monastery and would only be used on those rare ceremonial occasions - its existence in Llandeilo Fawr therefore probably only being known to a favoured few".

Now there was no stopping the young man's interest; but he still wanted to get the perspective right and so he interjected - "It seems then that the church in Wales was now standing alone, since Ireland, Scotland, Iona, Devon and Cornwall had all decided to fall in with the Easter dates of Rome. Only Wales had yet to agree to give up her ancient religious rites, so that, at the time this Gospel Book was produced, Wales was essentially going it alone, on her own as regards these rites certainly; all this time she was fighting continually on both her coasts and her borders with Mercia, perpetually it would seem trying to defend her identity and what was left of her country from every quarter. Surely it could be said that this was a strangely unsettled and dangerous period in which to produce such a work of art at Llandeilo Fawr, don't you think? - Even in the vale of Tywi itself we have seen the tension broken with raids by Seisyll, King of Ceredigion, on its western border; look what it says: KING SEISYLL ATTACKED DYFED AND DYNEVOR ABOUT 730 THUS CHANGING THE AREA FOR EVER (Dynevor is adjacent to Llandeilo).

It could have been during this unsettled period around 750 THAT THE GOSPEL BOOK WAS SOMEHOW FOUND TO BE MISSING DURING THE TURMOIL?"

It was the old man's turn now to bring them back now to the Book itself. "The first marginal note in the Gospel Book, misleadingly called 'Chad 1' states in Welsh:

'IT IS SHOWN HERE THAT GEHLI, THE SON OF ARHITIUD, BOUGHT THIS GOSPEL BOOK FROM CINGAL, AND GAVE HIM FOR IT HIS BEST HORSE; AND THAT FOR THE BENEFIT OF HIS SOUL HE OFFERED THIS GOSPEL TO GOD, AND ON THE ALTAR OF TEILO. - Gehli son of Arhituid- Cincenn son of Gripiud' ".

"So that some time during the second part of the eighth century the book had already left the church, was found and bought back again for the Altar of Teilo", interrupted the young man.

"Yes, that is so", said his old friend pointing to the notes written in the margin of the Gospel Book. "This is the first of six marginal notes in Welsh which were copied into the Gospel Book from other sources already in the monastery. Chad 1 is early ninth century.

'CHAD 2' was a copy of Teilo's witness and signature, referring to Caio, eleven miles north of Llandeilo Fawr. Probably this entry is early tenth century.

'CHAD 3 and 4' mention Trewyddog in the parish of Llan-crys fourteen miles to the north. Chad 3-5 are late ninth century.

'CHAD 5' is earlier than 840 written at Llandeilo Fawr by a professional scribe. It states that the four sons of Bleddri have given freedom to Bleiddud son of Julian and his seed for ever - but for a price, four pounds and eight ounces (of silver presumably). There were lay witnesses and clergy of Nobis, bishop of St Teilo.

'CHAD 6' mentions Llandybie six miles to the south". This is written by a less skilled hand. (These are the findings of Morfyd Owen and Dafyd Jenkins, on the Welsh Marginalia.)

The friends tried to trace on the map the places mentioned by the marginal notes. "It is interesting", the old man smiled, " to see how these places are all near Llandeilo Fawr and have nothing whatever to do with Lichfield. These land grants were made to the monastery at Llandeilo from Teilo's time onwards and show that there was a legal system behind them in the sixth century. These grants were copied into the margins in the more modern wording of the 8th and 9th centuries".

The old man was delighted with their findings and chuckled to himself as he sat back in his chair - "So late in the 9th century the active cult of Nobis, the Abbot/Bishop of Teilo, shows that the monastery was very much a thriving concern at Llandeilo Fawr".

"And here is the first inscription from its new home in Lichfield, Bishop Wynsi himself, Bishop of Lichfield 974-992. Well of course this isn't yet the end of the story, is it?" the other interjected, "for although we have the Book in the Cathedral records here in Lichfield, it seems that originally there were two Books here and somehow or other the four Gospels must have been complete once and then disappeared".

"I wonder" mused the old man "do you suppose that the missing part - some 200 pages! - became detached during the Civil War. It is known that the Duchess of Somerset looked after it and had the wooden chest made for it which she called 'the Ark', restoring it to the Cathedral in 1673".

"Perhaps they will never again be seen", replied the other," but I would like to think that now it has found a resting place with this great Cathedral showing it in controlled temperature and lighting, it may be safely handed down to posterity".

"May I tell you my vision?", mused the old man, "It is of the Christian churches working together. No more silly arguments over material treasures, but mutual help towards the oneness of Christendom, that 'The Kingdoms of this world may become the Kingdom of God and of His Christ'. A truly Celtic vision seen by those saints since the beginning of our era wholeheartedly fought for by Saint Teilo, that we may all be one and yet with our individual visions and contributions all building the City of God on earth".

"Who was this Bishop Nobis, then"? the young man enquired.

"Well here is his name in the margin, a margin which is in fact the beginnings for us of recorded history; for he was an uncle of the famous Bishop Asser of St David's at Menevia, who played such a crucial part at King Alfred's court and was himself something of an historian. But lets leave such minutiae and get back to our detective work, uprooting all we can of this Welsh/Mercian relationship. The ninth century saw the last mention of the Gospel Book at Llandeilo Fawr and in 814 the male line of Aircol Lawhir became extinct. Similarly after ravaging west Wales in 818, Cenwulf the last powerful Saxon King of Mercia died and the Danes poured into Mercia."

"So", burst in the young man, "Wales can get on with her own affairs for a bit! - and Ceredigion again rules the area which has formed Seisyllwg in Ystrad Tywi, until their King (of Ceredigion) Gwgon ap Meurig is drowned in 872; on his death Rhodri Mawr of North Wales succeeds to the southern throne in the usual way, by marrying

Gwgon's sister Angharad. Rhodri Mawr (Roderic the Great) has become King of Gwynedd in 844 on the death of his father: in 855 he inherits the kingdom of Powys from his uncle and in 872, the year after Alfred came to the throne of Wessex, he becomes ruler of Seisyllwg, his wife's property in her own right. He is now therefore king of most of Wales except Morgannwg, Gwent, Brycheiniog and Dyfed".

The old man took over, "Sadly Wales can never be settled for long, since at this time the rules of Welsh inheritance state that all sons inherit their father's property in equal measure so that Wales never develops centrally as a strong nation. Thus on Rhodri's death in 877, just five years after Wales has achieved partial unity, it is partitioned once again: he wasn't as prolific as some but he left six sons, the three eldest being Anarawd who took Gwynedd to the north, Cadell who was to rule his southern kingdom, Seisyllwg which included Ceredigion and Ystrad Tywi, leaving Mervyn with Powys in the middle. For each of these sons he built a palace and for Cadell this was to be in Dinevor , a less prominent spot than the former one on Argol; this Cadell was to live in fact both at Dinevor and in Ceridigion.

So there is a shift in the location of power in Southern Wales; Carmarthen, from the Dark gate in the town eastwards, was in Cadell's area; to the west of the Dark gate was the boundary with Dyfed. Being a seaport it was also vulnerable to Viking attacks from the sea; so that Dinevor's position inland became the seat of power in political terms for the future rulers of Deheubarth. The position on the estuary of the abbey in Carmarthen must also have been vulnerable and a cause for concern to the church. St David's was ravaged by the Norsemen many times, when they carried off all the church valuables, leaving a trail of destruction wherever they went".

"This must have been a dreadful time for the Welsh, for the monasteries were their great mouthpiece and political driving force, as well as their cultural centre; although some Norsemen settled, they were but few and in the main, it seems, coastal areas of Dyfed and the south-west, leaving names like Swansea and Caldey island, which at this time, I note, lost its old name of Ynis Pyr or Pyr's island after

Aircol's father, Pyr 'Tryphun'. In these few places they established trading posts, but more often they came to ravage Ceredigion and Ystrad Tywi, as in 895 when even Anarawd of Gwynedd came with an English raiding party and, a little later in 915 when Otar and Harold rounded Land's End, entered the Severn and even captured Cyfeiliawg, bishop of Llandaff.

I was also reading how the Norsemen, Vikings or Danes as they are variously called started their attacks on these coasts in 787, beginning by raiding the monasteries of their plate and valuables. By Alfred's time however they had settled in much of England, although as King of Wessex he had no intention of giving way as the King of Mercia had done. By their destruction of many monasteries and their capturing or killing of the monks, the Danes had torn the heart out of England; all that had been treasured and imparted by the monks was now being destroyed".

"Right again", agreed the old man, "the monasteries were absolutely essential to continuity of learning amongst other things, indeed England was even worse than Wales in this respect. So that the English King of the time, Alfred, had to begin his campaign to restore these seats of learning and to build up a literate and Christian country in England once more. He therefore turned to Asser of St David's for help, for not only were the remaining Welsh monasteries still continuing their traditions, but also the court at Gwynedd in Rhodri Mawr's time was, like Offa's earlier, renowned for its continental contacts; Rhodri's father was in touch with Charles the Bald of Burgundy, the son of Charlemagne, while Latin and Greek were known in the court of Gwynedd itself, an important aspect since Alfred was calling on scholars from abroad to his court also, prepared indeed to pay well for their information.

Asser, Abbot of St Davids, was to become King Alfred's biographer and deserves a few special words in our research, if not also because of some similarity to Teilo. He was a man of great learning, spending much of his time at the court of this English King Alfred, who came to value his learning and friendship; indeed a special relationship had begun between several leading princes in Wales and the English King at this time. King Alfred like his brothers was still illiterate at the age of twelve, when his mother arranged for him to learn to read. Asser taught the King Latin and did much translation for him. Alfred also saw to it that the law was amended and studied; he brought Mercian and Anglo-Saxon laws up to date and ensured that they were applied. It seems that he saved the Anglo-Saxon language by his demands for scholarship at this time and founded Oxford University. He even studied naval warfare, built up town walls and sectioned the country into shires; in fact his rule in every sphere set England on a new course, in spite of the fact that there was almost continuous war with the Danes throughout his reign, both on land and at sea".

The young man now returned to the fray bringing the conversation back to the Gospel Book - "|I Asser, 'Archbishop of the island of Britain', died in 910, a year or two after Rhodri Mawr's grandson, Howel the Good or Hywel Dda came to the throne of Ceredigion and Ystrad Tywi. Asser was a relation of Bishop Nobis of Llandeilo Fawr, whose name is inscribed in the Gospel Book at Llandeilo Fawr where he was Abbot/Bishop from 840 until 873. After this there is no further inscription in the Gospel Book until the name of Bishop Wynsi of Lichfield in 963-4, is inscribed on page one"

But the old man was not to be so easily deterred from his learned discourse. "After his call to Alfred's court in 884, he decided to divide his time between St David's and the English court, but Alfred gave him responsibility for the Episcopal care of Devon and Cornwall, as well as making him Bishop of Sherborne. It is from Asser that we have officially recorded history in Wales for the first time, the last date in his biography of King Alfred being 887. If ever there was a time for Bede to turn in his grave it was now, when, far from writing off Anglo-Saxon civilisation, the Welsh Bishop did so much to revive learning and scholarship in England. His Celtic influence was to be particularly felt in the resuscitation of the English Christian Church".

Determined however to keep hold of the main subject, 'the Book', the young man again interjected - "It follows then that towards the end of the ninth century the Welsh monastery of St David's was in good order, with a long tradition of scholarship. Llandeilo Fawr was thriving too under the custody of Asser's relative, Bishop Nobis, until the latter's death in 873, this fact being recorded in "the Gospels". We know that one of the reasons that Asser agreed to come to the court of King Alfred for part of the year was his concern about the political situation in Dyfed under the king of the time, Hyfaidd, who died in 892 and who was always harrying St David's; we know that he agreed as much because of his concern for the well-being of St David's, which sure enough was destroyed in 907, two years before Asser's death. He made his decision after a long illness in Caerwent, whilst returning from a visit to Alfred's court".

The old man nodded in agreement. "There is no doubt", he said, "that Asser's contacts with both Wales and Wessex at this time brought new insights into both churches. He must have kept the churchmen informed on this Roman route through Morgannwg and Gwent, in much the same way as his predecessor Teilo would have done three hundred years previously. Asser as Abbot in Menevia soon learned in practice that as Bishop of Sherborne his status was much higher than Abbot. The diocesan system in England had overtaken the ancient monastic of Bishops and Abbots, who had been almost interchangeable. The monasteries on the coasts, now stripped of their treasures, were losing their monks who would be captured by the Danes and sold into slavery. But monastic power and boundaries were always fluctuating in this period along with the political boundaries, so that the position at any one time remains obscure, until the introduction of fixed boundaries which coincided with the secular cantrefs a century later about 1027".

"That takes us up almost to the time of the Norman conquest then", said the young man.

"Well", the old man replied, "Wales was certainly very unstable now, for the in-fighting in Wales between minor princes during the early part of Alfred's reign became so trying for everyone that on the death of Rhodri Mawr in 881 many Welsh princes went to Alfred seeking his protection. This was to rebound on Wales very seriously later when the English considered this to be Welsh submission to the English throne.

Rhodri's grandson, Hywel Dda, married Elen of Dyfed, where he ruled from 892 until his father Cadell's death about 909. Hywel must have been in close contact for nearly twenty years with Asser until the latter's death in 910. At his father Cadell's death, Hywel came to rule a much wider area of south west Wales, a reign which was to last until 949 bringing a much more settled and creative phase for Wales. By the end indeed he was to rule both north and south Wales, as did his grandfather Rhodri Mawr before him. Like Alfred, Hywel codified the Laws of his country, for which purpose he gathered together many responsible men to advise him. Three copies of the Laws were made, two being placed at Dinevor and Gwynedd, the third to travel with him.

Alfred died in 899 but his son Edward became very powerful, ruling all England and conquering the Danes, although they were to rise again in 909 and ravage English Mercia once more. King Ethelred of Mercia died in 911 and his wife, Edward's sister Ethelfleda, ruled as 'The Lady of the Mercians' for the next eight years, whilst Edward was regaining his ravaged land, particularly London and Oxford. He continued for several years to consolidate his position all over England, fighting back another Danish attack on the Severn from Brittany.

Meanwhile his sister was building a new fortress every year in Mercia, including the fortress at Bridgenorth in 912, which strategically blocked the Severn channel to invaders. In some parts of England of course the Danes had now been settled for at least a generation, making a treaty with King Alfred, others even accepting Christianity, but on the whole war continued as the general rule especially between the Welsh and the Mercians".

"Now look at the Welsh hotheadedness again! Wouldn't you think that they could let sleeping dogs lie when they were so obviously politically vulnerable", burst out the young man as he read - "In 916 the murder of a Mercian Abbot by the Welsh was punished by an expedition which captured the wife of the King of Brycheiniog by Llangorse Lake near Brecon". Two years later King Edward's sister Ethelflaed died at Tamworth, the seat of Mercian government, her daughter temporarily taking her place, although Edward was soon to carry her off to Wessex and take command himself. The poets' obsession with revenge for that first act of brutality by the Mercians was still in Welsh memory!"

"Absolutely right", the old man nodded; "That act at Llangorse lake did not help them one jot, for the English could no longer trust them and finally the Welsh kings made their submission to Edward, 'those from Gwynedd and Dyfed and from the lands between Merioneth and Gower became his men'; the truth is that in 918 Hywel Dda and his brother, with their cousin Idwal Foel, King of Gwynedd, went to pay homage to Edward, King of Wessex; it was no more than a goodwill mission, to establish a common front against the Danes, a loose federation, far from submission by the Welsh king; this misconception came to be resented deeply by many of his subjects, when it was so recorded by the English later. Edward had already shown Wales his friendship by paying the ransom for the bishop of Llandaff, when captured by Viking raiders, while King Alfred had protected them in the past from the hostility of the Mercians. Now that the Mercians had shown their allegiance to the King, the Welsh also sought his 'protection' but that is of course a very different story from 'submission'".

"Perhaps Hywel Dda, the good, was misconstrued as being weak?" the young man asked.

"No I cant accept that", said the old man. Although often to be seen at the English court, where new administrative units were being devised for the towns, Hywel was far-seeing and astute. On Edward's death in 924 his son Athelstan, already powerful in Mercia, succeeded him; he was also firm, the Welsh princes now having to pay heavy tribute to him; the loose agreement of earlier days had now become submission. In 927 in fact Hywel as leader of those Welsh kings formally submitted to Athelstan at Hereford, when the river Wye in Hereford made the boundary between Welsh and English territory. Hywel was also present at the Witanagemot or parliament of the English King on most occasions.

In many ways Hywel was a most enlightened King; by gathering six representatives from each district in Wales, he formed a consensus of opinion from leaders of the community; by pooling their knowledge of local law and regional custom, they were able to draw up the future laws of Wales. These Laws came to be set down in three stages, the first at Hywel's initiative in this period either at Whitland or nearby in Dyfed; the second came with the reforms of the twelfth century at Whitland; the third with the Act of Union, Henry the Eighth bringing the Welsh in line with English law. The more I have studied them the more I realise that Hywel's law was the most civilised and intelligent of its age, indeed in some respects of any age. It again consisted of three parts, the law of the court, the law of the land and the customs of both. Women were held in equal honour to men and allowed their own property, while victim/family compensation was given proper pride of place for injury or death; you will note that it is only today appearing in English law, befogged as it has been for so long and still is by theories of State restitution, punishment and deterrence; these are but two aspects of this early codification which had united all Wales under one common law. The importance of Hywel Dda may be reflected in the fact that he was the only Welsh King to mint coins as did the English.

After the death of his wife Elen in 928, Hywel went on pilgrimage to Rome. One can but wonder what discussions he had with the Pope on the state of the Welsh Church. He may well have been worried about the integrity and defence of the monasteries of Wales, just as Asser had been for St David's before him; no doubt in the early years of his reign in Dyfed he had had many a discussion with Asser on this subject. He could not have failed to notice the discontent in the monasteries with English dominance, discontent which continued to grow and fester, becoming eventually a major focus for nationalism.

Hywel the good was both wise and astute, but as regards the real aim of this discussion he was no match for the forceful Athelstan".

The young man was still not fully persuaded by his old friend and felt it high time to put what he believed to be the crucial part of the sorry story. "Old friend", he said, "I think we have now reached the crunch point, for wasn't this the great period of Mercia? Athelstan was ambitious to gather as many treasures for the great monastery there as he possibly could. I have just been reading the vital link in Melville Richard's article in the National Library of Wales Journal xviii - 'The Lichfield' Gospels(Book of St Chad). I quote - 'He received gifts from all over Europe, gave richly in return, and gave especially to his followers, to his bishops and to churches in his own land. He particularly loved to give precious books to his monasteries". 'To Canterbury Cathedral he gave a Gospel Book which had belonged to the Abbot of Armagh; and another Gospel Book which Athelstan had received from his brother-in-law, Otto the Great of Germany...' Now that we have at last filled in the mass of historical detail, this is what I believe actually happened.

On May 28th 934 at Winchester, Hywel's name along with that of Tewdwr ab Elisedd of Brycheiniog is found on a charter at the Witanagemot. First comes Athelstan's name, followed by that of the Archbishops of Canterbury and York, then Hywel's followed by this Tewdwr and the Bishop of Lichfield'. In short, of all the many arguments I put my money on Melville Richards when he suggests in his article that 'Hywel Dda and Tewdwr, travelling from Llandeilo Fawr through Tewdwr's territory, brought the Gospel Book from Llandeilo Fawr and at Winchester handed it, in the presence of Athelstan to Aelfwine, Bishop of Lichfield. So why all the mystery, why the need for all these shrouds of concealment thereafter?"

The old man mused for a while at his friends words. "It was no doubt with great rejoicing that it finally came to rest at Lichfield and thereafter became known as 'The Book of Saint Chad' after their own great Bishop.

Enormous pressure must have been put on Hywel for him to have entered that renowned monastery at Llandeilo Fawr and removed the precious Book from its place of safekeeping by the altar. The monks must have watched this act in great horror, unless it was done stealthily by night. Hywel, as king of the area, was the only person who had the power to do such a terrible thing; there is no doubt at all that the English must have worked on his gentleness of character for some considerable time for him to have given in. He knew that this act of betrayal of his countrymen would undermine their confidence in him and his prestige as no other act could have done.

The old man had been silent for some while, when his young friend again burst in to his reverie. "As if this was not enough", he said returning to the charter, "we still find three years later in 937 at Hereford, Athelstan demanding an enormous tribute to be paid annually by the Welsh to the English King. The demand is twenty pounds of gold, three hundred pounds of silver and 25,000 oxen together with an unspecified number of hounds and hawks. This must have looked to the Welsh like an impossible yearly tribute. Nor was this the end of it - from now on the border was to lie along the river Wye and not as before along the river Severn. St Beuno's prophecy had come true. The ancient centres of Ambrosius and Dubricius were now in English territory. And now the nadir was to be demanded. At his coronation in 973, King Edgar, the last of this royal line, made six lesser kings pay homage to him by rowing him from his palace on the Dee to St John's church Chester - and back again - while he held the rudder.

"Well, my young friend", the old man resumed, looking up, "now perhaps you can understand these monks and the Welsh poets and their desolation at the tragic loss of their Gospel Book? In 934, a prophetic poem was composed by a monk in the south in Deheubarth, quite possibly Llandeilo Fawr, which revealed the depth of hatred of the Welsh for the English and their immense desire to unite and shake off the English yoke through a truly Welsh king. The poem, 'Armes Prydein', was composed during this decade of the thirties when Hywel had returned from Rome and when he was spending a lot of time in the English court, observing their ways and learning from them, as did many other Welsh princes. Athelstan was abroad developing relations with continental courts for some of this time, but he still maintained a firm hold on English affairs moving around the country and issuing many charters".

"The poets clearly foresaw the loss of their Book", the young man agreed. "But it is astounding to see what a thorough job the Mercians made of disguising its origins for now we know that "The Gospel Book was renamed 'The Lichfield Gospels' or 'Gospels of St Chad' after their patron saint at Lichfield Cathedral. Bishop Wynsi whose name appears on page one of the Gospel Book, became Bishop of Lichfield in 963-4 and died in 973-5.|i Melville Richards suggests that when the Book came to Lichfield it delighted the monks there more than anything else could, for it paid off a very old score. That score of course was the one mentioned in that other Welsh poem, 'The Elegy to Cynddylan'; it is attributed to Meigant about 660; it refers to a cattle raid on Lichfield, which included fifteen hundred

cattle and five herds of swine, eighty stallions and their harness....
and the attack on the monastery there; this Welsh attack itself
avenged the earlier massacre of the monks in 616 in the time of
Penda's son in the 650s, when Penda himself was ambushed and
killed".

The old man concluded the tale. "My son, I am most grateful; you're
with me to the end. In 942, nearly ten years before his reign of over
thirty years came to its close, on the death of his cousin Idwal Foel,
Hywel showed his political strength and skill by seizing the throne of
Gwynedd, thus re-uniting all Wales again without bloodshed for
almost a decade until his death in 949. During his long reign
however several kings had ruled England. With Athelstan dead in
939, the Danish invasions had started again in earnest. After the
death of this extraordinary man, Hywel Dda, his son Owain ruled in
the south for nearly forty years, followed by Maredudd, Hywel's
grandson; this Maredudd was to regain Gwynedd for a short time
before his death in 999, while the King of Brycheiniog also
recognised his overlordship.

To summarise all that I have said then, this whole period was one of
Danish harassment, of petty princes ever subdividing the Principality
after short periods of unity, of literary and poetic achievement,
especially the development of civilisation through law, but above all
it was a time of growth of national identity and it is significant that
Maredudd was called 'the glorious king of the Britons' at his death -
Henry the Seventh, call him Tudor or Tewdwr, was indeed not so far
away. This growth in national identity can be said to start with that
great war cry from 'Armes Prydein Vawr' - it is still for many -

THE GREAT PROPHECY OF BRITAIN.

The muse foretells, they will hasten we shall have wealth and
property and peace, and wide dominion, and ready leaders and after
commotion, settlement in every place. Brave men in battle-tumult,
mighty warriors, swift in attack, very stubborn in defence. The
warriors will scatter the foreigners as far as Caer Weir -they will
rejoice after the devastation, and there will be reconciliation between

the Cymri and the men of Dublin, the men of Cornwall and of Strathclyde will be made welcome among us.

12 The Britons will rise again. When they prevail for long it was prophesied the time when they will come, as rulers whose possession is by right of descent. The Men of the North will be in the place of honour about them, they will advance in the centre of their van of battle.

127 The Cymru will survive to order battle, and they will assemble the people of many lands, they will raise on high the holy standard of Dewi to lead the Irish by means of a linen banner.

171 Wise men foretold all that will happen: they will possess all from Manaw to Brittany, from Dyfed to Thanet, it will be theirs from the Wall to the Forth, along their estuaries their dominion will spread.

178 May the Cymru rise up a fair company; hosts about the ale-feast and the noise of warriors, and God's princes who have kept their faith.

195 Let us beseech the Lord who made Heaven and Earth, May Dewi be the leader of our warriors In straits it is the heavenly fortress and my God who is leader: He will not die, He will not escape, He will not retreat, He will not fade, reject, nor waver, nor will He diminish

But now I must prevail on your charity to complete the picture at least to the Norman conquest for the sake of posterity, for nothing much changes in that period.

In 988 the Viking invasions all over the south coast of Wales resulted in St David's again being burnt four times in twenty years and its bishop Morgeneu being killed; it did not prevent the monasteries continuing however, for from 1000 AD Wales continued to produce scholars of the first rank. The family of Sulien the Wise, himself born in Llanbadarn, were renowned. He was educated in Wales, then Scotland for five years and Ireland for thirteen, before he returned to Llanbadarn as a great teacher. He educated his four sons himself, the eldest, Rhygyfarch born in 1056, being twice bishop of St David's, where he was to write the Latin 'Life of St David', five hundred years after St David himself had founded that monastery. Rhygyfarch's intention was to put forward the claims of St Davids as a metropolitan church of Wales, independent of Canterbury. He used 68 chapters of old manuscript, found mostly at St David's as the basis of his 'Life'. He wrote in 1090, his son Sulien being brought up by the monks of Llanbadarn Fawr monastery, which continued to flourish until the fifteenth century.

Politically of course there was to be turmoil whilst various pretenders fought for the throne of Deheubarth, as in 1018 against Llywelyn ap Seisyll who had married the daughter of Maredudd. And again on Llywelyn's death in 1023, when they fought Gruffydd ap Llywelyn at the battle of Abergwili. Then came Gruffydd ap Llywelyn of north Wales who once again wanted to unite all Wales. He plundered Llanbadarn Fawr, while having to fight two kings for Deheubarth, the one in 1039 a great grandson of Hywel Dda, called Gruffydd ap Rhydderch from Gwent and Morganwg; the other, another grandson of Hywel Dda, Hywel ap Edwin, whom he had to fight at Pencader and to kill at Abertywi in 1044. Finally the Carew cross commemorates this other Hywel's brother, Maredudd ab Edwin.

By 1055 Gruffydd ap Llewellyn ruled Deheubarth, Morganwg and Gwent. He was however more than a local hero; he came to own a powerful fleet of ships and, although for a short period he was to fight against Mercia in 1039 and later on the Severn at Rhyd y Groes and around Offa's Dyke, he was to obtain Mercian help to attack Ystrad Tywi. It was because of this growing Welsh power through alliances with Swengen and Mercia, that they were able to take on Edward the Confessor until Edward banished Swengen altogether. Indeed this Welsh/Mercian co-operation was to continue against Harold of Wessex, when Harold attacked Gruffydd in 1063; fortunately after Edward died however, Harold had to turn quickly to fight William of Normandy instead in 1066, the result of which battle at least every schoolboy and schoolgirl seems to know.

In fact small wars were continuous all over Wales when Gruffydd died, but Maredudd ab Owen ruled in Deheubarth and Caradoc ab Gruffydd in Morganwg when the Normans came.

Do you want to know something, old friend!", said the younger man, "if you didn't look so utterly worn out, I would ask you to start all over again - to delve into all those other conundrums we have but touched upon. But I don't think you would make it!"

The two friends at Lichfield did not do all this research in one day, it had taken them several weeks to find out the bare political facts.

"Get along with you, let's have something useful in return what is your conclusion? where do we go from here?" the old man retorted.

"How on earth can anyone form a conclusion?" the other replied anyone can make up a good story, but then where would that leave us! Let's let bygones be bygones! Let's leave it like that, and let the matter rest in peace now. Too many wars, angry words and bitter feelings have been aroused over the years. It is my firm belief that it is now a matter of the past, let Christian love and charity prevail, we want no more dark ages. The world is a much smaller place and there are many more Welsh outside Wales than within. Let them call it 'The Book of Chad', 'Lichfield Gospels', whatever they like. It will always be 'The Book of Teilo' to us.

The old man closed the book and nodded his head, "Let the past be the past." he said.

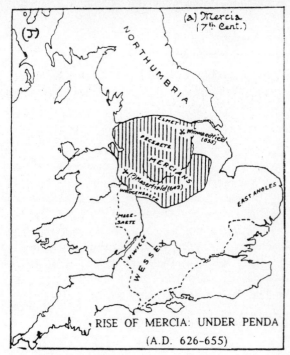

(a) Mercia
(7th Cent.)

NORTHUMBRIA

LINDSEY

PECSAETE

MERCIANS

✗ Winwaedfield (655)

✗ (?)Maserfield (642)

WROCENSAETE

EAST ANGLES

MAGE-SAETE

HWICCE

WESSEX

RISE OF MERCIA: UNDER PENDA

(A.D. 626–655)

(K)

NORTHUMBRIA

(b) Mercia
8th Cent.

MERCIA

OFFA'S DYKE

EAST ANGLES

HWICCE

Bensington (777)

KENT

WESSEX

SUSSEX

MERCIAN SUPREMACY UNDER OFFA

(8th Century)

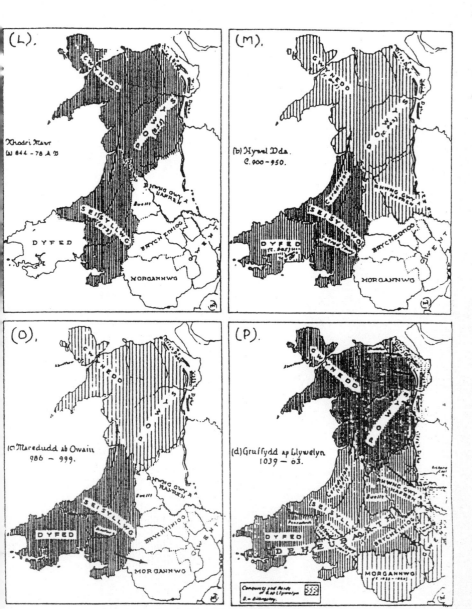

THE WELSH 'HEPTARCHY' (9th to 11th Centuries) :

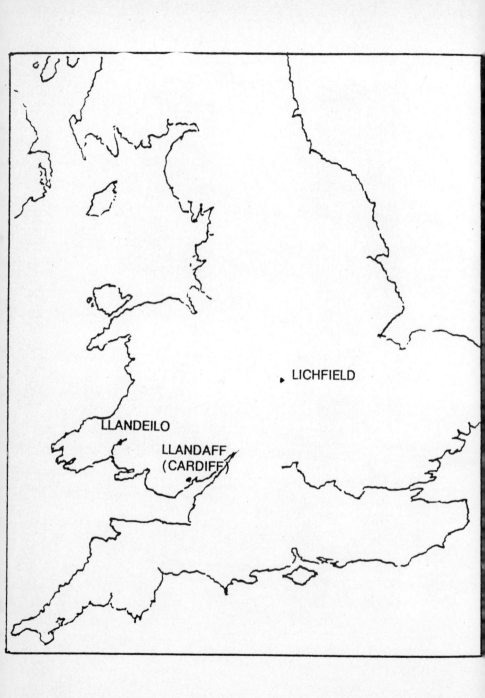

LICHFIELD

LLANDEILO

LLANDAFF
(CARDIFF)

The Right Reverend Father in God Adam Lord Bp of Sr This South Prospect of Llandaff Cathedral Church heretofore Suffragan to his See is most humbly Inscrib'd

Dauphin Lord Dolin M Burghers sculp

A The old Tower that a lower Wm Great Swan Chaquard B Upper D The lower ones in the South Plaster Houses w The School Houses E The School B G S Mann Bench tops of which are darkned & Dials of Bedford Towers C The Consistory Court Court thought gave it K Stair Case up to the School H V The Pen H V The School and the t upper ones work'd up new upper Windows in the Church Roof, informing to it W The Chap House K Room above y upper Church S Mary Church S Mary the old Ri't

A Scale of Yards

Golwg ar Eglwys Gadeiriol Llandaf o'r de. Llin-gefiad gan J. Lord, nua 1715

South prospect of Llandaff Cathedral Church. Engraving by J. Lord, c. 1715

Appendix (ii)

THE CHURCH

LLANDAFF

Church at Llandaff in Glamorgan, which became the centre of the cult of Dubricius, Teilo and Oudoceus, goes back to the earliest Christian legends and traditions in Britain, right back to Apostolic times. Succeeding invasions, Roman and otherwise, movements such as Celtic Christianity, and devastations like the Yellow plague have almost wiped out the hard evidence.

To quote Gildas c547 in 'The Ruin of Britain - "Meanwhile, to the island stiff with frost and cold, and in a far distant corner of the earth, remote from the visible sun, He, the true sun, even Christ, first yields His rays, I mean His precepts. He spread, not only from the temporal firmament, but from the highest arc of heaven beyond all times, his bright gleam to the whole world in the latest days as we know, of Tiberius Caesar." (AD 37 or 38). Among early martyrs he mentions Julius and Aaron of Caerleon and Amphibalus (Bishop and confessor of Llandaff) p.27, who like Alban died in the Diocletianic persecutions of the third century.

Other writers have referred to the Christian faith in early British history. Tertullian wrote "Those parts of Britain inaccessible to the Romans have been conquered by Christ" and Origen said c 240 that "Christianity was a unifying force amongst the British." There is a strong suggestion that the early evangelists were of Jewish origin, Aaron, Ilud being among the many with Jewish names. We should also be aware of the legends; one of these goes as follows: - Joseph of Arimathea escaped from Jerusalem by boat and together with other disciples of Jesus, landed at Marseilles where a delegation of chief Druids was sent from the King of the Silures to offer them sanctuary in Britain. Here he was received by the tribe of the Silures who inhabited the south-west and who protected and hid them in the islands amid the swamps around the Severn basin. Arviragus was their King, son of King Conobelinus (Shakespeare's Cymbeline), his cousin being the great Caratacus. These two men led the most powerful warrior kingdom in Britain. The details of Joseph's stay in Britain and the beginnings of the legend of Glastonbury can be gained from various sources, but the legend William of Malmesbury was told was that Christ Himself appeared in AD 60 at Glastonbury and instructed that a Church be built in honour of His Mother.

In the first century AD: Arviragus was to remain in Britain, but another legend avers that his cousin Caratacus who led the fighting against the Roman invaders was betrayed and taken prisoner to York and thence to Rome. He was absent for over eight years. His two daughters Eurgain and Gwladys and his son Linus accompanied him to Rome, where the British Royal family settled for some years. Caratacus so impressed his captors with his noble bearing during his trial and with the words in his defence at his trial that the Emperor Claudius allowed him to remain there on parole on condition that neither he nor any member of his family ever bore arms against Rome again. His daughter Gwladys(which means princess) was adopted by the Emperor Claudius and named Claudia; she later married Pudens they became hosts to St Paul when he was at Rome. Caratacus's son Linus was the first bishop of Rome in AD 58.

Eurgain was married to Salog the lord of Salisbury. She is recorded as the first British saint in St Prydain's genealogy. Returning to Britain after being taught by St Paul, she founded many colleges where theology and music were taught, wrote music and gave much land to the church in Glamorgan. Her love for music led to her founding the first Christian choirs at her colleges. When his parole was over Caratacus is said to have returned to Britain where he built a castle at St Donats (Aber Gweryd) on the coast of Glamorganshire, later being buried at Llan Ilud, where his father Bran, Eurgain, Salog and other members of his family were also buried in Glamorganshire.

These are the first CHRISTIAN LEGENDS FROM TWO SOURCES of the founding of the faith in Britain, claiming that Joseph's mission converted the Silurian Royal family; having been taught by St Paul in

Rome, they came back to the Glamorgan area to found these colleges of music and theology. The same soldiers of the second Roman Legion of Augustus, who had guarded Saint Paul when he was a prisoner in Rome and had been converted to Christianity by him there, were later in AD 75 based at Caerleon. This part of the country was therefore the first to experience the Christian Gospel. The church at LLandaff was of course this same area of the Severn basin.

The 'Book of Llandaff' states that this early site marks the place where King Lucius first planted a church. King Lucius (Lleurug Mawr or Great Light) was the great grandson of both Caratacus and Arviragus, his father being King Coel. He was recognised as a great luminary and in 156 AD was baptised at Winchester, then the capital of Britain. It was here that he proclaimed Christianity to be the national religion of Britain, taking the title 'Defender of the Faith', which was to remain with the British Royal family, to be re-iterated by Queen Elizabeth I, the Tudors being of this ancient British line. It was this same Lucius who wrote to Pope Eleutherius in Rome (177-192) for instruction as to the best way to govern his people; he also founded Archbishoprics at London, York and Caerleon-on-Usk. It seems that London and Llandaff may have been confused in the text which the Normans read on the founding by Lucius of a church at Llandaff. Certainly King Lucius minted coins showing the cross on one side and Luc on the other, whilst among others he built the London Church of St Peters Cornhill in 179, St Mellons near Cardiff and St Mary-de-Lode in Gloucester, where he was buried in 201 AD, to be re-buried later in St Peters Cornhill.

When in Bishop Urban's time (1107-1133), the Normans came to build the Cathedral in honour of the three saints, Dubricius, Teilo and Oudoceus (even bringing the bones of St Dubricius from Bardsey island to increase the prestige of the church), there was an ancient small church called 'The Little Minster' on the river Taff on this site (at Cardiff today); this ancient little church went back to Teilo's time and within it were Romano-British burials showing it to be an ancient site even then.

On his death Teilo was in overall charge of the whole of South Wales, whilst Deiniol had been given the care of north Wales by St

Dubricius. St Teilo's nephew Oudoceus appears to have kept the overall charge of the south, including Llandeilo fawr, Llandeilo fach, Llandough and Llandough fach (near Cardiff, a daughter church of the one at Cowbridge). Llancarvan and Llantwit each still having its own Abbot, Oudoceus's area would have included Gower and Glamorgan, stretching west as far as Dubricius's area of Herefordshire. Gradually with political changes due to constant fighting the church boundaries also altered. 8th Brycheiniog for instance was no longer part of Dyfed after the reign of Cathen, when we see the beginnings of the medieval division of land. At Argol the castle mound, which became Dryslwyn, was now the caput or head of the commote of Catheiniog, where taxes were collected for the local hundred families.

The Class system still held sway on Teilo's death, so that the problem of Llandeilo fawr was that of all monasteries, namely that they were by tradition hereditary. Thus, although he may have wished his natural successor to be his nephew Oudoceus, Teilo was a native of Penally so he was not of the local tribe in Llandeilo fawr. To get round this the Normans fabricated a legend saying that on his death Teilo's body was claimed by three churches, Llandaff, Llandeilo fawr and Penally, so that when the monks were praying for guidance as to where he should be buried, lo! there were suddenly three bodies of Teilo and he was thus buried in all three places.

But since Oudoceus does not play any part at Llandeilo fawr, one must assume his work was in another area. Yshmael the eldest is named in the south west region in Dyfed; his brother Teifi gave his name to the river in Cardiganshire, presumably his sphere of influence being to the west; another brother, Theodoric, was married to Urien Rheged's daughter Enhinti, their son Mouric founding a new dynasty on the Wye, Cadoc also giving him his kingdom of Glevissig when he retired. Mouric was thus King of Glevissig in Glamorgan and inherited Gower from his mother. His father Theodoric had returned to Brittany being King in the south there, later returning to Tintern to retire as a hermit. "While he was living that life, the Saxons began to invade his country against his son Mouric." Theodoric soon left his retirement however therefore to help his son to save his country, being killed himself at the battle of Ryt Tindern.

Mouric in deep distress pursued the Saxons, fighting them back over the Severn river. He buried his father on the island of Echni in the Severn sea, where a chapel was built on the spot where he died, to be blessed by Oudoceus. Mouric gave Mathern to the church of Llandaff forever the ancient palace at Mathern near Chepstow still existing today.

Oudoceus had oversight of his uncle Teilo's work in this large area, which extended from Loughor to the Wye including Brycheiniog as far as Hereford, and as Abbot of Mochros and bishop in Ergyng. He was followed in Mochros by Comerg, but while this Meurig ap Tewdrig (Mouric son of Theodoric) helped his uncle Oudoceus establish himself at Llandaff, from now onwards many lesser monasteries were to disappear as the main ones consolidated their position. However Oudoceus's name is today connected only with a Holy well at Dixton and Llandogo on the banks of the Wye.

Rationalisation was only gradually taking place, by the Norman period things had altered so much that the position needed further consolidation and clarification. Eventually some of the Llandeilo property went to St Davids. Llandeilo Fawr went on at least until 934 , after which it is not clear what happened; maybe it was destroyed, but with the loss of the Gospel Book, records ceased. By making Llandaff Teilo's house, the Normans could claim all the land grants made earlier to Teilo now belonged to Llandaff.

The 'Life of Oudoceus part I and II' appear to cover the lifetime of the three men, with some good stories but in no consecutive order. They tell of the creation of Llandaff over a long period as the centre of his cult. Teilo's cult was transferred from Llandeilo fawr, taking again with it considerable property which had belonged to Teilo, causing great resentment in Demetia. Thus the separate diocese of Menevia (St Davids) emerged. King Meurig ap Tewdrig gave Llandeilo fach to Llandaff and King Catoguan fixed the western boundary of Llandaff, St Davids losing the Gower peninsular which also went to Llandaff.

"Oudoceus departed from Demetia under a curse and from that time the Tywi divided the two bishoprics as it divided the two kingdoms," "Mouric and Catogaun repented and restored to the church of Llandaff, Penally, Llandeilo fawr and Gower." "Oudoceus went on a pilgrimage to Rome! and St Davids. He removed from St Davids and from his own Llandeilo fawr relics of the disciples of his uncle Teilo and put them in a suitable shrine. As he was returning through his bishopric to Llandaff, he was attacked by some disaffected and covetous persons at Pennalt in Kidwelly, who accused him of carrying off 'the treasures of St Dewi and St Teilo'. They were struck blind, and their arms, brandishing spears with which they were threatening the saint, became stiff, but on their repentance they were healed by his prayers." Perhaps Teilo's bell Bangu was amongst the relics which Oudoceus was trying to rescue!

Oudoceus's Norman 'Life' was written as a composite of at least two men, Eudoce who was probably the nephew of Teilo and uncle of King Mouric, and another Oudoceus, who was a contemporary of Mouric's grandson King Morcant, and yet another later Oudoceus, who was a predecessor of Bishop Berthguin of Llandaff. It was a patent forgery and has confused posterity ever since. By the time the Normans came to write the tale of the saints and founding of Llandaff, the true situation had long since been lost to posterity.

The Charters tell the tales, some being found at Llancarvan, some in other monasteries, but all eventually collected at Llandaff. Dr Wendy Davies has made a careful study of them explaining in 'An Early Welsh Microcosm' and in 'The Llandaff Charters' in more detail, how this came about. "The community and Episcopal role of Llandeilo fawr appear to have been displaced by the late tenth century. The Gospels found their way to Lichfield; Llandeilo fawr seems to have lost all Episcopal pretensions in the central medieval period among Teilo's houses (Llandeilo Berthan in Gwent, not Llandeilo fawr, was called Llanfawr (the great monastery); and Llandaff had become the house of Teilo by 1030. Joseph was consecrated bishop (1027-45) with English approval and the collecting of all the Charters began by 1040 as the single Bishopric in the south east".

The Episcopal records from the houses of Dubricius and Teilo(A+B), and Oudoceus(C) + Bishop Berthwyn (730-760), which constitute the Cadoc Charters now went to Llandaff. But there are no Charters for Llandaff itself. Llanarth, also an important residence of Teilo, and where he lived for a part of the time, seems to have been superseded

207

by Llanfawr. Twenty-one Charters made to Oudoceus cover the period of eleven Kings. The first made to Oudoceus is by his nephew Mouric, namely the church and lands of Llandeilo Fach,(Llandeilo Talybont). Another (referring to Gower)talks about Cingual, the dating cannot be fixed, while the name Cingual also in the Gospel Book, is unlikely to be the same man.

In the south-east there was a major change in the 8th and 9th century; Ergyng has disappeared from the records by the mid ninth century and by the eleventh century it has become the home of the house of Gwent, after which Llandaff itself begins to receive massive endowments. Llancarvan and the other monasteries had only Abbots in charge, Llandaff alone having a Bishop and considerable power, with courts of jurisdiction and great lands, canons and a choir. However by 915 we find Bishop Cimeilhau captured at Archenfeld, his ransom being paid by the English king. Meantime other monasteries suffered also monks often being captured in the Viking raids, seized and sold as slaves. By the time Joseph had become bishop of Llandaff from 1027-45, the monasteries had further declined as they were brought into line with the English.

The last Celtic bishop at Llandaff was Herewald, consecrated in 1056, in the period of Gruffydd ap Llywelyn, ten years before the Norman conquest. His son Lifris, based at Llancarvan became Archdeacon of Morgannwyg and Gwent itself becoming a separate archdeaconry. In 1063, the year that Herewald was assassinated, Ergyng became part of English Hereford. The Normans now gave Welsh church property to the English bishops, (Llancarvan to Gloucester, Llantwit and Llandough to Tewkesbury and so on). Urban arrived at Llandaff in 1107 to find that it had almost disappeared, there being only two canons left. In an endeavour to extend its boundaries from Hereford to St Davids, he claimed that his seat was the greatest in Wales and had once been an Archbishopric Geoffrey of Monmouth supported this by claiming that Dubricius was Archbishop of Caerleon. St Davids however countered this claim by saying in a letter to Pope Honorius II, that St Davids had been an Archbishopric since the beginnings of Christianity in Britain when Pope Eltheurius had sent to King Lucius the preachers Fagan and Duvian and founded three archbishoprics at London, York and

Caerleon and 28 bishoprics in the kingdom (these 28 correspond to Gildas's 28 cities, originally Druidical centres which became Christianised). St Davids went on to state that Dewi had been consecrated by Dubricius and the synod, so that the Archbishop's pallium had left Caerleon for St Davids. Bede supported this. They claimed that St Samson had the pallium at Dol (although Dol was never an Archbishopric). The argument was never resolved, although Bernard of St Davids may have had the pallium at some stage.

Both Bernard and Urban established dioceses in the Norman continental manner.

When the Norman task of founding their cathedral at Llandaff on a firm footing began, Urban, who still called himself bishop of Glamorgan, set about in 1107 building a new Cathedral beside the old church. He did away with Celtic liturgy and the cathedral now came under the jurisdiction of the Archbishop of Canterbury and the Pope, no longer a separate independent church. His claim for the territory and the authority now had to be pressed home. Pope Honorius gave judgements in 1119 and 1128 in Urban's favour, but when Bernard the bishop of St Davids entered the dispute they were called to appear before the Pope. Urban died in Rome before the disputes were settled in 1134. However both St Davids and Llandaff were soon going ahead on the Norman continental model. The Book of Llandaff was compiled by professional hagiographers who forged the 'Lives' of Dubricius, Teilo and Oudoceus and incorporated the Charters into the book.

The Norman Church was always closely connected to the castle and now from Cardiff the political and religious boundaries also corresponded. The Normans were a deeply religious people, their ideas were very different from the Celtic Church which they took over. Their language was French, not English and certainly not Welsh. The Class system of tribal monasteries, and more especially the Welsh laws of inheritance, must have made task of rationalisation extremely tedious for them. How could they ever hope to understand the political divisions and boundaries in a social system which did not rely on written records but on family customs, where the sons all inherited their father's property equally. In the English and Scottish systems of primogeniture the country became powerful and rich. The Welsh could never be rich or powerful under their rules of inheritance with such subdivision of wealth. There was no snobbery in Celtic society; everyone was equal except the current ruler as often gained through might as well as marriage; even women held property and had rights; in law everyone was of value. The Norman lords set themselves way above this itinerant population.

How far the situation had moved from the Age of the Saints when Kings and rulers set aside their possessions to serve the people, when saintliness had a different status than that in use by the Normans, when there was no such thing as the 'Celtic Church' as such, when Bishops such as Teilo or Dewi were but travelling evangelists, highly ascetic in character, even contributing to the conversion of their former conquerors in that seventh century. With the Norman conquest organisation gave weight and way to Rome; their church was lateral and worldly, unlike the Celtic saints who were open to God, other-worldly with simplicity of living and close to nature.

Of what Norman could it be said that his aim in life was simply Joy, so well expressed in that Celtic poem:

"I wish O Son of the living God, O ancient, eternal King, For a hidden little hut in the wilderness that it may be my dwelling. An all-grey lithe little lark to be by my side, A clear pool to wash away sins through the grace of the Holy Spirit. A southern aspect for warmth, a little brook across the floor, A choice land with many gracious gifts such as be good for every plant. A pleasant church and with the linen altar-cloth a dwelling for the God of heaven. Then shining candles above the pure white Scriptures.... This is the husbandry I would take, I would choose and I will not hide it. Fragrent leek, hens, salmon, trout, bees. Raiment and food enough for me from the King of fair fame. And I to be sitting for a while praying to God in every place."

What a far cry from the little "home made churches" of the saints to the beautiful architecture of the Norman arch and their central organisation and control! From Teilo, the holy man on whom the Christian community was focused, whose aim was to stimulate the spiritual life in a joyous building of regenerate men living in the City of God on earth; a life begun by the earliest Christians in this country, even anticipated by the druids whose central belief was the immortality of the soul; instead we find the churchianity of the Normans even though their mortal organisation and architecture are monumental. Furthermore it must be said that, but for the Normans, the cult of Teilo would be dead, but Teilo's 'Life' copied in part from Rhygyfarch's life of St David, is a collection without which we would know practically nothing of his existence apart from the church dedications. The Normans, however unsympathetic they may have been with the chaotic Welsh approach, did gather enough information together for posterity to get a glimpse of the greatness of the man. Llandaff stands for the Norman appreciation of this and Llandeilo Fawr appears to have been in the possession of Llandaff, until in the twelfth century the order of the White Canons set up their Premonstratensian monastery at Talley Abbey and appropriated the churches of Llandeilo Fawr and Llanegwad from Llandaff for the see of St David's.

Despite the Norman churchianity, we must remain grateful that we still can catch a glimpse of Saint Teilo's original vision. in the western part of our island where Teilo's monastic city at Llandeilo Fawr represented the birth and sunrise of the Creator - the crown of the gracious unknowable God.

DYNASTY OF KING BUDIC OF BRITTANY (TEILO'S NEPHEW'S RULE IN GLAMORGAN)

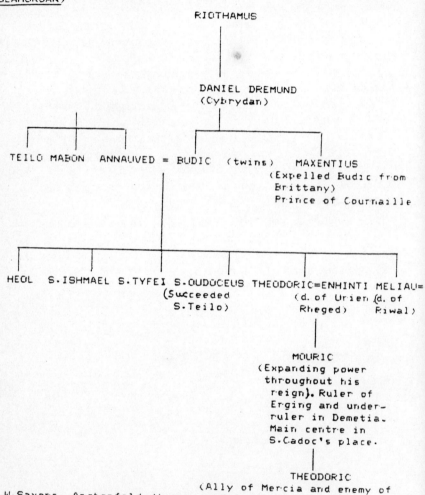

RIOTHAMUS

DANIEL DREMUND
(Cybrydan)

TEILO MABON   ANNAUVED = BUDIC   (twins)   MAXENTIUS
(Expelled Budic from
Brittany)
Prince of Cournaille

HEOL   S.ISHMAEL S.TYFEI S.OUDOCEUS THEODORIC=ENHINTI MELIAU=
(Succeeded   (d. of Urien (d. of
S.Teilo)   Rheged)   Riwal)

MOURIC
(Expanding power
throughout his
reign). Ruler of
Erging and under-
ruler in Demetia.
Main centre in
S.Cadoc's place.

THEODORIC
(Ally of Mercia and enemy of
W.Saxons. Archenfeld disappeared from his kingdom; 645 lost
Demetia and 647 slaughter in Gwent).

DRAMATIS PERSONAE

A Aaron and Julius - early Christian martyrs at Caerleon

Abelard-monk of the twelfth century

Aiden of Ferns in Ireland

Aiden, friend of Teilo

Aircol Lawhir (Agricola, Aergol) King of Demetia (Dyfed)

Ambrosius Aurelianus- Emperor - leader of the resistance to the Saxons

Ammwn Ddu (Black Amon) from Brittanny Anna his wife - from Gwent

Annauved - sister of saint Teilo

S.Anthony - and the Desert Fathers

Arthur

S.Anthony and the Desert Fathers

Augustine of Hippo in north Africa

Arthur nephew of Ambrosius Aurelianus

Bedevere - a knight of Arthur

Benlli - a tyrant

Boia - Celtic chieftain

S.Brendan of Clonfert in Ireland

S.Brieuc

Brochmail Ystragoth(teeth like tusks) Prince of Powys

Brychan - founder of Brecon

Brynach his son

King Budic exiled king of Southern Brittanny

Cadfan - leader of the saints from Brittany

Cadell Ddyrnllwg - founder of the dynasty of Powys (swineherd to the tyrant Benlli)

S.Cadoc - contemporary and friend of Teilo

Cai (Chei, Gaius, Si Kay)-foster brother of Arthur

Caracticus - early British leader

King Childebert of Paris- contemporary of Samson

S.Columbanus

King Mark Conomorus - father of Tristan

Cunedda Wledig (leader) - founder of the dynasty of the saints

S.Cybi Cynan Cynfach Oer

Dewi Sant (S.David)

Dewi Summus Sacredos founder of small churches in Hereford
Daniel Dremmund leader of a migration to Brittany (c460)

S.Deiniol

S.Dubricius founder and leader of the Celtic saints

Dyfan and Fagan Christian martyrs near Caerleon

Edern son of Vortigern

Eigr mother of Arthur

Eltherius,Pope

Emyr Llydaw (of Brittany)

Ensic father of S.Teilo

Erbdyl (Erdyl) mother of S.Dubricius

Erbin eldest son of King Aircol of Demetia

Fagan and Dyfan early martyrs

Finian of Clonard in Ireland

Flewin and Gredivil sons of Old Paulinus

Germanus of Auxerre

Germanus a teacher in Paris and later in Brittany

King Gerrenius of Din Gerran (now Cilgerran)

Gildas a monk and historian friend of Teilo

Godoelic and Brythonic Celtic language

Guinevere wife of Arthur

Gustilanus bishop and uncle of S.David

Gwladys

Gwidell Fitchi Irish pirates King

Gwynllwyi father of S.Cadoc ruler of E.Glamorgan

Heloise and Abelard

Iouill fictional character

S.Iltud the great teacher at LlanIltud Fawr

S.Ishmael nephew of Teilo

J S.Jerome translator of the Bible

L Liscki a Celtic chief

Mabon brother of Teilo

Maelgwyn Gwynedd king and contemporary of Teilo

Macliavus father of Caswallon great grandson of Cunedda

Magnus Maximus a Roman Emperor (Spanish) who married Elen

Margaret le ffay half-sister of Arthur

Meliau King of Leon son of Budic married to Riwal's daughter

Margaret le ffay wife of Urien Rheged

Mordred son of Arthur by Morgan le ffay

Morgan le ffay half sister to Arthur

S.Non mother of Dewi Sant (S.David)

S.Padarn

Paulinus Aurelianus founder of Pol de Leon

Old Paulinus (Paul Hen) brother of Urthwal

S.Patrick

King Pebiau father of Dubricius

Pedic founder of Kilpeck

King Perphirius father of Paul Aurelian

Princes of Powys

Riwal emigrated to Brittany

Sadwrn

King Sant father of S.David

S.Samson friend of Teilo

Saxons from Germany invading Britain

Taliesin a bard and contemporary of the saints

Tathan Irish teacher of Cadoc at Caerwent

Teilo

Theodoric a naval officer

Trephine one of the wives of King Mark

Tristan son of King Mark Conomorus

Umbraphael uncle of S.Samson brother of Amwn Ddu

Pope Urban

Urien Rheged a great prince of the north

Urthwal brother of old Paulinus

Uther Pendragon father of Arthur

Vortipor wicked son of King Aircol

Count Withurs uncle of Paul Aurelian living in Brittany.

Author's Notes:

There is mention of Bishop Nobis (840-873) who was Bishop in Llandeilo Fawr and is mentioned in the Book of Teilo or the Lichfield Gospels.

The young English Church. The first Celtic bishop of Mercia was an Irishman called Dimma, followed by Chad until his death in 672. From the time of Theodore, Archbishop of Canterbury, the parochial system developed with a centralised Episcopal system which became the model for the secular state, creating a new concept of kingship. National synods brought together rival factions, Theodore re-introducing Graeco-Roman culture, but in contrast, many monasteries being founded and thriving independently of Italy and

Gaul, because of local men who spoke and preached in English. New scriptoria and abbeys were founded at Hereford in 676 and Gloucester in 681, to name but two.

Prestatyn down to the Severn at Chepstow (168 miles). A hill fort 'Pen Offa' may have been used by Offa in Radnorshire, from where he could supervise the work which must have been carried out when there was a significant period of peace around 785 perhaps.

Around 930 a prophetic poem was composed by a monk from a monastery in the south, possibly Llandeilo Fawr in Deheubarth, which revealed hatred of the Welsh for the English and their desire to unite and throw off the English yoke through a truly Welsh king. The poem, 'Armes Prydain', was composed during this decade of the thirties when Hywel had returned from Rome and he was spending a lot of time in the English court, observing their ways and learning from them, as did many other Welsh princes. Athelstan was abroad developing relations with continental courts for some of this time, but he still maintained a firm hold on English affairs moving around the country and issuing many charters.

MARK CONOMORUS continued to run true to type. His marriages were many, because as soon as his wife became pregnant he would as often murder her, for he could not bear to have a rival. "When he had already done away with many women sprung from noble families - understandably parents began to feel much saddened on this account, and to move further away from him. Accordingly, in order not to become participator in his wickedness, no man of any discretion, whether in conference or in transacting business, would adhere to him in any manner whatsoever, or execute his mandates". (This passage comes from 'The Life of St Gildas" by a monk of the monastery of Rhys in Brittany.)

Mark was comparatively weak at Budic's death in 556; however he moved in to Carhaix and made it his capital. This was to lead to intensive plot and counterplot, conspiracy and intrigue. Macliavus,

216

the ruler in the south, broke his promise to protect Budic's son, the young Theodoric. and on Budic's death immediately drove Theodoric into exile and seized his territory. Likewise Budic's territory in the north-west was ruled by Budic's other son Meliau from Leon, the centre of Paul Aurelian's missionary work. Riwal of Dumnonia(Devon) who ruled in the adjacent area, marched in to Leon and killed Meliau. Budic's young grandson Melor, fled to Conomorus for protection at Carhaix; Mark tried to protect the boy, the lad was killed by Riwal's hired assassins; Melor is the patron saint of Amesbury in Wiltshire. Mark killed Riwal, ruler of east Dumnonia (Devon), and his son Iudal fled to Paris for protection, where King Childebert imprisoned him. On Riwal's death, Mark married his widow and marched on Leon. Mark then made his big mistake. He decided to support Chramm, the son of old King Childebert's brother Clothair, who had quarrelled with his father. When Childebert died the following year Clothair brought an army to kill his rebellious son Chramm, and his ally Conomorus brought over reinforcements from Britain which landed in the bay of Douarnenez on the Ile de Tristran. The story is confusing, but typical of this period - it no doubt reflected the loss of Teilo's presence as a peacemaker in the area.

Samson supported the prince of Dumnonia, Iudal, against Conomorus when Iudal was released by Clothair. Samson had an important foundation at Pental in Normandy, which had been given to him by Childebert and where he took Iudal for protection. They then went to raise an army from the Channel Islands to fight Conomorus, who moved north to meet Iudal for battle at Ploueneur Menez, south of Morlaix. During the battle Mark was wounded, fell from his horse and was trampled to death. He was taken back to Fowey and buried at Castle Dore. (Taken from John Morris'. 'The Age of Arthur')

URIEN RHEGED in the 560s was at the height of his power, all powerful in the north, conqueror of Powys and dominant from the Cheviots to the borders of Gwent.

When Urien started to spend more and more of his time in the north, seeing his land unprotected, the avaricious Cynan son of Brochmail Ystragoth began to form a plan. Cynan's great passion was conquest of land and possessions, being notorious again for setting fire to land of his enemies, while his joys were pomp and ostentation. Taliesin the bard, had earlier boasted that Cynan had conquests in Dyfed, Gwent, Anglesey and Cornwall, so that he did not have many friends among the Britons, for Powys originally extended east of Shrewsbury and north-east of Chester. Taliesin boasted of his patron Cynan, "I sang before a renowned lord where the Severn meanders, before Brochfael of Powys who loved my muse." Like his father Cynan had a congenital deformity of his jawbone and was very ugly; dubbed 'bone-lipped' Cynan, he also ruled in Urien's former territory between the Tawe and the Tywi, so that when the yellow pestilence broke out and Urien was called north to defend his lands in Strathclyde, Cynan took his place in the south.

BARDS. When Taliesin arrived at Urien's court he boasted of the gifts he had received from Cynan. "A hundred horses each with silver trapping. A hundred splendid mantles and a hundred bracelets; best of all a magnificent sword with a worthy scabbard." Urien would have to be equally generous! At one stage Taliesin put the cat among the pigeons by visiting the court of another local king, Gwallag, praising him also; this aroused Urien's violent anger.

Taliesin talks of Urien's silver hair and is most reflective when describing Urien riding to battle -"what if he were brought home on a bier, his cheeks stained with blood, his handsome body lifeless and his wife bereft of her husband?" In like manner he describes battle, where "I saw fierce men in hosts; mangled flesh in morning battle; tumult; champions worn out; warriors smeared with blood, their weary arms dropping from their weary, limp hands; warriors pillaging; blood on arms"; what a contrast to their proud array as they set out, picked men, wearing their gold torques around their necks! (Taken from Sir Ifor Williams 'Poems of Taliesin').

Urien's son Owain and his 'raven army' were also praised by the poets; the raven of course became the crest of the descendants of this Dynevor family. Urien's other children included Owain's twin sister Morvud, Rhiwallon, Elphin, and Rhun who converted Edwin to Christianity; also St Kentigern. Urien himself, was to be treacherously killed in jealousy - murdered and then decapitated, under that same Celtic belief that the head was an important prize of war containing the enemy's soul. His killer however suffered terrible remorse and returned to bury his body. Legend has it that his head was taken to the Tower of London. Urien is known sometimes as Bran, which means raven, ravens being kept in captivity at the Tower and when more are needed they are obtained from Dynevor Park. (Urien was however given several other titles such as 'Lord of the Evening' and 'Leader of Christendom').

There may have been a training school for bards on the cliff opposite Carreg Cennen, the place of the eagle's eyrie, the singing rock, at the source of the river Cennen flowing from between two cliff tops. Here in this wild and isolated spot, bards could learn the intricacies of their art; and youth with a musical bent could take the traditional training lasting many years. The bards would sing in the Celtic tongue, itself of course the rudiments of modern Welsh. Derwydd near Llandybie is within sight of Carreg Cennen but deep in a valley in the midst of a wood. Possibly a bardic nucleus also existed at Llandeilo Fach.

PELAGIUS - a final note. Pelagius's error is mortal sin; by denying what Christ did in His death and resurrection, we would deny Christ's redemptive work on earth ; Christ came to die as a ransom for any who choose to believe in the Trinity, namely, in the life and death of Jesus, in the power of God the Father in raising Him to life again and in the work of God the Holy Spirit at Pentecost and in the world ever since. If we want to free ourselves from the claims of mortality, if we wish for the freely offered guidance of Grace to prevent us from wandering away from the Truth and the Light time and again, we must accept that free-will is not enough in this temporal world; we must accept that Christ lived and died for us. By identifying with Christ's work and death we die as human beings, to be born again to live in His strength; we are re-born into a higher plane, a wider dimension, reborn to live in the new dynamic of the Holy Spirit. Often we will continue to fail to live up to such standards, but we can ask God's forgiveness and for His strength - to sin no more; and so gradually we increase in wisdom and develop the new life. This is very different from humanism; it is life raised to that highest plane with divine assistance". Chapter 8. page 21.

DEINIOL p.23 was Dubricius's constant companion at Henllan; later he had a large influence in mid-Wales.

DUBRICIUS The monastery overlooked the valley and the hills where his grandfather, Brychan, was born and had raised his large family. (p25).

Just outside Llandeilo, a little stream bubbled over the stones, a tributary of the Dulas beside the Talley road, named 'Erddyl' after Dubricius's mother, who was known also as Erbdyll or Efryddyl in Herefordshire, the daughter of King Pepiau of Archenfeld (Weston under Pennard) and Erging. A large area south of Hereford - Ynis Efrddyl- is also named after her; she always seems to have been associated with water. Dubricius's Norman name, Devereux, the Celtic equivalent of Dyfrig, is derived from the word water, after the legend of his birth. It goes like this: ' One day as the King returned from hunting, while his daughter was washing her hair, he noticed that she was pregnant; he was so angry that he ordered that she be put in a sack and drowned. But the river Wye washed her onto a sandbank. The King ordered that she be burnt and she was duly placed on a pyre, but she would not burn. The next day he found her nursing her baby, Dubricius'. The truth is harder to establish, but Brychan's son Brynach was Dubricius's father and Dubricius was born at Madley near the river Wye in Ynis Efrddyl. When his work at Henllan was overflowing he founded a settlement at Mochros, which translated means 'swine moor' and is now called Moccos near Madley, at that time 'well wooded and abounding in fish'. (Canon Doble)

Dr Wendy Davies covers the list of Dubricius and Teilo properties in her book on the Llandaff Charters in great detail (see reading list), as does Canon Doble in his treatise on the 'Life of Dubricius', when discussing the Book of Llandaff in relation to both Dubricius and Teilo.

Dubricius owned Welsh Bignor by inheritance from his grandfather, King Pepiau, the son-in-law of King Constantine Fendigaid, King of all Britain during the first quarter of the fourth century AD. Welsh Bignor, on the Wye near Whitchurch, was on a prominent Roman trade route and a very early Christian foundation. This is not far from the old Roman town of Ariconium (now Weston under Penyard itself) the great iron centre of Roman Britain, through which the very earliest trade routes came. Dubricius' churches, amongst them Moccos, Madley, Ballingham, Wormbridge, Llanwarne, S.Devereux and Henllan in south-west Herefordshire (said to be twenty-four in all in this area), together with his Bishopric at Llanarth, made up his chief responsibilities between the rivers Usk and Wye.

DEWI Chapter 12. page 1. 'Had custody of the mystic gifts bestowed to his father Sant for Dewi before his birth'. (J.E.Lloyd - History of Wales - chap V p.158 and chap VIII p268).

DEWI SANT - ST DAVID'S dedications (c.f. map - page) A group of Dewi churches close by are foundations of another Dewi, 'Dewi Summus Sacerdos' who also built Much Dewchurch, Little Dewchurch and Dewsall, and followed another saint Pedic at Kilpeck (Kil or cil meaning church); later this Dewi Sacerdos was to be forgotten, so that these churches became merged with Dewi Sant.

In Brittany close to Teilo's parish at Pledeliac, there is a holy well dedicated to Dewi; could it be that Dewi also brought a little party of frightened people from Llandybie in Wales to escape the yellow plague? Certainly Ploudavid is a large parish in King Mark's capital city on the bay of Douarnenez.

ST TEILO's dedications (c.f. map - page) A number of Teilo dedications are found in Dubricius's area, including Llandeilo Graban, Llandeilo Pertholey and Llandeilo Crosseny, while he later came to be associated with Llanarth.

One important dedication in Cournaille (Brittany) is Landeleau on the Aulne, east of Chateauneuf-du-Faou. He will always be remembered there by the people, for annually they proceed round his parish in their famous tromenie, from 7am till 5pm, following the course he took. They stop at St Elau's tree, where a sermon is preached, and as they process they sing a Breton hymn about Teilo. There is a dolmen there, called 'Ty Sant Heleau', two fields known as 'Parc Sant Elau-bras' and '-bihan' and another 'Goarem Sant Elau', while at the door of the church is a stone sarcophagus in which Teilo lay to do his penance.

Other places in Cornouaille with churches dedicated to Teilo include Leuhan about 15 Km SW of Landeleau in the parish of Plevin, now a ruined chapel; Plogonnec has a beautiful chapel dedicated to him (2.6 Km from the town); in the parish of Guengat is a granite chair called 'Chair of Delo', in which fever patients were placed for healing; on the river Oust, NW of Loudeac, Teilo is patron of St Thelo, while at Noyal there is a place called St Theleu and a possible monastery at Monterhelot also on the Oust. In Leon, Saint-Hilio may be a Teilo dedication, while further south near the department of Morbihan, close to Lorient, a village has the same name. By the parish of Pledeliac near Dinan, the church of St Teilo - St Thelo - adjoins the parish of Landebiea. as they do in Carmarthenshire (From Canon Doble's learned treatise on St Teilo). Very little has come down to us in history about Saint Teilo except what was written about him by the Norman monk at Llandaff in the 12th century.

YGRAIN . The character of Ygrain is wholly fictional. I have used her as a device to show Teilo's humanity . Also the Rev James McKinney indicated to me how useful she could be to exemplify Pelagianism in real life.

LLANDAFF. At Llandaff, Dubricius is named as the first bishop, though not the founder of the See; Teilo is named as the second bishop. However it is clear from the writing of Dr Wendy Davies in her chapter on the ' Original Charters', that it was not until the late tenth or early eleventh century that Llandaff became a bishopric. Earlier, she says, "there must have been at least two bishoprics, the one in Ergyng, centred on the house of Dubricius, which may have been at Henllan, the other possibly at Llandeilo Fawr. If the second was not at Llandeilo, then there certainly was a third bishopric there between the late sixth and early ninth century."

Suffice to say that the organisation of the later Norman church was very different to the Celtic church of St Dubricius' day and to that of the earliest written 'Life' that of St Samson. Which mentions 'Papa' Dubricius as being involved in many areas of South Wales overseeing the church and consecrating men to the priesthood. That he should have been honoured by the Normans and cited as first bishop of Llandaff seems wholly appropriate, whether in fact he had a church there or not. Certainly we know that Teilo had dedications in the area, indeed one is only two miles away. At Caerleon the position is unclear, but a charter under a heading dealing with two of Britain's earliest martyrs, Julius and Aaron, and all the territory which belonged to them there at Caerleon "which formerly belonged to Saint Dubricius " would connect Dubricius with the British Church in the days of the Roman Empire.

GILDAS, and TALIESIN compared, on some of the kings of the time.

GILDAS c 547.('The ruin of Britain' is our only contemporary written source of the period).

Off the shore at this time, Gildas, sick with dismay, wrote his tract on 'The Ruin of Britain', with all the spleen he could muster, on an island "along the Severn Sea by the island of Echni as far as the estuary of the Towy" - thought to be Flat Holm island. Gildas does not mention Arthur by name in his writing, although he is an admirer of Arthur's grandfather, Ambrosius. In the eyes of Gildas, Arthur perhaps fell below the standards of Ambrosius. There is a tale that suggests that Hueil, Gildas's older brother, rebelled and was killed in battle by Arthur; it is suggested that because Gildas could not forgive this act of Arthur he never mentioned his name. In the 'Life of Gildas', Arthur besieges Glastonbury because he is separated from his wife Guenuver. The five bad Kings about whom Gildas writes were Maelgwyn Gwynedd (Maglocunus) who was perhaps the strongest, living in north Wales; a grandson of Ambrosius, Aurelius Caninus is swallowed up in filth of murders, he is ruling Somerset, Gloucester, Monmouth and Glamorgan with his capital at Caerleon said to be the son of King Mark and brother of Tristan; Constantine of Dumnonia, the tyrannical whelp of the unclean lioness of Dumnonia! - the fourth was Cunoglas, meaning in Pictish "grey-haired"; the fifth was Vortipor of Dyfed who is likened to the pard (a leopard or panther).

The first, Gildas's schoolfellow Maelgwyn, was a great grandson of Cunedda, a stormy although brilliant war leader and king of Venedotiae (Gwynedd, north Wales), for which in contrast he was praised by Taliesin the poet in the Brythonic tongue, the beginnings of Welsh. Taliesin of course was himself a schoolmate of Gildas at

Llantwit major, although Gildas writes in Latin, while Taliesin uses his native tongue. Maelgwyn took monk's vows, then later left the monastery to take up his right of pre-eminence over the other princes. He put away his wife, then murdered his brother's son, took his nephew's wife and married her. Never did the country have unity again, such disunity among all the lesser kings allowed the Saxons to take advantage of the situation and to move west. Thus then is Gildas's description of Maelgwyn: "And thou, the island dragon, who hast driven many of the tyrants mentioned previously, though last in my writing, first in wickedness, exceeding many in power and at the same time in malice, more liberal in giving, more excessive in sin, strong in arms, but stronger in what destroys thy soul - thou Maclocunus, why dost thou obtusely wallow in such an old black pool of crimes, as high as mountains?"

THE LINE FROM NORTH WALES.

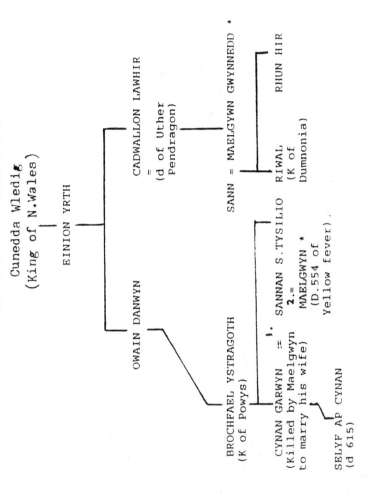

Cunedda Wledig
(King of N.Wales)

EINION YRTH

OWAIN DANWYN

CADWALLON LAWHIR
=
(d of Uther
Pendragon)

SANN = MAELGWN GWYNNEDD *

RIWAL,   RHUN HIR
(K of
Dumnonia)

BROCHFAEL YSTRAGOTH
(K of Powys)

CYNAN GARWYN = SANNAN S.TYSILIO
(Killed by Maelgwyn   1.
to marry his wife)   2.=
                       MAELGWYN *
SELYF AP CYNAN   (D.554 of
(d 615)   Yellow fever).

News came about 552 of Maelgwyn Gwynedd's death. Scared of the yellow pestilence, Maelgwyn locked himself in the church of Llanrhos, in Caernarvonshire, so that no one could contact him and, having renounced his priestly vows, cowering and trembling with the disease, he died. The poets had described it thus, "A strange creature will come from the marsh of Rhianedd, to punish the crimes of Maelgwyn Gwynedd; its hair, its teeth, and its eyes are yellow, and this will destroy Maelgwyn Gwynedd".

Maelgwyn's name is commemorated at Chateau Tremelgon near Vannes; perhaps he did flee for a while to Brittany; we cannot know. The Book of Llandaff tells us that: "Maelgwyn Gwynedd succeeded his father Caswallon in the sovereignty of North Wales in 517 and in 546 was elected King of the Britons, on the death of King Arthur. In 552, he endowed the See of Bangor with lands and privileges;" (he died during the plague years 547-555 approximately) "He likewise erected the town of Bangor Fawr and repaired Shrewsbury and the castle of Harlech." This novel assumes that Arthur died nearer to 537 than 546 and that Gildas wrote his book in the 540s

Of Aurelius Caninus I need say nothing more, since he has little to do with this book.

What then are the graphic epithets Gildas uses in this same book, 'The Ruin of Britain' about Constantine, King of Dumnonia, grandson of Ambrosius : "Art thou not swallowed up in the same, if not more destructive filth, murders, fornications, adulteries, like sea-waves rushing fatally upon thee?"

Of Cunoglas, like Dewi and Teilo also descended from Cunedda, and ruling between the Teifi and the Dee, he says: "Wallow in the old filth of wickedness from the years of thy youth, thou bear, rider of many and driver of a chariot belonging to a bear's den. Despiser of god and contemner of his decree, thou tawny (red-head) butcher...whom innumerable lapses drove away thy wife, cast thy eyes upon her dastardly sister who is under vow to God of perpetual chastity of widowhood. Provoking the saints by repeated injuries, groans and sighs of the saints. Cease from anger, forsake deadly wrath breathing against heaven. Change thy life.

VORTIPOR, the last of the five, is termed the 'Tyrant of Demetia'," foolishly stubborn. Like the pard art thou in manners and in wickedness of various colour, though thy head is now becoming grey, upon a throne full of guilt, and from top to bottom defiled by various murders and adulteries, thou worthless son of a good King, as Manessah of Hezekiah. What! do not such wide whirlpool of sins which thou suckest in like good wine, nay art thyself swallowed up by them, though the end of life is gradually drawing near - do these not satisfy thee? Why, to crown all thy sins, dost thou, when thine own wife had been removed and her death had been virtuous, by the violation of a shameless daughter, burden thy soul as with a weight impossible to remove? Spend not I beseech thee, the remainder of thy days offending God, because now it is the acceptable time and the day of salvation shines upon the faces of the penitent, during which thou canst well bring to pass that thy flight be not in the winter or on the Sabbath."

GILDAS IN IRELAND After his return to Britain Gildas concentrated on his mission to Ireland. Although the church was still not powerful enough to impose order in Ireland, even in Gildas's time the monasteries were becoming great centres of learning. We hear of his old pupil Finian of Clonard presiding over a community of over 3000 monks, writing to Gildas for advice on new rules for his community. The lives of these men were praised by Gildas. After a life of devoted and inspired teaching to the Irish especially, both at St Davids and in Ireland itself, as well as from Llancarvan in Cadoc's enormous monastery, Gildas withdrew to Brittany for his last days, to die in his abbey at Rhys.

BUDIC d. 556 AD was king of most of Brittany at his death. His grandfather Riothamus had led the second migration from Britain in the 460s and was the founder of the dynasty, to be followed by his son, Daniel Dremund, who had twin sons, Maxentius and Budic. Budic and his brother inherited their patrimony in their youth, but Budic was exiled and his brother took control; Budic returned with the help of Aircol Lawhir and Theodoric, the captain of Aircol's fleet, to recover this patrimony in Brittany and to rule for nearly forty years. Budic named his son Theodoric after the sea captain who had helped him so well (extract from John Morris - 'The Age of Arthur').

THEODORIC, Teilo's own nephew (his sister Annauved's son), became involved in the fighting: he had married Enhinti, the (?sister) daughter of Urien Rheged. Annauved named her son Theodoric after Arthur's naval commander who had helped her husband King Budic regain his kingdom of Quimper in Brittany. The commander old Theodoric was now retired and living in Cornwall, a very old man, who could look out on the waves and the sea shore, dreaming of those exploits with Arthur in his youth.

Some twenty years after settling in Britain, in 577, the younger Theodoric returned with an army to his birthplace in Brittany to retrieve his father's kingdom of Quimper where Macliavus had been succeeded by his son Waroc in Vannes. (the city to which Padarn returned during the plague). At about the same time Mouric, the son of Theodoric and Enhinti, was called by St Cadoc, who had returned home from Ireland, to take on the Kingship of east Glamorgan, since Cadoc was beginning to find it all too much for him; it was a wise choice, for Mouric ruled for 30 years, free from the petty jealousies which often brought down local kings. Towards the end of his life, after Waroc had defeated him, Theodoric returned as a religious hermit to live near his son Mouric, but, as the Saxons advanced, he was to come out of retreat once more to help his son and to be killed at Tintern Ford on the Wye. The grieving Mouric was to pursue his beaten enemy with much vengeance. (John Morris 'The Age of Arthur')

CADOC was growing old and wished to retire. When he returned to Lancarvan he nominated Elli his successor and retired to a place called Beneventum, which could not have been too far away from Lancarvan for we are told that Elli had to visit him every year to keep Cadoc informed of what was going on at Lancarvan. Perhaps it was the old city of Bovium in Glamorgan or maybe near Abergavenny. At any rate at Beneventum Cadoc arrived to find that the walls were crumbling and with many gaps, for they were made of clay. Since he was soon to be made Abbot over a large monastery there, he ordered that the walls be repaired with stone. However the place was attacked and plundered by the Saxons shortly after, and many people killed, including St Cadoc who, celebrating Holy Communion, was transfixed with a spear to fall dead at the very altar. It was some time before the monks of Lancarvan were allowed into the city to take Cadoc's body for burial in Lancarvan. But even here the body was not safe, for a marauding band led by the same Cynan, son of Brochmail Ystragoth King of Powys, attacked the monastery, his coffin being struck by a pagan staff, whereupon the legend says St Cadoc roared like a bull from within! Near Argol in a dingle by the tump at Llanegwad, there is a place known to this day as Cadoc's mound, but the truth is no one knows where he was buried. (Taken from the 'Life of St Cadoc)

BIBLIOGRAPHY

Books and articles used in preparation
of the Life of Saint Teilo

A

Alcock. Leslie,	Arthur's Britain	Penguin 1971
Alexander. J.J.G	Insular MSS 6th-9th century	Harvey Miller
Andere. Mary,	Herefordshire. The Enchanted Land	Express Logic 1974
ARMES PRYDEIN		
Ashe. Geoffrey,	A certain very special book.	Speculum 1981 56.2
Ashe. Geoffrey	King Arthur's Avalon	Collins. 1957. Fontana 1973
	Kings and Queens of early Britain.	Methuen 1982
	Quest for Arthur's Britain	Granada Publishing 1971
	Camelot and the vision of Avalon Attwater.	
	Donald Penguin Dictionary of Saints.	1965
	King Arthur. Tintagel.	Tintagel Parish Council 1982
Austerberry. Jennie	Chad Bishop and Saint	English Life Publications 1984

B

Bagoly. Suzanne,	Edition Critique de la vie de Saint	Thelyau. 1980-1981
Baring Gould and Fisher	The Lives of the saints	
Bamm. Peter,	The Kingdoms of Christ	Thames and Hudson 1959
Bede	A History of the English Church and People.	
	(Trans. Leo Shirley Price.) Penguin 1955	
Bowen. Prof. E.G	St David of History (an address given to the friends of St David's Cathedral)	1982
	The Book of Llanbadarn Fawr.	1979
	Travels of St Samson of Dol	
	Settlements of the Celtic Saints in Wales	
	U.W.P. Cardiff 1956	
	Antiquity Vol x1x	
Bridgeman. G.T.D	History of the Princes of S.Wales.	1876
Bright	Waymarks in Church history	
Brooke. Christopher.	The Archbishops of St Davids Llandaff and Caerleon on Usk	Caerleon on Usk
	The Saxon and Norman Kings.	Fontana 1963
Brown. Peter	Augustine of Hippo.	Faber 1967
Browne. Rev. Canon	The Church in these Isles before Augustine.	1894
Bromwich. Rachel	Troioedd Ynys Prydein Augustine. 1894	U.W.P. 1963
Butler. Lawrence,	The Monastic City in Wales, myth or reality. B.B.C.S.1979	

Bulleid. Arthur   The Lake Villages of Somerset.
                                        Somerset Archaeological Society. 1966

C
Cable. James(trans)   The death of King Arthur   Penguin 1971
Cadoc.Life of   (Lifris) BCS 1944.   History and Law Series
Caerleon Roman Ampitheatre.   HMSO
Caerwent Roman City   HMSO
Caldey Abbey and Island
Carr. A.D.and Hywel Dda: The Law   Dafydd Jenkins. Gomer Press 1986
Carlsile. Nicholas   Topographical Dictionary: Llaniltud Fawr. 1811
Casselli. Giovani   The Roman Empire in the Dark ages   Macdonald 1981
Chadwick. Henry   The Early Church   Penguin 1967
Chadwick. H.M   Foundations of the early British Kingdoms.
Chadwick. Nora   The Celts   Pelican 1979
Chadwick. Owen   Evidence of dedications in the early history of the Welsh
                        Church   Cambridge U.P. 1954
B.M.Cotton   MS Vespasian Axiv closely linked with the book of
                        Llandav in actual writing.

D
Davies. Wendy   The Llandaff Charters   NLW 1979
                        An early Welsh Microcosm Historical Soc. studies no9
1978

                        Journal of theological studies: notes and studies. p.204 I; p.

                        59 II. (F.C.Burkitt)
Doble. Canon   S.Dubricius   Welsh saints series
                        S.Samson of Dol and Golant in Cornwall
                                                         Welsh Saints series
                        (Also Cressage and S.Samson. Antiquites of Shropshire)
                                                                  S.Iltud
                        Lives of the Welsh Saints 1971 UWP (Ed. D.Simon Evans)
                        S.Paul Aurelian:Bishop and Confessor S.Teilo (traced to an
                        older 3rd life by Rhygyfarch)
Donaldson.Christopher. S Martins Church Canterbury   1966
Mac Dougal   Racial Myth in English History
                                        University Press of New England 1982

E
Evans.Gwenogvryn   Book of Taliesin
Evans. Gwengvryn   Book of Llandav. Gwysaney MS.

E.D.Jones and E.L.Bevan Papers on the B. of Llandav 1945-46. BNLW. Vol iv
pp46-49 nos 3 and 4.

Evans. Michael C.S.   The Llandyfan Forges SN 170659
                         Carmarthenshire Antiquary p131
Evans. Gwynfor   Land of My Fathers   John Penry Press 1974 Swansea
Evans. Wade   Welsh Christian Origins   1964 pp161
                         Description of Pembrokeshire
                         Welsh medieval law I and II
                         II p42 Arcoyl or Castel Arcoyl

F
Fenn. R.W.D   The Pre-Norman Diocese of Llandaff
                         Story of the Church in Glamorgan
                         560-960 Ed. E.T.Davies. SPCK 1962

G
Gallico. Paul   The Steadfast Man   Michael Joseph 1958
Gildas   Gildae : The ruin of Britain   Lost Letters, The Penitential
                         The Lorica of Gildas. ed. Hugh Williams 1899 Pub.David
                         Nutt for the Hon.Soc Cymmrodorion
Glamorgan   Glamorgan vol 1.part 3.   HMSO RCAM 1976
                         Early Christian Period.
Glastonbury   Early Church at Glastonbury
                         Charters of the Early Church (excavations on Tor 5th
                         century monastic site)
Golden Grove   Golden Grove Book (4 vols)Record Office Carmarthen
Graham-Campbell   The Vikings
Dafydd Kidd   British Museum   1980

H
Hughes. Lynne   A Carmarthenshire Anthology   Christopher Davies 1984

J
James. Heather   Roman West Wales.   Rampart Press Carmarthen 1982
Jarrett. Michael G   Excavations at Llys Brychan
                                      Llangadog 1961 Carms Antiquarian
Johnson. Stephen   Roman Fortifications on the Saxon Shore.
                                      Dept of the Environment HMO 1977
Jones. Rev.Daven   The Early Cymry and their Church
                                      W.Spurrell and sons Carmarthen 1910
Jones. Gwyn   The Mabinogion (Tales from)
Jones. Thomas   Golanz Press 1985 also J.M.Dent   1949

Jones. Thomas   Sir John Rhys   Memorial Lecture 1967 British Academy
                       The Black Book of Carmarthen
                       Stanzas of the Graves
                       The Black Book of Carmarthen
Jones. Thomas   Brut y Tywysogyon. Red Book of Hergest   UWP 1955
Jones. Thornley   Saints,Knights and Llanau   Gomer Press 1975
Jowett. George P.   The Drama of the Lost Disciples Covenant Publishing 1980

K
Kerr. Donald   St Patrick Catholic Truth Society   1983
Kelly. L.V.   A History guide to Llantwit Major   1976
Kentigern S.   The Lives of the Saints

L
Leyland   (Itinerary vii part 2 marginal page 152).
                       (Later ed. by Toulmin Smith)
                       Castel Argoel ie. site of old Dynevor Castle at Dryslwyn.
Llandaff   Book of Llandaff
Lloyd. J.E.   A History of Carmarthenshire
Loomis. R.S.   Arthurian Literature in the middle ages.
                                         OUP 1959 Clarendon Press

M
Mathews. John   The Grail Quest for the Eternal   Thames and Hudson 1981
Mee. Arthur   The King's England. Herefordshire.
                                              Hodder and Stoughton 1938
McEvedy. Colin   The Penguin Atlas of medieval history.   1961
Meyrick.   History and Antiquities of Cardiganshire   1808
Morris. John   Dates of the Celtic Saintes The Age of Arthur
                                              Phillimore 1973 Vols 1-3
Mountney. Rev Michael The Saints of Herefordshire   Express Logic 1976 Hereford
Morgan. Rev R.W.   The British Kymry and Britons of Cambria:
                       Outlines of history and institutions.   1857

O
Owen. G   Dimetian and Gwentian Codes (Ancient Laws of Wales)
                                         BBCS vol vii 1933-1935.3.Argoel
                       History of Pembrokeshire
                       The Kymrie Vol 4. p 407. Gron gaer (round fort)Caer
                       Gathen = old name Grongaer Argol(p.407)

	BCS History and Law p.40	
Owen. Morfyd and Dafyd Jenkins.	The Welsh Marginalia of the Lichfield Gospels.	
Ordinance Survey	Map of Roman Britain	1978

P

Pearce. Rev E.H.	English Christianity and its beginnings	1908 SPCK
Pearce. Susan	The Kingdom of Dumnonia AD 350-1150.	1978
Piggott. Stuart	The Druids	Pelican 1968
Plummer. Alfred	The Churches in Britain before AD 1000	
		(Library of historic theology).

R

Radford. C.A.Ralegh	Glastonbury Abbey. The Isle of Avalon.	
		Pitkin Pictures 1973
	The Nature of Ecclesiastical Architecture of Wales 1100-1285	
	Justinia Prima (Tsaritsin Grad) 5th century city in south	
		Serbia.
	Antiquity	
	The earliest Irish churches.	
	Ulster journal of Archaeology	vol 40 1977
	The Celtic Monastery in Britain	
	Lecture to Dublin meeting	Arch Camb. 1962
	Two dateable cross shafts at Llantwit Major Arch Camb	
		1983
Richards. Melville	The Lichfield Gospels (Book of St Chad).	NLW Journal
		xviii pp 134-144
Richards. Rev Rice	An essay on the Welsh Saints.	1836
Rees. Prof. William	An Historical Atlas of Wales.	Faber and Faber
Rowan.	Art in Wales 2000 BC- AD 1850.	UWP Cardiff 1978

S

Salway.Peter	Scandanavian Settlement in Ystrad Tywi	
	Oxford History of England.	Clarendon Press 1981
Skene. W.F.	Four Ancient Books: Triads of Arthur and his warriors.	
Saklatvala. Beram	Roman Britain's Last Champion	David and Charles 1967
Smith. Lesley M.	The Making of Britain. The Dark Ages.	Macmillan 1984
Smith. Malcolm	Introduction to the Triads of Britain. Compiled by Iola	
	Morganawg.	Wildwood House 1977
Stein. Dr Wendy	Thesis on Lichfield Gospels	Cathedral Library 1980

Stenton. Sir Frank   Anglo-Saxon England. The Oxford History of England
Clarendon Press 1943

T
Tacitus   The Agricola and the Germania   Penguin 1948
Taylor. Canon T.   Life of Saint Samson   SPCK 1925
Thomas. Charles   Early Christian Archaeology in N. Britain.   OUP 1971
Thomas. Gwyn   The Mabinogion   Crossley-Holland. Gollancz 1985
Thomas. Gwyn   The Mabinogion
Jones. Thomas   J.M.Dent 1949

U
Unstead. R.J.   The Medieval Scene   A.C. Black 1978
Ure. Percy Neville   Justinian and his Age   Penguin 1951

V
Victory. Sian   The Celtic Church in Wales   SPCK 1977

W
Walker. David   A History of the Church in Wales   1976
White. T.H.   Once and Future King. Collins   1939
Williams. Glanmore   Religion. Language and Nationality in Wales   UWP 1979
Williams. J.E.Caerwyn   The Poets of the Welsh Princes   U.W.P. 1978
Williams. A.H.   History of Wales
Williams. Rhys Davis   Notes taken on lectures by Alan Morgan
Williams. Sir Ifor   The Beginnings of Welsh Poetry   1972
        The Poems of Taliesin   1975
        The Prophecy of Britain from the Book of Taliesin
        Dublin Institute of advanced Studies(English version
Rachel Bromwich translated in 1982)
Wilson. P.A.   Romano-British and Welsh Christianity, continuity or
        discontinuity
        BCS Vol 3 1966-67 History and Law review.

Also published by Llanerch

THE LEGENDARY XII HIDES OF GLASTONBURY

by Ray Gibbs. History, Archaeology and the
legends of Joseph of Arimathea and King Arthur.

THE ADORNMENT OF THE SPIRITUAL MARRIAGE, THE SPARKLING STONE and the BOOK OF SUPREME TRUTH

by John of Ruysbroeck, edited by Evelyn Underhill.

THE DARK AGE SAINTS OF SOMERSET

by John Seal. An account of the Celtic Church and
early Monasticism, Glastonbury and its saints, the
Chedder saints and the saints of Blue Anchor Bay.

SYMBOLISM OF THE CELTIC CROSS

by Derek Bryce, with drawings by J Romilly Allen.

CELTIC CROSSES OF WALES

by J Romilly Allen (modern edited text).

TALIESIN POEMS

Translated by Meirion Pennar, Illustrated. Including the poems
considered most likely to be ancient and authentic by Ifor Williams.

THE BLACK BOOK OF CARMARTHEN

Translated by Meirion Pennar. Including the Merlin poems.

THE GODODDIN of Aneirin

Translated by Steve Short.

For a complete list, write to:
LLANERCH PUBLISHERS
Felinfach, Lampeter, Dyfed, Wales; SA48 8PJ.